D1600693

Harry Belten and the Mendelssohn Violin Concerto

The Iowa School of Letters Award for Short Fiction

Harry Belten and the Mendelssohn Violin Concerto

Barry Targan

UNIVERSITY OF IOWA PRESS
IOWA CITY
1975

The previously published stories in this collection appear by permission:

"Harry Belten and the Mendelssohn Violin Concerto," *Esquire* 66 (July, 1966).
"And Their Fathers Who Begat Them," *Esquire* 69 (January, 1968).
"Old Vemish," *Salmagundi* 24 (Fall, 1973).
". . . and still the heart doth sing," *Sou'wester* New Series: 1 (Winter, 1973).
"Tickets," *Prairie Schooner* 39 (Winter, 1965/66).
"In Excelsis Deo," Twigs 8 (Fall, 1971).

"Little Parameters," *Salmagundi* 19 (Spring, 1972).
"Leaving," *Denver Quarterly* 6 (Autumn, 1971).
"Leave My Mother Alone," *Quarterly Review of Literature* 17 (1971).
"Charity Begins," *Seneca Review* 1 (May, 1970).
"The Man Who Lived," *Southern Review* 10 (Summer, 1974).
"The Clay War," *American Review* 18 (September, 1973).
"Natural As Can Be," *Salmagundi* 12 (1970).

"Harry Belten and the Mendelssohn Violin Concerto" appeared in *Stories From the Sixties,* New York: Doubleday, 1971; "Old Vemish" in *The Best American Short Stories 1974,* New York: Houghton Mifflin, 1974.

Library of Congress Cataloging in Publication Data

Targan, Barry 1932-
Harry Belten and the Mendelssohn violin concerto.

"The Iowa School of Letters award for short fiction."
CONTENTS: Harry Belten and the Mendelssohn violin concerto.—Little parameters.—Old Vemish. [etc.]
I. Title
PZ4.T184Har [PS3570.A59] 813'.5'4 75-17705
ISBN 0-87745-060-9

University of Iowa Press, Iowa City 52242

Printed in the United States of America

For Arleen

Contents

Harry Belten And The Mendelssohn Violin Concerto

If a thing is worth doing, surely it is worth doing badly

ALICE BELTEN LABORED up the thin wooden outer stairway leading to Josephine Goss's tiny apartment above Fulmer's dress shop. She opened the weather-stained door, streamed into the limited sitting room, and cried, "Oh, Josie. I think my Harry's going crazy." From the day thirty-one years before, when Alice and Harry had married, Josephine Goss, Alice's best friend, had suspected that Harry Belten was crazy. Thirty-one years' knowledge of him fed the suspicion. Her friend's announcement came now as no surprise.

"The violin again?" she asked, but as though she knew.

"Yes," Alice said, almost sobbing, "but worse this time, much worse. Oh God!" She put her hands to her head. "Why was I born?"

"Well, what is it?" Josephine asked.

"Oh God," Alice moaned.

"*What is it?*" Josephine lanced at her.

Alice snapped her head up, to attention. "A concert. He's going to give a concert. He's going to play in front of people."

Josephine slumped a little in her disappointment. "Is that all? He's played in front of people before, the jerk. Do you want some tea?" she asked in a tone which considered the subject changed.

"No, I don't want any tea. Who could drink? Who could eat? It's not the same. This time it's for *real.* Don't you understand?" Alice waved her hands upward. "This time he thinks he's Heifetz. He's renting an orchestra, a hall. He's going to a big city. He's going to advertise. Oh God! Oh God!" She collapsed into the tears she had sought all day.

Josephine revived. "Well I'll be. . . ." She smiled. "So the jerk has finally flipped for real. Where's he getting the money?"

"A mortgage," Alice managed. "A second mortgage." Although not relieved, she was calming. "Harry figures it'll cost about three thousand dollars."

"Three thousand dollars!" Josephine shouted. It was more serious than she had thought. "Does he stand to make anything?"

"No."

"No?"

"Nothing."

"Nothing? Nothing? Get a lawyer," she said and she rose to do it.

Harry Belten sold hardware and appliances for Alexander White, whose store was located in the town of Tyler, population four thousand, southwest New York—the Southern Tier. He had worked for Alexander White for thirty-two years, ever since he came up from the Appalachian coal country of western Pennsylvania on his way to Buffalo and saw the little sign in the general-store window advertising for a clerk. Harry had had the usual young-man dreams of life in the big city, but he had come up in the Depression. He had figured quickly on that distant afternoon that a sure job in Tyler was better than a possible soup line in Buffalo, so he stopped and he stayed. Within a year he had married Alice Miller, the young waitress and cashier at what was then Mosely's filling station, bus depot, and restaurant—the only one in Tyler. Two years later Alice was pregnant and gave birth in a hot August to a son, Jackson (after Andrew Jackson, a childhood hero of Harry's). Two years after that Harry started to pay for a house. That was in 1939. He didn't have the down payment, but in 1939, in or around

Tyler, a bank had to take some risk if it wanted to do any business at all. And Harry Belten, after six years in Tyler and at the same job, was considered by all to be, and in fact was, reliable.

His life had closed in upon him quickly. But, he sometimes reflected, he would not have arranged it to be anything other than what it was.

In 1941 Harry Belten bought a violin and began to learn to play it. Once a week, on Sunday afternoon, he would take the short bus ride over to neighboring Chamsford to Miss Houghton, a retired schoolteacher who gave music lessons to an occasional pupil. A couple of jokes were made about it in Tyler at the time, but the war was starting and all interest went there. Alice was pregnant again, and in 1942 gave birth to a daughter, Jane. Harry started working part time in a ball-bearing factory in Buffalo. He drove up with four other men from Tyler three times a week. Mr. White didn't object, for there wasn't much to sell in the hardware line anymore, and besides, it was patriotic. Through it all Harry practiced the violin. Hardly anyone knew and no one cared, except maybe Josephine Goss, who never tired of remembering that Harry's violin playing and the Second World War started together.

"Harry," Alexander White called out from his little cubbyhole office in the back of the store, "could you come back here a minute please?"

"Right away, Alex," Harry answered. He took eighty cents out of a dollar for nails, handed the customer his change, and walked to the back of the store. "Keep an eye on the front," he said to Martin Bollard, who was stacking paint cans, as he passed him. While not technically a manager—besides himself and White there were only two others—Harry was by far the senior clerk. Frequently he would open and close the store, and more than once, when the boss took a vacation or had an operation, he had run the entire business, from ordering stock to making the bank deposits and ledger entries. Over the accumulating years White had sometimes reminded himself that you don't find a Harry Belten every day of the week or around some corner.

Harry squeezed into the office and sat down in the old ladder-back chair. "What can I do for you, Alex?"

"Oh, nothing . . . nothing," the older man said. He was looking at a household-supplies catalog on the desk, thumbing through it. After a few seconds he said, "You know these new ceramic-lined garbage pails? You think we should try a gross?"

"Too many," Harry said. "We don't sell a gross of pails in a year."

"Yeah, yeah. That's right, Harry. It was just that the discount looked so good." He thumbed the catalog some more. "Harry," he started again, "yesterday at lunch down at Kiwanis I heard a couple of guys saying you was going to give a violin concert?"

"Yes sir, Alex. That's correct. As a matter of fact," he continued, "I'd been meaning to talk to you about it." Harry rushed on into his own interest and with an assurance that left his employer out. He made it all seem so "done," so finished, so accomplished. "You see, I figure I'll need a year to get ready, to really get ready. I mean I know all the fingerings and bowings of the pieces I'll be playing. But what I need is *polish.* So I've contacted a teacher—you know, a really top professional teacher. And, well, my lessons are on Monday afternoons starting in a month. The end of April that is." Alexander White looked sideways and up at Harry.

"Harry," he said slowly, smilingly, "the store isn't closed on Mondays. It's closed on Wednesday afternoons. Can't you take your lessons on Wednesday?"

"No," Harry said. "Karnovsky is busy on Wednesday. Maybe," he offered, "we could close the store on Monday and open on Wednesday instead?" White gave a slight start at such a suggestion. "Anyway, I've got to have off Monday afternoons. Without pay, of course." Alexander White shook his hand in front of his eyes and smiled again.

"Harry, when did you say the concert was? In a year, right? And you said just now that you knew all the fingers and bows?"

"Fingerings and bowings," Harry corrected.

"Fingerings and bowings. Yeah. You said so yourself all you need was polish. Okay. Good! But Harry, why a *year*? I mean how much polish do you need for Tyler anyway?"

"Oh," Harry said, "the concert isn't going to be in Tyler. Oh no sir." Harry was igniting. It was something that Alexander White did not behold easily: this fifty-one-year-old man—his slightly crumpled face, the two deep thrusts of baldness on his head, the darkening and sagging flesh beneath the eyes—beginning to burn, to be lustrous. "This isn't going to be like with the quartet that time or like with Tingle on the piano. No sir, Alex. This is *it*! I'm giving the concert in Oswego."

"Uuuh," White grunted as though he had been poked sharply above the stomach.

"I'm renting the Oswego Symphony Orchestra—two days for rehearsals, one day for the performance," Harry continued.

"Uuuh. Aaah," White grunted and wheezed again, nodding, his eyes wincing and watering a little.

"Are you okay, Alex?" Harry asked.

"Harry!" Martin Bollard shouted from the front of the store. It meant that there were customers waiting.

"Be right there," Harry shouted back. He stood to leave and started to squeeze his way out. "And I'm renting the auditorium there," he said over his shoulder and was gone back to work.

"Eeeh. Uuuh," White grunted in conclusion, his breath escaping him. The corners of his mouth turned down. He had blanched and the color had not come back. He said softly to himself, "Then it's true," and waited as if for refutation from a spirit more benign than Harry's demonic one. "But Harry," he rose up, "you're not that kind of fiddler!"

"Mr. Belten, in all candor, you are not a concert-caliber violinist." Karnovsky was speaking. His English was perfect, tempered by a soft, prewar Viennese lilt which could bring delicate memories of music and a time past. Harry had just finished playing a Spanish dance by Sarasate. He put his violin down on top of the piano and turned to the old, gentle man. It was the first time Karnovsky had heard him play.

"I know," Harry said. "I know. But I don't want to be a concert violinist. All I want to do is to give this one concert." Somewhere Karnovsky sighed. Harry went on. "I know all the notes for all the pieces I'm going to play, all the fingerings and bowings. What I need now is polish."

"Mr. Belten, what you need is . . ." but Karnovsky did not finish. "Mr. Belten, there is more to concertizing than all the notes, all the fingerings and bowings. There is a certain . . ." and again he did not finish. "Mr. Belten, have you ever heard Heifetz? Milstein? Stern? Either on records or live?" Harry nodded. "Well that, Mr. Belten, that kind of polish you aren't . . . I'm not able to give you." Karnovsky ended, embarrassed by his special exertion. He was a small man, bald and portly. His eyebrows flickered with every nuance of meaning or emotion, either when he spoke or when he played. He stood now before Harry, slightly red, his eyes wide. Harry soothed him.

"Ah, Mr. Karnovsky, that kind of playing no man can give to another. I don't ask so much from you. Just listen and suggest. Do to me what you would do to a good fiddler." Karnovsky could not look at him longer this way. He turned around.

"What do you propose to play for your concert, Mr. Belten?" Suspicions began to rise in Karnovsky's mind.

"I thought I'd start with the Vivaldi *Concerto in A Minor.*" Karnovsky nodded. "The Chausson's *Poème,* then the two Beethoven *Romances,* then something by Sarasate. . . ." Karnovsky's head continued to bob. "And finish up with the Mendelssohn." Karnovsky could not help it. He spun around on Harry.

"The *Mendelssohn*?"

"Yes."

"The Mendelssohn? The Mendelssohn *Violin Concerto*? You are going to play the Mendelssohn? You know the Mendelssohn?"

"Yes," Harry said, "Yes. Yes." He was himself excited by the excitement of the older man, but in a different way.

"How do you know the Mendelssohn?" Karnovsky asked him. His tone was tougher. A fool was a fool, but music was music. Some claims you don't make. Some things you don't say.

"I've studied it," Harry answered.

"How long?" Karnovsky probed. "With whom?"

"Eighteen years. With myself. Ever since I learned how to play in all the positions, I've worked on the Mendelssohn. Every day a little bit. Phrase by phrase. No matter what I practiced, I always saved a little time for the Mendelssohn. I thought the last forty measures of the third movement would kill me. It took me four-and-a-half years." Harry looked up at Karnovsky, but that innocent man had staggered back to the piano bench and collapsed. "It's taken a long time," Harry smiled. No matter what else, he was enjoying talking about his music.

"Eighteen *years*?" Karnovsky croaked from behind the piano.

"Eighteen years," Harry reaffirmed, "and now I'm almost ready." *But is the world?* Karnovsky thought to himself. His own wryness softened him toward this strange and earnest man.

"It's fifteen dollars an hour, you know," he tried finally.

"Right," Harry said. Karnovsky fumbled in his pocket and withdrew a white Life-Saver. He rubbed it in his fingers and then flipped it like a coin in the air. He caught it in his hand and put it into his mouth. Outside, March rain slicked the grimy streets.

"Okay," he muttered. "Like we agreed before you . . . when we spoke . . . on the . . . ." The eyebrows fluttered. "Go," he said. "Get the fiddle. We begin." Harry obeyed.

"Then you're really going through with it?" Alice asked.

"Of course," Harry said, swallowing quickly the last of his Jell-O. He pushed his chair back and stood up.

"Where are you going?" Alice asked.

"I've got something Karnovsky showed me that I want to work on. It's terrific." He smiled. "Already I'm learning stuff

I never dreamed of." He started to leave.

"Harry," Alice said, getting up too, "first let's talk a little, huh?"

"Okay," he said, "talk."

"Come into the living room" she said, and walked into it. Harry followed. They both sat down on the sofa. Alice said, "Harry, tell me. Why are you doing it?"

"Doing what?" he asked.

"Throwing three thousand bucks out the window, is what," Alice said, her voice beginning to rise, partly in offended surprise at his question, at his innocence.

"What are you talking about, 'throw out the window'? What kind of talk is that. Is lessons from Louis Karnovsky throwing money away? Is performing the Mendelssohn *Violin Concerto* with a full, professional orchestra behind you throwing money away? What are you talking about? Drinking! That's throwing money away. Gambling! That's throwing money away. But the Mendelssohn *Violin Concerto*? Jeezzz," he concluded turning away his head, not without impatience.

Alice sat there trying to put it together. Something had gotten confused, switched around. It had all seemed so obvious at first. But now it was she who seemed under attack. *What had drinking to do with anything?* she wondered. *Who was doing what wrong?* She gave it up to try another way.

"Do you remember when you and the other guys played together and sometimes put on a show . . . concert . . . in the Grange Hall?"

Harry smiled and then laughed. "Yeah," he said. "Boy, were we a lousy string quartet." But it was a pleasant memory and an important one, and it released him from both his excitement and his scorn.

Shortly after the war some gust of chance, bred out of the new mobility enforced upon the land, brought to Tyler a cellist in the form of a traveling salesman. His name was Fred Miller and he represented a company which sold electric milking machines, their necessary supporting equipment, and other dairy sundries. It was not the first merchandise Fred Miller had hawked across America; it proved not to be the last—only one more item of an endless linkage of products which seemed to gain their reality more from such as he than from their own actual application. Who, after all, can believe in the abstraction of an electric milking machine, of plastic dolls, of suppositories, of Idaho? But Fred Miller was real, full of some American juice that pumped vitality into whatever he touched. And he had brought his cello with him.

After they played, over beer and sandwiches, Fred Miller would tell them about America and about music. "Once," he would begin, "when I was selling automobile accessories [or brushes or aluminum storm windows or animal food] in Denver, one night after supper I was outside the hotel when looking up the street I saw on the movie marquee, instead of the usual announcement of 'Fair star in a country far,' the single word 'Francescatti.' " (The other three would look at each other knowingly.) "Of course, I hurried to the theatre." And then he would take them through the music, through the performance, piece by piece, gesture by gesture, play by play.

"And there he was, not more than twenty bars away from his entrance, big as life and cool as day, wiping his hands on his handkerchief, that forty-grand Strad sticking out from under his chin. *And then he starts to mess with the bow.* Yep. He's got both hands on the bow tightening the hairs. It's a bar to go. It's two beats away. You're sure he's missed it and *wham.* Faster than the speed of light he's whacked that old bow down on the cleanest harmonic A you've ever heard, and it's off to the races, playing triple stops all the way and never missing nothing. Hand me a beer, will you, Harry?" And only then would the three of them breathe.

There was the one about when Milstein lost his bow and it almost stabbed a lady in the eighth row. Or the Heifetz one, where he didn't move anything but his fingers and his bow arm, not even his eyes, through the entire Beethoven *Concerto.* There was Stern and Rosand and Oistrakh and Fuchs and Ricci and Piatigorsky and Feuermann and Rose and the Juilliard and the Hungarian and the Budapest and Koussevitsky and Toscanini and Ormandy and the gossip and the feuds and the apocryphal. All of music came to Tyler on those Thursday nights mixed gloriously with the exotic names of Seattle and Madison and Butte and Tucson and with the rubber, steel, plastic, and edible works of all our hands and days.

One Tuesday Fred Miller came into the hardware store to tell Harry that he was leaving. The electric-milking-machine business hadn't made it and he was off to Chicago to pick up a new line. There wasn't even time for a farewell performance. For a few weeks after, Harry, Tingle, and the reconstructed viola player from Bath had tried some improvised trios, but the spirit had gone out of the thing. Harry would sometimes play to Tingle's piano accompaniment or to Music Minus One records. But mostly he played alone.

"Harry," Alice broke in upon him gently, for she sensed where he had been, "Harry, all I'm trying to say is that for people who don't have a lot of money, three thousand dollars is a lot of money to spend . . . on anything!"

"I'll say," Harry agreed, getting up. "I'll be five years at least paying this thing off." He walked away to the room at the back of the house in which he had practiced for twenty-four years. Alice sat, miserable in her dumbness, frustrated and frightened. Something was catching and pulling at her which she couldn't understand. What was she worried about? When he had spent the eight hundred dollars on the new violin, she had not flinched. She had taken the six hundred dollars of hi-fi equipment in her wifely stride, indeed, had come to like it. All their married life they had lived in genteel debt. She looked then as she had in other anxious times for reference and stability to the bedrock of her life, but what she found there only defeated her further: the children were grown and married, the boy, even, had gone to college; all the insurance and the pension plans were paid to date; the second mortgage on the house—which would pay for all of this concertizing—would only push back the final ownership slightly, for the house, on a thirty-year mortgage to begin with, had only four more years to go. The impedimenta of existence were under control.

As Alice sat in the midst of this, the phone rang. She rose to answer it. What was the problem? Was there a problem? Whose problem? It was all so hard. Alice could have wept.

"Hello, Alice." It was Josephine Goss.

"Yes."

"I've been talking to the lawyer." Josephine sounded excited in the way people do who act after obliterating ages of inaction have taught them to forget the taste—giddy, high-pitched, trying to outrun the end of it. "He says you can't do anything legal to stop Harry unless he really is crazy, and if he really is crazy, you've got to be able to prove it."

"So?" 'Alice said, bracing for the lash of her friend's attitude her questions always earned.

"*So?* So you got to get him to a psychiatrist, so that's what." All at once Alice was deeply frightened, only to discover in the center of her fear the finest speck of relief. Terrible as it was to contemplate, was this the answer? Was this why nothing made sense with Harry anymore? Was he really mad?

From the back of the house Harry's violin sounded above it all.

Harry came out of the storeroom with an armload of brooms.

"Well, if it ain't Pangini himself," Billy Rostend shouted out.

"Paganini," Harry corrected him, laughing, "the greatest of them all." He put the brooms down. "What can I do for you, Billy?"

"I came for some more of that off-white caulking compound I bought last week. But what I'd really like is to know what is all this about you giving a concert in Oswego. You really going to leave all us poor people and become a big star?"

"Not a chance," Harry said. "How many tubes do you want?"

"Eight. But no kidding, Harry, what's the story?" Alexander White put down the hatchet he had been using to break open nail kegs to listen. The shy, ubiquitous Tingle, a frequent visitor to the store, slipped quietly behind a rack of wooden handles for picks and axes. Martin Bollard and Mrs. George Preble, who had been talking closely and earnestly about an electric toaster at the front of the store, paused at the loudness of Billy's voice and at the question too. There were many in Tyler who wanted to know the story.

"No story," Harry answered him. "I've got this feeling, you see, that I've always wanted to give a real, big-time concert. And now I'm going to do it. That's all. It's that simple." He had been figuring on a pad. "That'll be $3.12, Billy. Do you want a bag?" Billy became conspiratorial. He dropped his voice to a whisper, but it was sharp and whistling.

"Come on, Harry, what gives?" It was more a command than a question, the kind of thing living for three decades in a small town permits, where any sense of secret is affront.

"It's nothing more than what I just told you, Billy. It's something I've always wanted to do, and now I'm going to do it."

"Yeah!" Billy spat at him. "Well, I'll believe that when I believe a lot of other things." He scooped up the tubes of caulking and slammed out of the store. Mrs. George Preble followed, either unnerved by the encounter or bent on gossip, without buying the toaster. Harry looked at Martin Bollard and shrugged his shoulders, but what could Martin say, who also wanted answers to the question Billy had asked. Only the wraithlike Tingle, glancing quickly about himself twice, looked at Harry, smiled, and then was gone.

"Harry, could I see you a minute," Alexander White called to him.

In back, in the little office, White explained to Harry that "it" was all over the town, indeed, all over the entire area of the county that had contact with Tyler. He explained to Harry that business was a "funny thing" and that people were "fickle." He explained that if a man didn't like you he would drive (county roads being so good now) ten miles out of his way to do his business elsewhere. After more than thirty years people didn't distinguish between Harry Belten and White's Hardware. What Harry did reflected on the business. And what Harry was doing, whatever it was, wasn't good for it. Harry listened carefully and attentively, as he always had. In thirty-two years he had never sassed the boss or had a cross word with him. He wasn't going to start now. Whatever was bugging Alexander White and the town of Tyler was something they were going to have to learn to live with until April twenty-eight, eight months away.

"Yes, sir," Harry said. After almost a minute, when Alexander White didn't say anything more, Harry went back to work. And Alexander White went back to opening nail kegs, smashing vigorously and repeatedly at the lids, splintering them beyond necessity.

When Harry came into Karnovsky's studio and said hello, Karnovsky's expressive eyebrows pumped up and down four times before he said a thing. The grey-and-yellow sallowness of the old man's skin took on an illusory undercast of healthy pink from the blood that had risen.

"Mr. Belten, from the beginning I have felt strangely about our relationship. I never minced words. I told you from the beginning that you didn't have it to be a concert violinist. That the idea of you concertizing, beginning to concertize, you, a man your age, was . . . was . . . *crazy!*" Harry had never seen the gentle Karnovsky sputter before. It affected him deeply. "But okay, I thought," Karnovsky continued, "so who cares. So a man from the Southern Tier wants to put on a performance with the local high-school orchestra or something. So okay, I thought. So who cares." He was using his arms to form his accusation the way that a conductor forms a symphony. Karnovsky brought his orchestra to a climax. "But now I find that you have engaged the Oswego Symphony Orchestra and are going to perform in . . . in public! *You are doing this thing for real!*" Not in years, perhaps never before, had Karnovsky shouted so loudly. The sound of his reaching voice surprised him, shocked him, and he fell silent, but he continued to look at Harry, his eyebrows bounding.

After a moment Harry asked, "Am I committing some crime? What is this terrible thing I am about to do?"

Karnovsky hadn't thought about it in those terms. Six weeks earlier he had told Bronson, his stuffy colleague at the university where he was Professor of Violin, about Harry. A frustrated Heifetz, he had called him. He had also used the word "nut," but gently and with humor. So it was that when at lunch that very day, Bronson had told him that his Harry Belten had hired a professional orchestra and had rented a hall in the middle of the downtown of a large city, Karnovsky felt unjustly sinned against, like the man who wakens belatedly to the fact that "the joke's on him." He considered, and reasonably, the effect that this might have upon his reputation. To be linked with this mad venture was not something you could easily explain away to the musical world. And Karnovsky had a reputation big enough to be shot at by the droning snipers who, living only off of wakes, do what they can to bring them about. Finally, there was the central offense of his musicianship. After fifty-five years of experience as performer and teacher, he knew what Harry's performance would sound like. It wouldn't be unbearably bad, but it didn't belong where Harry was intent on putting it. Maybe, he thought, that would be the best approach.

"Mr. Belten, the musicians will laugh at you. Anyone in your audience—if you even have an audience—who has heard a professional play the Mendelssohn will laugh at you."

"So." Harry shrugged it off. "What's so terrible about that? They laughed at you once."

"What?" Karnovsky started. "What are you talking about?"

"In 1942, when you played the Schoenberg *Violin Concerto* for the first time in Chicago. Worse than laugh at you, they booed and shouted and hissed, even. And one lady threw her pocketbook and it hit you on the knee. I read about it all in *Grant's History of Music Since 1930*."

Who could help but be softened? Karnovsky smiled. "Believe me, that performance I'll never forget. Still, in Italy in 1939, in Milan, it was worse. Three guys in the audience tried to get up on the stage, to kill me I guess, at least from the way they were screaming and shaking their fists. Thank God there were some police there. I was touring with the Schoenberg *Concerto* then, so I guess they had heard about the trouble it was causing and that's why the police were there." He was warming to his memory and smiling broadly now. *It is a good thing,* he thought, *to have a big, good thing to remember.*

"So what's the difference?" Harry asked.

"What?" Karnovsky came back to the room slowly.

"They laughed at you. They'll laugh at me. What's the difference?"

Repentantly softened, Karnovsky gently said, "It wasn't me they were laughing at, it was the music." He looked away from Harry. "With you it will be you."

"Oh, of course," Harry agreed. "What I meant was what is the difference to the performer?" Harry really wanted to know. "Does the performer take the cheers for himself but leave the boos for the composer? In Italy they were going to kill *you,* not Schoenberg."

Karnovsky had moved to the large window and looked out, his back to Harry. March had turned to May. He heard Harry unzip the canvas cover of his violin case.

"No lesson," he said without turning. He heard Harry zip the case closed again. "Next week," he whispered, but Harry heard and left. Karnovsky stood before the window a long time. Auer had Heifetz, he thought. Kneisel had Fuchs. And I got Harry Belten.

"You're home early," Alice called out.

"Yeah. It's too hot to sell, too hot to buy. White closed up early." He had the evening paper under his arm and in his hand the mail.

"Oh, the mail," Alice said. "I forgot to get it. Anything?"

Harry was looking. He saw a letter addressed to him from the Oswego Symphony, opened it and read.

"Ha!" he shouted, flinging his hand upward.

"What is it?" Alice came over to him.

"It's from the Oswego Symphony. They want to cancel the agreement. They say they didn't know I was going to use the orchestra to give my own public performance." Harry hit the letter with his fist. "They want out. Listen." Harry read from the letter.

". . . given the peculiar nature of the circumstances surrounding your engagement of the orchestra and considering that it is a civically sponsored organization which must consider the feelings and needs both present and future of the community, I am sure that you will be sensitive to the position in which we find ourselves. It has taken many years to establish in the minds and hearts of our people here a sense of respect and trust in the orchestra, and while this is not to say that your intended performance would violate that trust, yet it must be obvious to you that it would perhaps severely qualify it. It goes without saying that upon receipt of the contract, your check will be returned at once along with a cash consideration of fifty dollars for whatever inconvenience this will have involved you in."

Somewhere in the middle of the first ponderous sentence, Alice had gotten lost. "Harry," she asked, "What does it mean?"

"Wait," Harry said as he read the letter again. And then he laughed, splendidly and loud. "It means," he gasped out to her, "that they are offering me my first chance to make money from the violin—by *not* playing." He roared. "Well, the hell with them!" he shouted up at the ceiling. "A contract is a contract. We play!" And he thundered off to his music room to write a letter saying so.

"Harry," Alice called after him. "Harry," she trailed off. But he was gone. She had meant to tell him that the children were coming that night for supper. And she had meant to tell him that Tingle had quietly left at the front door that morning a bundle of large maroon-and-black posters announcing the debut of Harry Belten in Oswego. But, then, it seemed that it was not important to tell him, that until all of this was settled one way or another she would not be able to tell what was important or what was not. Under her flaming flesh, she felt heavy, sodden, cold.

Throughout supper he regaled them with his excitement. Although neither of his children had become musicians,

Jackson had learned the piano and Jane the violin. But once past high school they had left their instruments and their skill in that inevitable pile of lost things heaped up by the newer and for a time more attractive urgencies. College had engulfed the boy, marriage and babies the girl. As children they had made their music and had even liked it, but the vital whip of love had never struck them. Still, they had lived too long in that house and with that man not to be sympathetic to his joy. It was, then, wrenchingly difficult when, after supper, after the ice cream on the summer porch which he and his father had built, Jackson told his father that everyone was concerned by what they thought was Harry's strange behavior. Would he consent to be examined?

"Examined?" Harry asked.

"By a doctor," his son answered.

The daughter looked away.

"What's the matter?" Harry looked around surprised. "I feel fine."

"By a different kind of doctor, Dad."

"Oh," Harry said, and quickly understood. "By a . . . uh . . . a psychiatrist?"

"Yes." Jackson's voice hurried on to add, to adjust, to soften. "Dad . . . it's not that we. . . ."

But Harry cut him off. "Okay," he said.

They all turned and leaned toward him as though they expected him to fall down.

"Daddy?" his daughter began, putting her hand out to him. She didn't think that he had understood. She wanted him to be certain that he understood what was implied. But he forestalled her, them.

"It's okay," he said, nodding. "I understand. A psychiatrist. Make the arrangements." And then, to help them out of their confused silence and their embarrassment, he said, "Look. I really may be nuts or something, but not," he added, "the way everybody thinks." And with the confidence of a man who knows a thing or two about his own madness, he kissed them all good night and went to bed.

By the middle of September all kinds of arrangements had been made or remained to be made. First of all, there was the Oswego Symphony. A series of letters between Mr. Arthur Stennis, manager of the orchestra, and Harry had accomplished nothing. It was finally suggested that Harry meet with the Board of Directors personally. A date, Tuesday afternoon, September 21, was set. Then there was the psychiatrist. For convenience, an appointment had been made for Tuesday morning. The psychiatrist was in Rochester. Harry's plan was to have his lesson as usual Monday afternoon, sleep over in Buffalo, drive to Rochester and the psychiatrist the following morning, and then on to Oswego and the Board of the Symphony in the afternoon; home that night and back to work on Wednesday. That was the way he explained it to Alexander White at the store.

After lunch on the twentieth of September Harry prepared to enter upon his quest. He knew it was off to a battle that he went, so he girded himself and planned. And it was the first time he would be sleeping away from home without his wife since he took his son camping fourteen years before. He was enjoying the excitement.

"Is everything in the suitcase?" he asked Alice.

"Yes," she said.

"Are you sure?"

"Yes, yes. I've checked it a dozen times." She held up the list and read it off. "Toothbrush, shaving, underwear, shirt, handkerchief."

"Tie?"

"Tie."

"Okay," he said. "Tonight I'll call you from the Lake View Hotel and tomorrow after the doctor I'll call you too. I won't call after the meeting. I'll just drive right home." He picked up the suitcase and walked toward the door. "Wish me luck," he said.

"Oh, Harry," Alice called and ran to him. She kissed him very hard on his cheek and hugged him to her. "Good luck," she said.

Harry smiled at the irony. "With whom?" he asked.

"With . . . with *all* of them," she said, laughing and squeezing his arm.

At the door he picked up his violin case and, hoisting it under his arm in exaggerated imitation of an old-time movie gangster, turned and sprayed the room. "Rat-a-tat-tat."

They both laughed. Harry kissed his wife and left the house, his weapon ready in his hand.

The psychiatrist was fat and reddish, his freckles still numerous and prominent. He sat behind an expensive-looking desklike table and smoked a large, curved pipe. Harry thought that he looked like a nice man.

"Good morning, Mr. Belten," he said, gesturing for Harry to be seated. "Please, be comfortable."

"That pipe smells wonderful," Harry said. The doctor wrote on a legal-size yellow pad on the desk. "Did you write that down?" Harry asked.

The doctor looked up and smiled. "Not exactly. I wrote down something about what you said."

"Oh," Harry nodded.

"Mr. Belten, do you know why you're here?" the psychiatrist asked.

"Certainly," Harry answered. "For you to see if I'm crazy."

"Not exactly. In fact, not at all." The word "crazy" made the doctor's ears redden. "Your family felt that your behavior in the past six months exhibited a definite break with your behavior patterns of the past and felt that, with your consent, an examination now would be useful in determining any potential developments of an aberrated nature. Are you laughing?" he asked Harry, a bit put off.

"I was just thinking, my family felt that, all that?"

The doctor laughed too.

"Doctor, do you know why my family felt whatever it was you said they felt and wanted me examined? I'll tell you. One: Because they can't understand why I want to give this big, public concert. Two: Because it's costing me three thousand dollars, which for me is a lot of money. And three: Because my wife's best friend, who has always disliked me for no good reason, put the bug into my wife."

"Suppose you tell me about it," the doctor said.

Although not certain what the doctor meant by "it" Harry told him plenty. He told him about Alexander White and the hardware business and about Tyler, about Fred Miller and about Miss Houghton, the old violin teacher, and about Karnovsky, the new one, and about the teachers in-between. He told him about Josephine Goss and about his children, about his wife and about the gentle Tingle and about when he bought the new violin. It took a long time to tell all the things that Harry was telling. The doctor was writing rapidly.

"Are you writing down things about that too?" Harry asked.

The doctor paused and looked up at Harry. "Do you want to see what I'm writing?" he asked.

"No," Harry said. "I trust you."

The doctor leaned forward. "Good," he said. "Now, what do you mean by 'trust me'?"

"I mean," Harry answered, "that you'll see I'm not craz . . . not . . . ah . . ." he gave it up with a shrug . . . "*crazy* and that you'll tell my family that and they'll feel better and won't try to stop me from giving the concert."

The doctor leaned back heavily. His pipe had gone out. "Mr. Belten, I can tell you right now that you're not *crazy*—as you put it—and that I have nothing to do with stopping you from giving your concert. Even if I thought you were *crazy* I couldn't stop you. It would have to go through the courts, there would have to be a trial. . . ."

"Fine," Harry interrupted. He stood up. "Just tell them that nothing's wrong with me."

"I didn't say that," the doctor said.

Harry sat down. "What do you mean?" he asked.

"Well." The doctor lit his pipe at length. "Sometimes people can be 'sane' and still 'have something wrong with them.' " He was uncomfortable with Harry's phrasing but decided to use it for the sake of clarity. "By helping the individual to find out what that thing is, we help him to lead a . . . a . . . *happier* life."

"Oh, I get it." Harry brightened. "We find out why I want to give the concert so that when I do give it I'll enjoy it even more?"

"Not exactly." The doctor smiled, but something in what Harry had said lurked dangerously over him. He stiffened slightly as he said, "By finding out why you want to give it maybe we discover that it isn't so important after all, that maybe, finally, you don't really need to give it, that you would be just as happy, maybe happier, by *not* giving it." He continued, his pipe steaming, "There are all kinds of possibilities. It might easily be that your apparent compulsion to give this concert is in reality a way of striking back at the subconscious frustrations of a small life, a way of grasping out for some of the excitement, some of the thrill that you never had."

"Sure," Harry said. "Now that you put it that way, I can see where it could be that too." Harry smiled. "That's pretty good." The doctor smiled. "Still, I don't see where that means that I *shouldn't* have the thrill, the excitement of giving the concert. Maybe after the concert I won't have anymore—what did you call them—'subconscious frustrations.' Maybe the best thing for me *is* to give the concert."

There was a long silence. The doctor let his pipe go out and stared at Harry. At last he said, "Why not?"

It didn't take the Board, or more precisely, Mr. Arthur Stennis, manager of the orchestra and secretary to the Board, more than ten minutes to come to the point. To wit: even though they (he) had executed a contract with one Harry Belten, the Board felt that the reputation of the orchestra had to be protected and that there were sufficient grounds to charge misrepresentation on his part and take the whole thing to court if necessary, which action could cost Harry Belten a small fortune. Why didn't he take their generous offer (now up to two hundred dollars) for returning the contract and forget the whole thing?

"Because," Harry explained again, "I don't want the money. I want to give a concert with a professional orchestra." But that simple answer, which had alienated others, did not aid him here.

He looked around him at the other eight members of the Board. Five were women, all older than Harry, all looking identical in their rinsed-grey hair and in those graceless clothes designed to capture women in their age. They all wore rimless glasses and peered out at Harry, silently, flatly, properly. No help there, he thought. There was the conductor, Morgenstern, a good minor-leaguer. He had said nothing and had not even looked at Harry from the time both had entered the room. Next to him was the treasurer, elected to the Board but, Harry knew, strictly a hired hand. He would take no opposite side. Finally there was Mr. Stanley Knox, eight-three years old and one of the wealthier men in Oswego, improbably but defiantly present. Although Harry had never seen this ancient man before that afternoon, he knew instinctively that he knew him well. Stanley Knox wore the high-button boot of the past. The too-large check of his unlikely shirt, the width of his tie, the white, green-lined workman's suspenders which Harry glimpsed under the Montgomery Ward suit marked Stanley Knox for what he basically was: for all that counted, just one more of Harry's customers. He had dealt with Stanley Knoxes for more than thirty years. Had he learned anything in all that time that would matter now? Yes.

"It isn't fair," Harry said.

"It might not seem fair to you," Stennis countered, "but would it be fair to the people of Oswego?" He looked around the table in that kind of bowing gesture which suggested that he spoke for them all.

But Harry pursued. "You start by being fair to one man at a time." He paused for that to work. Then he continued. "But *besides* me," he said, waving himself out of the picture, "it isn't fair to the musicians. You talk about the good of the orchestra, but you take bread out of the musicians' mouths. Do you think *they* would mind playing with me?"

"What does each man lose?" Stanley Knox asked of anyone. His eyes were rheumy and his teeth chattered in his head.

"For two rehearsals and the performance, between thirty and forty dollars a man," Harry answered.

Stanley Knox looked at Stennis. "Hee, hee," he began. His head lolled for a moment and then straightened. "That's a lot of money for a man to lose."

"Mr. Knox," Stennis explained in the tone affected for the young and the senile, "the thirty dollars lost now could mean much more to the individual members of the orchestra in the years to come. The thirty dollars now should be looked at as an investment in the future, a future of faith and trust that the Oswego Symphony will bring to its people the *best* in music *all* of the time." He said the last looking, glaring, at Harry.

The old man leaned forward in his chair, shaking, and said, "Forty bucks now is forty bucks now." His spittle flew around him. He slapped his open palm down upon the sleek conference table. And then he asked Stennis, "Have you ever heard him play?" Stennis told him no. "Then how do you know he's so bad?" The old ladies, who had been watching either Harry or Stanley Knox, now turned to Stennis. It was the first sign that Harry had a chance.

Then Stennis said, too prissily, too impatiently, "Because at fifty-one years of age you *don't* start a career as a concert violinist. You *don't* start giving concerts."

But that was exactly the wrong thing to say.

"Get your fiddle and play for us," the old man said to Harry. Harry got up and walked to the back of the room where his violin case rested on a table. He took the violin out of the case. Behind him he could hear Stennis squawk:

"Mr. Knox. This is *still* a Board meeting and we are *still* subject to the rules of parliamentary procedure."

"Shut up, Stennis," Stanley Knox said. Harry came forward and played. After he finished a pleasant little minuet of Haydn's he saw the old ladies smiling.

"Very nice," Stanley Knox said.

Stennis interrupted him, feverishly. "But Haydn minuets don't prove anything. My twelve-year-old *daughter* can play that, for God's sake."

Stanley Knox paid him no heed. "Do you know *Turkey in the Straw?*"

Harry nodded and played. Stennis was frantic. As Harry finished, he stood up. "Mr. Knox. I must insist on order." He looked around him for support, and, much as they were enjoying the music, the old ladies nodded, reluctantly, in agreement—Board business was, after all, Board business.

But Stanley Knox slapped the table for his own order. "Quiet," he commanded. "Let the boy play. Play *The Fiddler's Contest,*" he ordered Harry.

"*Mr. Knox!*" Stennis shouted.

"*Quiet!*" Knox shouted back. "Let the boy play."

Harry played.

Stennis hit his hand to his head and rushed noisily from the room.

One by one the old ladies tiptoed out, and then the treasurer left, and then Morgenstern, who walked by Harry and neither looked at him nor smiled nor frowned. Harry played on.

"Let the boy play," Stanley Knox roared, pounding the table. "Let the boy play."

By the time Alexander White ate lunch on Monday, April 24, Harry was halfway to Buffalo and his last lesson with Karnovsky. "Well, this is the week," he had cheerfully observed for White that morning. "It sure is," his wearied boss had replied. Although it was spring and the busier time of the year in the hardware business, he had suggested that Harry take off Tuesday as well as the other three and a half days of the week. Harry had objected that he didn't mind working Tuesday. "I know," White told him. "It's me. I object. Go. Get this thing over with." So Harry went. Now Alexander White sat in the Tyler Arms coffee shop-restaurant on Route 39 eating a chicken-salad sandwich. It was two in the afternoon, but he couldn't have gotten away sooner. Louis Bertrand came into the shop and walked over to where Alexander White was sitting.

"Mind if I join you, Alex?" he asked.

"No, no. Sit down," White said, gesturing to the seat opposite him. But even before Bertrand had settled creakingly down onto the cane chair, White regretted it.

"So Harry's gone and left you," he observed lightly.

For a fact, White thought, everything travels fast in a small town. "No, no. He had three-and-a-half days off so I gave him the fourth too. Let him get it out of his system. Thank God when this week is over." He went to bite into the other half of his sandwich but found that he didn't want it. He sipped at his coffee several times. Thank God when this week is over, he thought.

"But will it be over? Will he get it out of his system?"

"What? What do you mean? You don't think he's going to become a musician, do you? A gypsy?" With his voice Alexander White turned the idea down. He knew his man.

"Why not?" Louis Bertrand asked.

"*Why not? Why not?* Because a man lives and works in a place all his life, he doesn't just like that leave it. Because . . . because he likes it here, the people, his job and everything. And besides, he couldn't afford it even if he wanted to."

"Couldn't he?"

In all the weeks, in all the months that Alexander White had been engulfed and upset by the impinging consequences of Harry's action, he had never been frightened because he had never imagined conclusions more complex than the return to normal which he expected to take place after the concert. But now, for the first time, he imagined more largely.

"What does that mean?" he asked Louis Bertrand steadily and hard.

"I don't say it means anything." He looked away from White over to where George Latham, owner of the Tyler Arms, was sitting drinking coffee. He raised his voice to attract an ally. There had been something in Alexander White's tone. "But when a clerk starts spending three thousand bucks on nothing and takes off a week just like that and buys fancy violins, well . . . ." George Latham had come over and so had George Smiter, who had just entered. Bertrand looked up at them.

"Well *what*?" White demanded.

"Now take it easy, Alex," George Latham soothed him. "Lou didn't mean anything."

"*The hell he didn't.* Are you accusing Harry of something? Are you saying he's been stealing from me?" No one had said it and none of them thought that it was so, but anger breeds its kind, and mystery compounds it. It wasn't long before they were all arguing heatedly, not to prove a point but to attack an enigma. All except Alexander White, who found out that in thirty-two years men could be honest and loyal and even courageous, and that in the face of that exciting truth violin concerts or what have you for whatever reasons didn't matter much. Uncertain of Harry's compelling vision, unnerved by the ardor of his dream, certain only of the quality of the man and what that demanded of himself, he defended Harry and his concert stoutly. He was surprised to hear the things he was saying, surprised that he was saying them. But he felt freed and good.

In the Green Room Karnovsky paced incessantly.

"Relax," Harry said to him. Karnovsky looked up to see if it was a joke. Harry was tuning his violin.

"I'm relaxed," he said. "I'm relaxed. Here. Give me that," he commanded Harry and grabbed the violin away from him. He began to tune it himself, but it was in tune. He gave it back to Harry. "And don't forget, in the *tutti* in the second movement of the Vivaldi, you have got to come up *over* the orchestra, *over* it."

An electrician knocked at the door. "How do you want the house lights?" he asked Harry.

"What?" Harry said, turning to Karnovsky.

"Halfway," Karnovsky said to the electrician, who left. "Never play in a dark house," he explained to Harry. "You should always be able to see them or else you'll forget that they're there and then the music will die. But don't look at them," he rushed to add.

Harry laughed. "Okay," he said. Then he heard the merest sound of applause. The conductor had taken his place. Harry moved for the door.

"Good luck," Karnovsky said from back in the room.

"Thanks," Harry said. And then, turning, he asked, "You care?"

"I care," Karnovsky said slowly. "I care."

In the great auditorium, built to seat some five thousand, scattered even beyond random were, here and there, a hundred twenty-seven people. Most had come from Tyler, but at least thirty were people who would come to hear a live performance, especially a live performance of the Mendelssohn, anywhere, anytime. In their time they had experienced much. But what, they wondered this night as Morgenstern mounted the podium, was this? Certainly it was Morgenstern and indeed that was the orchestra and there, walking gaily out upon the stage, was a man with a violin in his hand. The house lights were sinking, as in all the concerts of the past. But where were the people? What was going on? Some four or five, unnerved by the hallucinated spectacle, stood up and raced out of the auditorium. But it was only after Harry had been playing (the Vivaldi) for three or four minutes, had wandered for ten measures until he and the orchestra agreed upon the tempo, had come in flat on two successive entrances, and had scratched loudly once, that the others—the strangers—began to get nervous. Now a fine anxiety sprang up in them. Their minds raced over the familiar grounds of their expectations—the orchestra, the conductor, the hall, the music—but nothing held together and no equation that they could imagine explained anything. One woman felt in herself the faint scurryings of hysteria, the flutters of demonic laughter, but she struggled out of the hall in time. Among the other strangers there was much nudging of neighbors and shrugs of unknowing. Then, each reassured that he was not alone in whatever mad thing it was that was happening, they sank down into the wonder of it all. And Harry got, if not good, better. He played through the rest of the first half of the concert pleasantly enough and without incident.

There was no intermission. The time for the Mendelssohn had come.

The Mendelssohn *Concerto in E minor for Violin and Orchestra, Op. 64* was completed September 16, 1844, and was first performed by the celebrated virtuoso Ferdinand David in Leipzig, March 13, 1845. From its first performance and ever after it was and is greatly received in its glory. Every major violinist since David has lived long enough to perform it well. And of concerti for the violin it is preeminent, for it combines a great display of violin technique with lyric magnificence, holding the possibilities of ordered sound at once beyond and above satisfying description. Nowhere in all the vast world of violin literature does the instrument so perfectly emerge as a disciple of itself. No one performs the Mendelssohn *Violin Concerto* publicly without entering into, at least touching upon, its tradition.

After a measure and a half, the violin and the orchestra engage each other and stay, throughout the piece, deeply involved in the other's fate. But the music is for the violin after all, so it is important that the violinist establish at once his mastery over the orchestra, determine in his entrance the tempo and the dynamic pattern that the orchestra must bow to. This Harry did. But he did not do much more. Playing with a reasonable precision and, even, polish; with, even, a certain technical assurance which allowed his tone to bloom, he played well enough but not grandly. As he concluded the first movement he thought to himself, with neither chagrin nor surprise, "Well, Belten. You're no Heifetz," and at the end of the lovely, melancholy second movement, "You're no Oistrakh, either." It was really just as he expected it would be. He was enjoying it immensely.

In the Mendelssohn *Violin Concerto* there are no pauses between the three movements. Part of the greatness of the piece lies in its extraordinary sense of continuity, in its terrific pressure of building, in its tightening, mounting pace (even the cadenza is made an integral part of the overall development). Because there are no pauses and because of the length of the piece and because of the great physical stress put upon the instrument by the demands of the music, there is an increased possibility for one of the strings to lose that exact and critical degree of tautness which gives it—and all the notes played upon it—the correct pitch. If such a thing happens, then the entire harmonic sense of the music is thrown into jeopardy.

Deep into the third movement, at the end of the recapitulation in the new key, Morgenstern heard it happen. He glanced quickly over at Harry. And Glickman, the concertmaster, heard it. He glanced up at Morgenstern. And Karnovsky heard it too. In the many times that he himself had performed the Mendelssohn, this same thing had happened to him only two terrible times. He remembered them like nightmares, perfectly. There was only one thing to do. The performer must adjust his fingering of the notes played on the weakened string. In effect, he must play all the notes on that one string slightly off, slightly wrong, while playing the notes on all the other three strings correctly. Karnovsky tightened in his seat while his fingers twitched with the frustrated knowledge that he could not give to Harry up on the stage. He was suffocating in his black rage at the injustice about to overtake this good man. That the years of absurd dreaming, the months of aching practice should be cast away by the failure of a miserable piece of gut strangled Karnovsky almost to the point of fainting.

Even before Morgenstern had looked at him (and with the first real emotion Harry had seen on that man's face), Harry had heard the pitch drop on the D string. Only his motor responses formed out of his eighteen years of love carried him through the next three speeding measures as terror exploded in him. He had time to think two things: *I know what should be done,* and *Do it.* He did it. It almost worked.

Harry Belten played the worst finale to the Mendelssohn *Violin Concerto* probably ever played with a real orchestra and before the public, any public. But it was still recognizably the Mendelssohn, it was not too badly out of tune, and if he was missing here and there on the incredibly diffficult adjustments to the flatted D string, there were many places where he wasn't missing at all. Besides

Karnovsky, Morgenstern, and Glickman, nobody in the tiny audience in the Coliseum knew what was going on. What they knew was what they heard: to most, sounds which could not help but excite; to the more knowledgeable, a poor performance of a great piece of music. But what Karnovsky knew made him almost weep in his pride and in his joy. And then, in that wonder-filled conclusion, violin and orchestra welded themselves together in an affirming shout of splendor and success. The Mendelssohn *Concerto in E minor for Violin and Orchestra, Op. 64,* was over.

In all his life Harry did not remember shaking as he was shaking now as Morgenstern and then the concertmaster grasped his hand in the traditional gesture made at concert's end. His sweat was thick upon him. He turned, smiling, to the world. Out of the great silence someone clapped. One clap. It rang like a shot through the empty hall, ricocheting from high beam to vacant seat and back. And then another clap. And then a clapping, an uncoordinated, hesitant buzz of sound rising up into the half gloom of the hollow dome. Then someone shouted out, "Hey, Harry. That was terrific."

"Yeah," fourteen rows back a voice agreed, "terrific." Two on either distant side of the auditorium whistled shrilly their appreciation. Someone pounded his feet. Joe Lombardy remembered a picture he had seen on TV once where after a concert they had shouted *bravo.*

"Bravo," he shouted. He was on his feet, waving to the stage. "Hey, Harry. Bravo." He looked around him to bring in the others. "Bravo," he shouted again. Others joined, almost chanting: "Bravo. Bravo. Bravo. Bravo." And the sounds flew upward like sparks from fire glowing and dying in the dark.

"Encore," Joe Lombardy, remembering more, shouted out. "Encore," he screamed, pleased with himself. "Encore," he knifed through the thinly spread tumult.

"Encore," the others yelled. "Encore. Encore." What there was there of Tyler cheered.

Alice Belten, sitting between her two children, holding their hands, her eyes full, laughing, was at ease. She looked up at the man on the stage. He threw her a kiss. And she kissed him back.

Then Harry Belten tuned his violin, placed it under his chin, and played his encore. And then he played another one.

Little Parameters

—It should be emphasized, however, that the probability function does not in itself represent a course of events in the course of time. It represents a tendency for events and our knowledge of events.
Werner Heisenberg

IF I AM convinced of anything at all it is that no event necessarily determines any other. At best one moment nudges the next into the curious ambit of yet more, like the jets of Kennedy in their holding patterns, like the arrow in flight which is never at any one place—or is always in one infinitely small place—at a time, like the same river which you cannot step into even once. No. Cause is our species' central fiction, and like any good fiction, it is more important than fact, *truer* as it impells us to our fates—an irony too subtle for gods to have imagined. Thus Sara and our son William, Sara's father, me—we spend our lives triangulating America seeking love and justice where the others are not, offering salvation at the end of a spear, living after a while for our pain like cancer patients at the close. For certainly it is the sandbed of our mutual suffering upon which we structure what is left of our lives, or so we presume. And I, I have more time than the others for it. I have nothing else to do.

I married Sara when I was twenty-five, she twenty-three. I was in the Army when we met, with a year more to serve, but in June, with three months of duty left, we had firmly decided upon each other. And we thought (with all the leisure and pay of a married Army clerk-typist, Specialist 4th Class to use for an extended honeymoon) that getting married now would be better than getting married in September when all at once we would be in a new city and I back into graduate school. We sought to keep the variables to a minimum. And we were right.

Those three months were an idyl neither of us, even in our most recriminating moments, will challenge. We bought a new car with my old one and much of the wedding present money and drove and drove the summer long it seemed everywhere that I could get back from by eight-thirty in the morning. (I was on a civilian component assignment and was stationed in the post office in Trenton, New Jersey, not the worst of Army circumstances.) On weekends and with an occasional Friday off, we traveled even further along the Eastern seaboard and into each other.

It was three months indispensably lovely, a vast capital upon whose high interest we lived in the narrowing years that followed. Until we woke one day to discover how much each of us had embezzled from our principal. But then that was the life for me.

It was clearly not the life for Sara's father, not the life that he wanted for her, not the life that he would madly insist upon later. But for those three months, even Aaron Krale granted us our unimpeded, elated existence.

Perhaps we should never have left it. Perhaps Sara and I should have headed south to St. Thomas or Bermuda or St. Kitts into the mythic equipoise of endless summer where what rots is buried more quickly by what grows. But it was not into that summer that we went when, in September, I was freed from the Army. It was north to Cambridge.

And our life (which I do not intend to reassemble here) was good all over again in this new way. I to find my mind and language again after the bludgeoning of twenty-four months of typing Army correspondence, Sara to establish herself in the atelier of a convenient art group. We were both back to our personal life's work in a week, every hour full of our business, saving the inbetween time for hunting Cambridge and Boston for our sparse furnishings, and Friday afternoon for the cornucopian glory of Haymarket

Square, where we bought our food for the week. Friendships were everywhere, a thick, continuous, mainly worthwhile moss-like bed of them. By June we had been here forever.

We stayed in Cambridge that first summer excepting Cape Ann excursions. I had lost two years of my career and wanted to get back some of it. Sara and two others had a show, and she sold two-hundred and fifty dollars worth of her prints. We treated ourselves to a Maine week on most of it. And even then, through most of that year, Aaron Krale kept his distance, though we began to discover him in our (Sara's) mail here and there.

Aaron Krale lived now and prospered in Des Moines, Iowa, a city of about 200,000 at the juncture of the Des Moines and Racoon Rivers. It is the capital of the state. I have never seen it and do not expect to. Nor can I imagine it—Des Moines or Iowa or any of that great prairie which is the center of this continent, although I have traveled across it at least a dozen times. Perhaps it is Eastern snobbishness, but I think not: what, after all, has the East to be lordly about? Rather, I think of the prairie as someplace to which no one went, a place to which no one *intended* to go, but where wagon trains broke down and dissolved or where river travel stopped for wood and provisions.

Gentlemen adventurers and puritan fathers sailed to America and made it a commercial nation and a New Jerusalem; Fremont and the '49ers and assorted brigands etched in our western destiny. But the rest of the land was only something to build railroads across, and here and there people simply fell off and did not die, sunk a fence post, opened a saloon, grew grain for horses, incorporated, voted, and invented a history. Aaron Krale, a century later, went to Des Moines on purpose.

Sara was seventeen, ready for her senior year in high school in Upper Darby, a suburb of Philadelphia, when her father moved her and her mother to Des Moines. He had worked in something broadly called Fabrics all his life. Sometimes he was a salesman on the road, sometimes he was vaguely involved in manufacturing material, sometimes he did not work at all. But he was always prepared—*preparing*—for enormous success. He never thought of himself as earning a living, Sara would tell me. Everything was a step—a run—at the "killing," at the swift and broad trading coup which alone could bring to Aaron Krale the success that mattered to him: Triumph. Aggressive and obsessive as a general or an athlete, the goal for Aaron Krale was spiritual—other worldly—after all. To have "made it" was what mattered, not the money nor any of the things that it could buy, including the security a constant income would provide. If security was what had mattered he would have settled in with a good line or two of children's clothes long ago.

But Aaron Krale's time and chance finally did come, and he bought a small factory and its two discount outlets. In five years he had driven—beaten—it into an enormous success, himself into wealth. It was all as he had never lost faith it would be. The money meant nearly nothing.

After her senior year in high school, Sara returned East to college, to Bryn Mawr, near to Philadelphia, near enough to Upper Darby and old friends. Except for Christmas vacation visits, Sara never went back. Even in the summers she traveled. Today she does not remember the names of any of the streets of Des Moines, Iowa.

Does anything ever begin in exactly the neat locateable way that *Beginning* implies, or are *Beginnings* merely explanations of convenience, the best we can come up with given our faltering, limited ontological thresholds and needs? The sperm and the egg? The first flash of lightning into the elemental seas and the amino acids that remained? But what about the precedent electrons? What about the vitalist patterns that drew the materials to them? Who was Aaron Krale when he sent us that first check? Who was I when I refused it? Who did we become?

Dear Sara, and Louis too,

Enclosed is a check for $100 because what I read and hear is that graduate students in history don't make much money, not even if they are veterans. And artists neither. Spend it in good health.

The letter went on to report dutifully that the mother was fine, the business good as ever, and the Iowa weather as predictably winter-foul as it could be. The letter had been dictated to and typed by /pw: Phoebe Wrightman, one of the secretaries. My answer, as far as I remember it:

Dear Aaron,

We are returning your check because we don't think parents should support their children beyond a certain age. Going to graduate school (and the attendant "poverty") is not a disaster, an unfortunate interlude in our lives. What we are doing is our life. Now we are poor, later we will be better off though never rich. But what we do now, though it prepares for later, is not done to get to later. Is this clear enough? What is going on now is natural, part of the condition of the situation we have willingly entered into. If we had gone into something else—business or government work, then we would have more money now but less time and leisure to pursue what mainly interests us: for me, the history of ideas; for Sara, the forming of color and line. So thank you for the generosity of your gift, but we are ok for this moment in our life. We have sufficient for what we should need for the life we have chosen.

But did I really say "we," or was it "I"? Did I ever make that distinction in our years together? I cannot be certain now although I remember the length at which Sara and I discussed the check and my answer. I remember her support and her prediction of his rage. And rage he did.

Dear Sufficient Ones,

I may not be educated in school, but I'm no dummy either, so I'll tell you this for free. Money is not Evil but pain and suffering is. It never hurts to have a little more than you need because you never know when you'll need a little more. Life is full of dangers. Don't be so smart to think it won't be full of dangers to you.

And more of the like, a fulminating page of it, again typed by /pw.

I do remember that Sara urged me not to answer this letter. She told me about his rages and how shallow they actually were, not mean-spirited. She and her mother had long ago learned to hove to and ride out his momentary short-lived blasts. Let it be, she urged. Nothing you say will change him; he can't understand what you are trying to tell him. He can't really understand what we are doing. He has always been confused and frightened easily by any strength that he can't see or measure or buy or sell. What is the gain to us? Besides, it is his way of loving.

No, I argued with her. That is not loving. That is possessing, and they are not the same. Aaron Krale is a spoiled brat who throws tantrums at his womenfolk unless they do his bidding. But there is more to it than that, I explained my position. In his letter—in him—there is nothing but contempt for what I do, for what you do. He is a vandal. But what it really comes to is this: Aaron Krale has no prerogatives around here. No parents do in their children's lives, fancy to the contrary though they might. Simply I will not have Aaron Krale or the Aaron Krales of this world presumptuously telling me about my life, or affecting it at all. I will not tolerate their impudence.

Why not just disregard it? Sara advised. What he says, after all, comes to nothing. Why spend yourself? And of course she was right, which is what I know now. But not then.

> *Dear Aaron,*
>
> *I did not call money evil nor imply that you were. Simply we are not in pain nor are we suffering. All I said and say again is that we want to live according to our means and that to do so is our right. No one should or can insist otherwise. So please don't be angry with us for choosing to live by our own lights. And thanks again for your generosity.*

And that was the end of it, or so I thought, for his next letter was a month in coming, and when it did, it was calm: there was no check nor mention of money nor of our past exchange.

But when Sara's birthday came, in February, he sent her—not us—*her,* five hundred dollars. As was his custom, he had looked for and found a loophole: the way of his world. With some of the money she bought lots of supplies for her work and special pieces of this and that for the apartment. The rest went into the bank to inflate our account for a few months as we nibbled it back to the lean and then to the bone again. And with some of it she bought me a gorgeous swiveling reading lamp that I had lingered over time and again in the Co-op. And I accepted it with a good grace, for if I am a fool, at least I am not petty. At least not always.

In May the Aaron Krales visited us, a small arc in the circle of a vast business trip. Aaron and Esther stayed downtown, for our apartment was much too small, but they ate with us, or we with them, daily for three days, during which we toured them from the U.S.S. Constitution to Newberry Street, from Lexington and Concord to the Widener Library.

"Very impressive," Aaron Krale said of it, of its Gutenberg Bible and First Folio. "I know of the Wideners from Philly. Do you know up in Oak Lane?" he said to Sara. "Where Aunt Miriam used to live near, in Cheltenham? We'd go up there Thanksgivings? Well up there was the Widener estate. They gave it to an art school I think. Sure, the Wideners," Aaron Krale said looking up at the monument to their dead son.

All in all it was a successful visit up to the end, busy but well-paced, and with nightly gaps for each side to rest before remounting; and lacking in any of the tensions I, frankly, expected. Aaron Krale was perfectly willing to be a guest, and he kept his wallet sheathed except for those permissible moments when he reached for the checks at Durgin Park and the Oyster House and the Parker House.

But on Friday night, the last night of their visit, Aaron Krale asked us what our plans were for the summer coming: he was talking to me. I thought we might stay in Cambridge again, using it as a base for long leaps into Maine or

Vermont or New Hampshire or wherever the camping was good. A casual summer: a little work, a little play, a generally fallow time saving up for the cold and exuberance of winter.

What Aaron Krale wanted to know was how would we like to come to Des Moines for the summer, or part of it, to see his business operation.

When we are young all of us, I suppose, sooner or later enter into the thrilling and frightening contemplation of the Mysteries: the blackness of Death, the endlessness of Space, the enormity of Time, the saltiness of the sea, where the mountains come from. I remember my breathless grapple with Fire. To think that the immense cauldron of the sun and the microscopic cells in my body were similarly active, that the flare of a match and the burst of a bomb were identical, to think all that made me swoony. My world was on fire: grass, engines, pulsating birds, my brain. Everything in the universe was doing the same thing: burning and burning. So what distinguished us was not what we did but the rate at which we did it, burned; or else how quickly some one else could channel and control the burning when it came too quickly. It was the difference between the handgrenade and the rifle shot, the difference between the precise mortar shell and the careless pioneer hoist by his own petard.

So after three decent days, Aaron Krale broke the ground rules of conduct and lit a torch in his cellar, in his magazine. Maybe that is what he came to do.

About a summer in Iowa? I don't think so I told him evenly, but I must have been glowing. I *felt* like I was glowing. Even now, these years later, I can feel again the hot constriction around my forehead and temples of that moment, the hot compress of anger and defense. It should have warned him. But could anything have? And was it warning that he wanted, or the combat instead? For how can you Win without a war?

"You're not doing anything this summer. You just said. So come to Iowa and . . . ."

". . . learn something worthwhile?" I finished for him. He did not dispute that. I had indeed taken the words from his mouth, but he would accept them whichever way they got said. So I had to explain all over again that what we did was not "nothing" to us, as meaningless and frivolous as it might seem to him or to others. And I had to add that it was extremely important to any good relationship between people that each respect the other's necessities. And all at once Aaron Krale was over the top, flying about the room, smearing the walls with his voice, staining the air with his wiping gestures, particles of him swirling in the violent air.

"What are you giving me, huh? Like you got respect for what I do? Baloney! You think I'm nothing, that I do nothing important. So that's what I think about you too. Only I want to give you something. I want to GIVE you good whatever you think of me, see. What I'm making is finally for you. When I'm done with it you could make a million from it, more. A young man you could retire. You could do your history like . . . a gentleman, not like a . . . a . . . like *this*." He described our apartment with a jerk of his head.

"You're talking about our home," I said. "You're *insulting* us, don't you see that?"

"HOME? You call this a HOME?" He was truly out of control. "Even in my worst days on the road, with the worst crap, *seconds* even in back streets in Baltimore and Winston-Salem and Charlottesville, I gave them better than this." "Them" was his wife and my wife whom he thought of exclusively as his daughter.

"Aaron!" I shouted back like slapping an hysteric. "You can't talk to people this way. You can't talk to people about their home this way."

"HOME! I could give you a mansion. But OK. So I could give you the chance to *earn* a mansion, god forbid you should take something from me."

"You don't want to give me anything, Aaron."

"HER," he screamed. "HER."

But what was *my* point in all of this? The women would say nothing, and if I stopped then so too would he. I, after all, was the material he was bursting into his spasmic ravings. After a minute of my silence, he fumed out and walked through our doorway and from the apartment house to wait for his wife on Chauncy Street in May. It was the last time I ever saw him.

"Well," Esther Krale said in another minute. "I guess we'd better be leaving." And I never saw her again either.

What can I say about Esther Krale? From personal experiences I can hardly know her. (We have spent less than ten days even near enough to talk to each other.) I never saw her in her own home. Our wedding was East, where most of the Krales' relatives and life-long friends still lived. But if I did know her better, I doubt that I would know her more. From what Sara tells me, describes for me (told, described), I think not.

Esther Krale appeared to be as blandly accepting of life as she actually was, an unquestioning corpuscle in life's veins. Sara does not remember her mother in any of those sharp, chiseled ways in which we do our important remembering. There are no incidents, no perfectly fossilized sorrows or joys that she can pick up and handle and observe in the precise details of their happening, no picnics nor arguments, no shopping trips, no confidences, no memory of learning to cook and sew, no rough loving, no silly laughter. No evocative odors to surprise her in the present and sweep her back twenty years. Sara knew her mother only as a gauzy penumbra, a hovering presence, but not even so hovering, more like an atmosphere, the slightest pressure on the skin in August when the barometer falls slower than a feather.

It cannot even be equanimity that I am describing that Sara described, for equanimity is a condition in which tensions work for and not against themselves. But there were no opposites, no surfaces and depths, no dimensions to Esther Krale. She was more like the thinnest film of water on a table top, narrowed to a single band of molecules, too insubstantial to puddle; or to break. Only a dampness. It was probably just as well for her with Aaron Krale her husband.

There is some of her mother in Sara, but more as a toner in a pigment than as a color itself. Mainly she is derived from her father. She is quickly intelligent, energetic, glittery. She is capable of huge determinations that can come at times close to possessing her, a compulsive lash which she forgets she wields, as when occasionally I have gone to fetch her from her studio to find her as crumpled as the broad lithographic sheets she has ripped apart, crumpled by her failure to make ink stain paper according to her will. But that is not Sara either, for unlike either of her parents, she is sweet though like an elegant candy after a gaudy meal: a lucid, definable taste. And she is gentle, though firm in her gentleness like in the hands of the doctor who probed me as I grew up. She is very firm.

In November Sara was pregnant. We had not planned it, but we had not *not* planned it either. We had conceived a child in that state in which most, I guess, are conceived: against the practical logics but out of compelling love; and adventure, of course. We were very happy about the pregnancy, and I read with an avidity equal to Sara's about what was coming. We read ourselves through infant feeding problems to childhood diseases beyond to the social problems of ten-year-olds (Little League tensions, sexual awareness). Our child-to-be was one of our more constant topics, and as Sara swelled with him or her (we were determined not to call the foetus "it"), so too did our interest. We were delighted with ourselves the way people must be who are elected into a select club or who get to buy a house in a neighborhood which immediately bestows upon them the rights and privileges of a subtle royalty. We felt very special indeed, closely (and smugly) a part of Life Forces and Oversouls and Humanity. But even now I think that that is true, that making a child links you up with the universe, for better or worse: its terrific beauties and terrifying truths, such as they are. Even now I instinctively do not trust people who have not made children.

My graduate work was going along splendidly. I had a small Fellowship now and a teaching Assistantship to go along with the GI Bill, so even with the pregnancy we were a little ahead of the game of penury. I had finished almost all of my course work, passed my language requirements, and would spend this third year preparing for pre-lims (which I took successfully in May) and working on my dissertation: "Elizabeth and the Sydneys in the Early Years of the Reign: 1556-1575." (I leave you with the title alone, for only someone who loved Elizabeth second only to Sara would much care about what I was exploring.) So I was getting on, a better graduate experience by far than that had by many. And though I had hoped and planned to use a fourth year to complete the dissertation and to polish it leisurely into a book, I was yet more delighted to seek my first whole professorial position. I was excited now to begin, now that there was a real starting line to approach, a real race to be run. So along with studying for exams and writing on the Sydneys, I wrote job applications and assembled my dossier.

By late April I had the job I wanted, *we* wanted: an Instructorship (automatically an assistant professor upon the acceptance of my dissertation) at Clinton College, a fine small liberal arts college in the softening land down near the Maryland-Pennsylvania border off beyond the Chadds Ford country made known so well by Andrew Wyeth. It was rural, which was what we wanted, but not so far from Philadelphia, Wilmington, Baltimore, or even Washington that we need fall out of touch because of distances. I would teach two sections of Western Civilization each semester and a course in Sixteenth Century and then Seventeenth Century History, which was ideal. Whatever Sara and I had ever wanted we were getting.

In June, still in Cambridge, the baby, William, was born, healthy and lusty as one hopes his baby will be. We moved to Clintonville in August, to an ancient excellently conditioned house on the edge of the village, our back door opening on to blue fields and into the rising nubbed hills already dying into early yellowish Fall. We rented and had an option to purchase. By the time classes began in mid-September we knew villager and faculty with the sudden and deeper warmth that one can still find in some countrysides, the way one finds other signs of a near past along the by-passed lanes: White Flash Atlantic gasoline, the yawning Fisk Tire boy ("Time to Retire") the script "Ford" on the blue background. In October I could look back upon the ascending and lengthening curve of my life: as precise as calculus, it stretched out toward my future with the strength of a cantilever. It was a well-proportioned curve that one could build upon.

But by that March I was fired, or as the euphemisms of academe have it, had been given a terminal contract. My next year at Clinton College would be my last. For whatever solace it might provide, I was assured that it was not *me.* Indeed, seven of the newest faculty were cut. The war baby boom was over, enrollment was down, operating costs were up, the economy at large was too nervously uncertain (or downright gloomy) to bring forth the usual crops of endowments, grants, and contributions. Education as a career had dived suddenly into a Great Depression which did not seem to have any reason for lessening. When a bubble bursts there are no pieces to put back together; you can only wait for a new bubble. All in all it was to be a harrowing time for all colleges, more so for the small independent colleges like Clinton, and much more so for me and my six soon-to-be-jobless colleagues, though as I was soon to find out, our number was legion.

I remember a cartoon in which a bridge over a river, just built, meets the road on the other side. But there they miss each other by a lane, so that the left lanes run into each but the right ones end empty, blank. Someone, somewhere many miles back, on one side or another (or on both?) miscalculated by an inch which grew. *Now* what? the cartoon by implication asks.

The humor is the classic humor of frustration, the slow, helplessness of failure in the midst of all our precautions—the noisy cat when we would sleep, the mud-spattering car on our way to the church. But it is humor only so far as we avoid knowledge of consequences: there is no next panel to the cartoon. After the man slips on the banana peel, we do not see him fail to rise as the blood spreads out to halo his head like a Byzantine saint. We are not around when the shrieking ambulance comes to scoop him up. Now that the bridge and the road do not meet, now that the tons of concrete and steel are poured and welded and set, what happens to whom? Is the chief engineer shot (or more likely his subordinates)? Or is it the foreman of the surveying crew? Or the road-bed graders? Blame is what we are after, by which we mean Cause. And because we assume it—Cause—we find it, Cause in the sense of the rigorously definable once-and-for-all. But I do not believe it, not in the final determinate assumption that Cause demands. If we, our lives, are *Caused,* then they are always, continuously, being Caused, and that is not what the rhetoricians of systems mean. Why did the road and the bridge not meet? Why indeed.

We did not worry much, at least not directly, through the summer. We bravely put in the garden (no perennials, we joked) and watched our William grow heavy and raucous. At my graduation in June I found how common my fate was, and how bleak the professional future. We were all stunned by the swiftness and the completeness with which our careers seemed to have ended. I at least had the cushion of a job, even if only for the year, which is more than many had who had stayed at the university to finish as I had planned to do. Well, I reasoned, if they had no life now to begin, at least they had no life to undo. But that kind of arithmetic did nothing for anyone.

I did not get another job. Through the winter I wrote three hundred letters, and one gross sign of what we were all up against was that the rejection letter, once traditionally typed, was now Xeroxed or offset: the number of job requests pouring in would have meant a department secretary her day to answer.

By April I had taken to panicking in the early morning, around three o'clock. Then Sara would come and soothe me and I would fall back to sleep to wake again by eight to be at my mailbox by nine. By nine-fifteen it was bad all over again. By the beginning of May I was seriously bashed in by the demonic irony of getting two articles accepted by major scholarly publications. And when, soon after, a chapter from my dissertation was selected for an anthology on sixteenth century life in England, I could take no more.

Rather, I had taken enough. I stopped trying to be only a professor or student of history any longer. No one, no *they* or *it,* had done me in. It had happened. Now I would have to try to start *something;* I would have to try beginning again. So Aaron Krale's letter came at a bad time.

Dear Children and Grandchild,

It is naturally with great unhappiness for you that I see by all the newspapers and magazines that times are tough for the teachers. And also that you have not yet gotten a new job. [Sara had been keeping him posted.] It is a crying shame that people so important to the society as teachers should be having such a tough time. But what can be done? Things are a little tough all over. Even with me I've had to cut back production, only even with cutting back I'm busier than I can handle. What I could really use is some smart help.

I know how you feel about this so please don't get angry. Just hear my proposition. The way I see it, if you don't get a job teaching, then you'll have to get a job doing something else. So why not work here, for me, at a very good salary?

Also there is this advantage. There is just starting here in Des Moines a two-year community college and by coincidence I am a lodge member and good friend of one of the Board. I told him about Louis, his schooling and writing, and my friend thinks somebody like Lew could maybe fit in well with the new school. Anyway, I include the address and other information as well as my friend's name and address to write to if Louis is interested.

I thought maybe he could work part time for me, or else full time for me and part time for the school, if that comes through. Or else full time for me.

My friend tells me too that there are excellent research facilities at Drake University which is here in Des Moines, which you could use. Also I add we are only 320 miles from Chicago, 110 miles from Iowa City, where the University of Iowa is, and 30 miles from Ames, where Iowa State University is.

Let me know what you think. Any details you want I can give you in plenty, just say the word. If you work for me, let me tell you honestly, I am not so bad to work for. You could ask anyone. I am not a bad boss.

I will write again with more home news soon. Send pictures of my beautiful grandson. If you need anything, just say the word.

Love from your father and mother
Aaron

ak/lm

"Who is 'lm'?" I asked. "What happened to Phoebe Wrightman?"

"Is that all you can say?" Sara said.

"Yes. For the moment, yes." But I didn't have many moments left. And by the first of August they had run out.

We returned to Cambridge, to North Cambridge nearer to Arlington. I began to look for work, for anything. But if I was unqualified for much—mechanic, press operator, short-order cook—then I was overqualified for nearly the rest. As one job agency explained it (accurately): I would always be looking for the chance to get back to college teaching, so employers didn't want personnel who had more than what was needed for what they were hiring. And as for editorial positions or advertising or public relations—they were too few and we were too many.

I began application for welfare, which I rather quickly got, which surprised me—and offended me—as if there were no argument, no doubt that I was through, no amazement or incredulity that I should be useless; that society in its beneficence would care for its aged and infirm and for me.

With what we had saved in the past two years against this day, along with the $137.30 a month from Welfare, we would last out the year. By then something would happen, a teaching job (unlikely) perhaps, but certainly a future. For we would only permit ourselves one year of living like this. During it we would sort our alternatives and create and discover new ones. We were resourceful people, young and strong. If we were down, we were far from out. That sort of thing. We would work at summer resorts in Maine and winter in Florida—or the reverse. I would apprentice as a carpenter. Sara would draw charcoal portraits at Super Markets and county fairs. Supervisory positions in Vista or the Peace Corps awaited. And on.

It was an endless list, heady and enticing, like the blazing wardrobe room of an old theater where in an afternoon one could prance into and out of time, condition, and circumstance—the bewigged fop to the sabled Hamlet, a pirate from Penzance or a captain in the Lafayette Escardille. Sara and William and I became all the things there were to become in that blue September in the Commons.

But one day in February in the North Cambridge apartment alone with William, I was made as vacant as the city snow, cold and sad, a man easy at last to do nothing but suffer the vicissitudes, to endure as numbly as the snowmounded fireplug the utter exhaustion of doubt as much as of hope, my life become a terrifyingly vast hollow from whose sides no echo or light reflected. I had that Vision, and it cracked me forever. From that day to this one I have taken into me that imprint of Despair so that whatever else, whatever joys and accomplishments may yet remain, will be forever tinged and discolored by it, all of our lonely pageants perceived in their insubstantiality, and faded. February and I had come to the bottom of things together. In the deep, empty well of the year, I knew I would never wholly climb out.

Sara returned at three o'clock. She too had been unable to get steady employment, but had gotten a week of work now and then on rush layout and production jobs as well as an occasional piece of free lance. We couldn't pay for her part of the art group any more and so she sketched at home and worked on some large, listless acrylics. She came in, some groceries in one arm, mail in another hand, snow melting on her brow. She settled, made coffee, and we sat down to the mail.

There was always a lot of mail. Almost all to whom we wrote replied, and we wrote to many: for jobs, for information, to friends to make sure that they at least were still there and had not dissolved like the rest of our world.

Today there was the usual crop of rejections, requests for my dossier, government (federal and state) pamphlets, an immigrant's kit from Canada (we were considering), and a letter from Aaron Krale. It was Sara's birthday again. I had forgotten, but he had not. The check was for a thousand.

> *Dear Sara and Louis and William,*
>
> *Happy birthday. Business is good, better, best, so use this in good health and never worry if you need more, just say the word.*
>
> *Your mother is fine and sends her regards and thanks for the pictures of Willie, who is certainly growing up big and strong. Your mother clucks from the picture that she sees he has patches on his winter coat, but you know your mother.*
>
> *The business is so good I am thinking of maybe taking in a small part partner. I should be slowing down instead of speeding up. Help I can hire, but you need someone who has a stake in the business if you want him to really take care of things.*

The letter went on and on. If Aaron Krale was a busy man, he wasn't busy that day. Or else he was busy in a different direction.

"The letter is comical, it's so obvious," I said.

"Would it be so terrible for you to work for him?" Sara asked. She had never said that before, or even indicated ever considering it. And maybe she wasn't even then. Maybe it was simply the natural time to speculate, to examine, to once more turn our lives in our hands like a globe and to study the terrain of it for insights and solutions. So we talked.

Me: 1. To work for Aaron Krale would be dishonest, a false pretense on my part. I would always be trying to get back to my profession which, incredibly, I must continue to believe I someday will. Therefore: I would leave his employment with a day's notice if necessary. That is not what he has in mind when he wants me to come to work for him. He wants me—us (YOU)—for keeps.

2. Aaron Krale wants his own way. That's what his life is about. What he enjoys is winning in the games he invents, is overcoming the difficulties he sets himself. I don't want to be a part of that. I don't like Aaron Krale or people like him.

Sara: 1. It would be no less dishonest leaving a stranger than it would be leaving him. In fact you could even make that a condition—the clear understanding that you might leave at any moment.

2. You can't make the boss's personality a factor in getting a job. If you could get a job tomorrow from someone maybe a lot worse that he, you'd take the job, wouldn't you?

and 3. Pride is a luxury.

"And we can't afford luxuries right now, can we?" I said. "Is that the point?" I drank hard at my coffee. "Why the hell not? We've got a tax-free thousand bucks. We're rich, baby, *rich.* You're an heiress, for christsake."

"Oh, Lou," she reached across to me, but I pulled back my hand, not through with my self-pity.

"Why work at all? For anybody? Just get him to send us a grand a month. You could get a studio and I'd go back to the Sixteenth Century and Willie would go to nursery school. Just say the word. Remember, if you need more, just say the word. So maybe you should say $1500 a month so we can save something for a summer vacation. Where would you like? Martha's Vineyard? Nantuckett?? Would you like a trip to Europe, perhaps?"

"Yes," she said. "Yes. I'd like that very much." And then she said. "Don't make such a virtue out of our necessity," and rose to wash the coffee cups. What a great line! Even then, through my increasingly self-seeking sorrow, I think I admired it, and surely I do now, even if I could not allow it to guide me.

Sara did not "just say the word" then, and it was not to the islands or Europe that we went but to the hospital. I with appendecitis, Willie with a broken arm. The thousand went quickly. And I became more Job-like, but without either his faith or courage, only his afflictions, only his boils and running sores.

And at last came the pestilence of Aaron Krale's money, for when Sara, in the great dignity of her love for her son and husband, afforded herself no luxuries and did "say the word," the money came in bales: five thousand for openers, no strings attached. And she and Willie did mend and thaw through the summer in Chilmark on the Vineyard. But I, I would not, and even now.

It has been two years since that breaking February. Sara and Willie live in Philadelphia. I see them about once a month. Sometimes we all take day-long rides down to the Maryland border, to Clintonville, which Willie, of course, does not remember. We do not look up anyone; we only linger a little in that earlier time. Sara and I do not know where we are or exactly how we got here, only that we are like galaxies on opposite sides of the universe, out of our own control, thrusting away from each other with rising velocity so that soon, I am fearful, we will fall out of each other's ken, able to communicate only indirectly through our satellite.

My career is still a shambles, though knitting up, a patchwork affair of part-time teaching in an evening college, reading for an educational testing bureau, book reviewing for the Christian Science Monitor, and some at-home editorial work for a local publisher of high school texts.

I have not won reinstatement. And as time passes my chances of return lessen, although there are recent possibilities of a Fulbright, but what would I go for, or come back to? But it may be an opportunity not to be missed. I talk to Sara about it when we meet.

But Sara has decided to accept her patrimony and to give her son and herself (and me if I would) what we should have—the valid adornments of a life well-lived. And in truth I am pleased for her and Willie that the abundances of travel and material, of unenforced leisure and self-expressive opportunities are theirs, that neither of them will live a crabbed existence. But I cannot partake of it myself.

And there has been bitterness. Aaron Krale and I have written to each other and still do with the violence of men tumbling down mountainsides with their hands at each other's throat, too busy injuring to stop their own fall. He curses me and beats me with the club of his common sense, and I hit him with all I have left, which is to forbid him Willie. I tell him I forbid him to see his grandson. And I tell this to Sara. We are not actually (is law actual?) separated and so I have partly the right to determine in this matter. And Sara, who does not want to leave me, yet, will not turn our lives on this one issue. She agrees but cheats to placate him and does allow Aaron and Esther to visit, though she will not visit them in Des Moines, much less go to live there, as he desires and urges. I find out usually by what Willie says (Sara will not confuse him, will not tell him to lie to his father), and I fight with her half-heartedly, for I do not care if Aaron sees his grandchild. Only that he must do it this way, *my way*. For I am the abiding obstacle in his life now, the irritant grain of sand he cannot make a pearl upon, me, the irrational historian of grief.

So I have come to live in all this, the little parameter of my life.

And Aaron Krale, he waits.

Old Vemish

THE S.S. SOLAR sailed from New York City, Pier 62, precisely at ten o'clock on the morning of a clear April for twelve Caribbean days (seven, really, counting off getting there and getting back) and eleven nights. By 10:45 the glistening red, white, and blue ship, about 14,000 tons, its 250 passengers and crew of eighty, had sailed smoothly beneath the Verrazano Bridge through the Narrows into the Lower Bay, and then into the calm Atlantic heading south.

It has been a fine leaving, fruitbasket parties and all, a calypso band, streamers and confetti even. But by 12:30, Clifton Booth had his troubles. Not that he hadn't expected them. As a Tour Director for five years with the Lootens Line and as a specialist in geriatric cruises ("The time to ship out is when you have the time"), the solving of troubles was what Clifton Booth more than half existed for.

About the time the ship had cleared the smokey land for certain, the dramatic Battery shrinking in smudged silvery sticks, the whining complaints began to flicker down upon him like a new and larger confetti than that at the recent dock. Arthur Lewis, one of Clifton Booth's three assistants (they stood watches just like any Ablebodied Seaman), brought him, about every fifteen minutes, a wailing sheath of urgently scribbled protests and pleas: someone had lost his teeth, others were suddenly displeased with their cabins, seasickness swept over them like a plague.

But mainly there was just the grumpiness of the old that flared whenever they were dislocated, shifted out of the comforting familiarity of personal routines and the securing knowledge of where the bathroom is in the dark and what all the creaking and vibrations in their own houses meant. It was just the newness, Clifton Booth knew, that unnerved them for a while. That is why he stayed in his cabin for the first two hours of actual seatime and did not heed any of the yellow notes. By the afternoon the teeth would be found, the cabins unpacked in and made homelike, and the captain would have announced that the ship's stabilizers were now operating, thereby making seasickness modernly impossible, and the last queasiness would instantly disappear.

All except Clifton Booth's.

Unfortunately, but in a minor way, Clifton Booth needed a few hours at the beginning of each tour to regain his "sea stomach," although his difficulty wasn't a matter of equilibrium in the inner ear.

"Nerves," Clifton Booth said to Arthur Lewis. "Nervousness. Not *about* anything, do you see; just nervousness *in itself*. Do you know what I mean, Arthur?"

"Yes sir. I think so, sir," Arthur replied placing the newest messages upon the rising pile on the table next to the Director's bunk-bed.

"How are they going?" Booth asked, not looking out from under the damp, cool compress over his eyes.

"About the same, sir. In number and content. The only thing different so far is a complaint about a bridge partner."

"A *what?*" Clifton Booth said, almost rising. "A *bridge partner?* Oh God," he said sinking back laughing. "And I thought I had heard them all." He sighed happily. He was feeling much better. He drifted off to visions of blue St. Croix, of a pleasant afternoon's talk with Martinson in his cool English garden in the middle of tropical Guadeloupe, of the Barbados rug by a native weaver from high in the hills which he had decided at last to buy for his New York apartment.

He awoke in ten minutes to the yellow rustling by his ear.

"Fewer now," Arthur Lewis said to him, "And the complaints about the tour are beginning. Phase two."

"Ah," Booth sighed again, his strength and stability almost returned now as the pieces to his pattern, smoothed and worn by five years of experience, slipped easily almost all into their managed place. "It's going to be a good trip, this one. I can feel it." He took off the compress. All his color was back, replacing the yellowish stain around his temples and the corners of his mouth. "After a while, Arthur, you can *tell* about these things." He sat up. "You can just *tell.*"

But he was wrong. He hadn't yet encountered Martin Vemish.

Martin Vemish was sixty years old, a short man, gleamingly bald, but not fat although a little stout. He looked open and hard, smooth-faced but uncompromising, well-tailored but like a man high in the echelons of a Labor union who seemed uncomfortable to be there in his fancy office, remembering as he did the raw battles at Gate Four of Henry Ford's Rouge plant, and things like that. But Martin Vemish's stern appearance owed more, probably, to the fat, inelegant cigar he was always puckered upon than to any individual facial feature. He was, however, *as a person,* what he looked like.

Martin Vemish owned a wall paper and paint store in Ogahala Park on Long Island, about twenty miles from the city, a community at once as old as Eastern America, but as new as last week. He had owned the store early in his life, for forty years, getting into business and a large inventory six months before the Crash, long before latex paints and rollers and do-it-yourself housewives, in the years when wall paper was the major wall covering. For many years now, however, as he watched Ogahala Park turn from trees into houses, he had sold much more paint than paper, though he had his preferences. ("There's nothing *to* paint. Nothing to see, to *feel.* The paint covers. The paper *is!*") But he was in business and so he sold paint.

Still, affection and loyalty paid off. With the new affluence that had descended upon his corridor of Long Island, he sold a lot of paint, but paper made a comeback, and his sentimentally large selection and knowledge of papers had quickly established him as the wall paper center of the Ogahala Park area and even beyond. Because of this more than himself alone, he had grown near to "rich," or what his father would have called "rich." To Vemish, today, it was merely called "plenty." He had "plenty." You had to have it, or someone did, for you to leave your business and go sailing around the Caribbean for twelve days in the S.S. Solar, not that he wanted to be there.

He and his gray wife, Sara, were there in the light on the third deck of the starboard side of the throbbing ship because of their son, or, more exactly, because of their daughter-in-law, Norma, whom, even after thirteen years, Martin Vemish had never gotten to like very much. Still, a man's wife is his own concern, even if the man is of your flesh, so Vemish had been silent, utterly civil, and generous at every bad turn of Herbert's faltering business life. He, Vemish, had maintained Herbert and Norma and the two grandchildren in a manner that Herbert's and Norma's earliest young hopes for Herbert's ventures had taught Herbert and Norma to expect. They had always lived in a nice house and drove a nice car and wore nice clothing just as if Herbert were a successful shoe salesman or civil servant working in the Post Office, which he was not.

What he had been for eleven years was everything and nothing—a nice guy looking for a big break who never found it. What he was now and had been for the past two years was his father's partner.

After Herbert's final failure (selling space in a giant frozen food locker which he had rented too far out on the Island), Martin Vemish decided to pull Herbert into the business. Years back, even when the boy was still in the Army, he had offered him. What, after all, was he supposed to do with the business when he was through with it? What are sons for, anyway? But Herbert had refused through a glass of larger dreams, and Vemish, and Sara, too, had let him go in peace, even if they did stand around to pick him up when he got knocked down.

Vemish and his wife were strong like rocks are, not like rivers. Their strength was more in remaining than in doing;

but they were parents too. So when the frozen food locker business failed and the home mortgage payment came due (along with the car and the electric and a dozen others) after eleven years Martin Vemish pushed his son a little, and from the other side, Norma pushed him a lot. By the end of a nice evening, Vemish had his man.

Now, two years later, he was reaping one of his rewards: a vacation.

In forty years he had never taken a formal vacation because he and Sara didn't feel anything about them. In the '30s of the Depression no one in a little business took a vacation: there was too much of doing nothing in a day as it was. And later, after the war, it wasn't natural to him to start something new. If sometimes he didn't want to work or Sara wanted to visit her sister in Rochester, New York, or it was too hot, he would simply close the store for a day and sometimes two and go away. That was all. Vacations just never occurred to them. Where they were and what they did pleased them enough. But one of the strongest levers Norma had used on Herbert two years before at the partner-making was that, as his father's partner, he could make it possible now for his father and mother to go on a vacation, to "get away."

"Do you know that they've never, *never,* taken a real vacation?" she had said. "Can you imagine, Herb? Can you imagine? *Forty years with no vacation.*" There was horror in her voice.

Herbert Vemish, like his father, figured that what a man did with his own life was his own affair, but this, as Norma was insistently pointing out, was different. A son, after all, did have some obligations.

"And Herb, darling," Norma had put her hand on his arm, "Martin and Sara aren't getting any younger. It's not so easy anymore." Then, urgently, "Herbie, Herbie, have a little consideration for *them.*" That did it.

Herbert Vemish turned and looked at his father and then at his mother and said, "Ok." He put out his hand to his father. "Partner."

Martin Vemish looked at his son looking at him *that way* and wanted to protest, wanted to make it harshly clear to him that at fifty-eight he, Martin Vemish, was healthy and vigorous enough to make it to seventy-eight, at which time he could be looked at *that way,* maybe. Not until. But the whole point was to get Herbert to do what he was doing right now: agreeing. If Norma's argument worked, so let it. Martin Vemish took his son's hand and shook upon the deal. He and Sara had gotten what they wanted, Norma had gotten what she wanted, and Herbie was pleased to be able to do something good for his aging parents, so what the hell.

Except that Herbie started to do good to them right away. He was familiar enough with the paint and paper business from high school days when he had worked after school and weekends so that in less than a month he could pretty much run things. Besides, there wasn't much that could go wrong, and, anyway, if Herbert Vemish hadn't been a success in his commercial ventures, at least he wasn't a fool. Thirty days into his partnership he began to urge his father to "Take a nap" or "Take the afternoon off" or "Go up to the mountains for the weekend." As the summer drew on he began asking his father where they were planning to go.

"Go? Go where?" his father asked.

"On your vacation," the son answered, a gallon of Bone-white Flat Interior in either hand.

"Vacations, vacations! Will you stop already with your vacations!"

"No!" the son shouted back. "No! You're fifty-nine! A year from now you'll be sixty! *SIXTY!*" He said it the way they say "Bad breath" or "Body Odor" on the TV commercials. "You've got to start taking it *easier.*"

Martin Vemish walked away from his son that day and disregarded the subject whenever he, frequently, brought it up, but after two years the father calculated that the weekly turmoil of Herbie's now obsessive concern was costing him more of his inner peace than any vacation possibly could: he finally agreed. After all, it wasn't that he *disliked* vacations; he didn't even know anything about them.

"All right! *ALL RIGHT!*" he shouted at his son across a rising square of five pound packages of Plaster of Paris that the two of them were stacking up in a corner of the store. It was February and snowing, and the son had been at him from the first thing in the morning. "*ALL RIGHT! I'LL GO!* Make the plans! Buy the tickets! Send me! Just leave me alone already!"

At supper he told Sara, and even as they were finishing their after-dinner tea the phone rang with Norma to tell them that she had selected a Caribbean cruise. She told them how long they would be gone, where they would go, what they could buy at what low prices, how warm it would be, and about thirty other things. She didn't tell them until another time that the cruise was restricted to sixty-year-olds and up, and up. When she did tell them, the way she put it was, "And one of the absolutely best things about *this* cruise is that you'll have so much in common with every one else."

Right then Martin Vemish almost cancelled out. It would have been a good day for Clifton Booth if he had.

At three o'clock Clifton Booth put on his lightly braided uniform and called an assembly of his charges, at which time he introduced himself and his assistants much in the manner of a Dean on first meeting with the collected Freshmen. There was a continual bantering going on between Clifton Booth and himself, a delicious interior dialogue that his Graciousness permitted them a glance at—light, fluffy as sea foam, witty, assuring, charming; but firm, too. He told them in detail about the numerous activities that he had planned for them on shipboard. He talked about the games, the dances, the bridge tournaments, the shuffleboard and other contests (and the prizes), the movies, the lectures, the concerts. He told them about the food: its staggering variety, its incredible abundance, its unending availability, and the special dietary considerations that some might need (low salt menus and the like). He explained to them their proper procedure while ashore at the daily stops the ship would make: first the guided tour for those who wanted it

("Though I can promise you that the tours are unquestionably *the* way to see the most in the time available") and then the period for shopping. ("Although I guess the husbands would just as soon we didn't leave the ship at all.") Laughter.

He told a delighting story of a clever woman shopper who brought from an out-of-the-way shop on Martinique what turned out to be a real "find": a handcarved (not turned) salad bowl made of Martinique teak, perhaps the rarest wood in this hemisphere, maybe, even, the world. His audience ooo-ed. Similar things were always happening.

And then he told them of the laggardly pair, continually late for everything, who, after a number of close calls, finally missed the boat in St. Kitts and had to stay there three days before another cruise boat came along to save them.

"*Three days* they lost out of their once-in-a-lifetime cruise. *Three days* in St. Kitts with nothing to do but sit on the beach and stare at the water." He let his lovely voice show compassion for their loss, but pique at their foolishness. He let his voice rise up to drive into his listeners the critical importance of promptness in returning to the boat.

"Where ever you are," he admonished now, strictly, "keep an ear tuned to the boat whistle. When you hear the whistle it will mean you've got an hour to get aboard ship. *Aboard* it." He said it all again and added details.

This was a no-nonsense thing. Fun was fun, but there were still obligations, duties. "Let's remember," he said, his voice soothing down into his peroration, "While we're all on this ship together, we are like a little world. We've got to be considerate of each other in order for any of us to live happily. We've got to think of the next guy. So let's see if we can't do a better job on the world of this ship, the good old S.S. Solar, than we, as mankind, have done on the world of the old ship Earth."

Somehow it all sounded so familiar, as if they had all been here before.

Still they applauded strongly and started to nod in sage agreement. It sure wasn't an easy thing to do, running a cruise and looking out for the happiness and safety of 250 people. They felt that they should feel thankful to have someone as pleasant and sensible as Director Booth to take care of them. Well, they were going to do whatever *they* could to make it easier for him to make it easier for them. With a little pitching in all around there was no reason why the next eleven days and ten nights couldn't be as nice as any they had ever spent—nicer, even. At least now they had a clearer understanding of why they were here.

Clifton Booth praised them, then, for their considerate attention and announced that an Introduction Tea would start at four o'clock in the Main Lounge. He hoped to meet all of them individually there and that they would all get to know each other. Once more they applauded back what was now their affection.

All but Martin and Sara Vemish, who had not attended the meeting.

Back in the office that adjoined Booth's stateroom, Arthur Lewis reported the Vemishes.

"Are you sure they *knew* about the meeting? Are you sure they *understood?*" Clifton Booth was standing before his mirror straightening himself out. He spoke to the reflection of his assistant.

"Yes sir. When I saw them sitting there I asked them if they knew about the meeting. They did. I explained that it was a very important meeting because it outlined the basic procedures for the cruise."

"And?" Booth was impatient. Recalcitrants were such a bother.

"They said they didn't care. They liked it out on deck."

"And?"

"That was all, sir."

"What do you mean, 'That was all?' " Booth turned and put on his lordly white, black-beaked hat and started for the door.

"That's all they said, sir. That's all they would say," Arthur Lewis said, saying all *he* could say, again to the back of Clifton Booth as he moved into action.

When it came to tactics the only ones that Martin Vemish knew about were grim. In 1948 when Macy's, the first of the big department stores to open branches in the suburbs, opened in the new Ogahala Park Shopping Center and started to move for all the business, including the paint business, in the area—for *all* of it—Martin Vemish fought back the only way a man who doesn't fight much fights when he has to: deadly. Restraint, after all, is a condition of experience, a knowledge earned from the *use* of power. Martin Vemish, lacking experience, knew nothing about restraint. He went for Macy's throat. Macy's was threatening him and it was all he knew what to do.

He advertised for the first time: in newspapers, with handbills, with posters on telephone poles as if he were running for political office. He cut prices below even what Macy's was selling at, and *then* he ran special sales. He wrote sputtering letters to the Chamber of Commerce and worse to the Letters-to-the-Editor page of the paper trumpeting his outrage. He cut the letters out of the newspaper and pasted them in the window of his store between the red and blue signs that were giving his business away gallon by gallon. "Communists," he called Macy's in his letter. He compared them to the Russians overpowering the courageous little countries of eastern Europe. "Un-American," "Death of the Free Enterprise System," "Low Prices Today, Macy's Prices Tomorrow" were some of his titles.

During the winter, when business was slow, nobody painting much of anything but chairs, cabinets, and a few interior walls, he almost went broke. There were bitter days in February when he looked over the classified section wondering about what sort of job he might soon have to get.

But in the spring he won. Macy's relented, withdrawing to its enormous share of the market. From then on Vemish's business rose from the ashes.

Had he known more about the world than he did, perhaps Martin Vemish would not have fought with Macy's the way he had, but he did not know, and he never found out, and, anyway, he couldn't stop himself from fighting against a thing he hadn't started.

Clifton Booth knew none of this as he approached the Vemishes, their eyes shut, their faces uplifted to the western sun, at pleasant ease thirty miles abeam of Stone Harbor, New Jersey.

"Hello," Clifton Booth said, coming between Martin Vemish and the sun.

"Hello," Vemish said looking up into the shadow over him. Sara opened her eyes but said nothing.

"I'm Clifton Booth, your Tour Director."

"*Your* Tour Director, not mine," Vemish said.

Clifton Booth had floundered about in real estate before he became, at forty, a Tour Director, and found his destiny. He was as successful at the one job as he had not been at the other, as if large parcels of land were too difficult for him to manage compared to the handling of the smaller geographies of old people on tightly scheduled boats. He was very good at it, at adjusting the old people to his organization for them, for he was, as he had discovered, his century's surrogate king, the *technician* of power, the Manager.

From the start he had indicated great skill in Tour Directing and had moved from an assistantship to his own boat in exactly one year, half the usual time. In the Lootens Line it was generally conceded that no one ran a better, a more orderly cruise than he, a "tighter" ship. There was even talk that he would be the successor to the post of Chief Director, whose responsibility it was to oversee the training of the others as well as to sit in upon cruise policy decisions. All in all, Clifton Booth knew where he stood, and why.

Confidently Booth approached the Vemishes another way. He had ways and ways. On every cruise he met some petulant, persistently cantankerous anger of an old one, who had been abraded in some way by a petty feature or detail of the planned and plotted existence that he had signed on for for twelve days and eleven nights. The outburst would flash until he, Booth, came and put it out. He understood: it was the way of the old. He was a gentle man, and patient. His patience was a weapon, and a great one. But not his only one. He knew a lot of things to do to people to get them straightened out and running true to his form in no time at all.

Only with Martin Vemish it was different. With him it wasn't some little senile bitching or petty gripe; it was a deeper anger and an abiding one, and over and through it all flickered contemptuous fire. Vemish despised the idea of the cruise itself. He saw it as a shoddy trick that the strong young played upon the weakening old, a facade that children insisted their parents put on as the final price to pay for affection, as the last humiliating demand for their death. Vemish hated it and Clifton Booth, the agent, even as he looked at him for the first time. This *attendant,* the ship his home, this "parent" to the childish and cowered old, himself rooted in no fading memories dissolving in time's acid, stretched beyond no context other than himself, bound to shore by no perdurable threads of kindred love—it was easy for him to imagine things to be other than they were and to manage a world as he thought it was and therefore should be. And wasn't that what he was getting paid by the children to do?

Martin Vemish didn't want to be on the S.S. Solar's geriatric tour, not for twelve days or twelve minutes, but if he had to be, then he would be there on his own terms, which is exactly what he told Director Booth.

"Listen," finally he said, not bothering to take the cigar out of his mouth, "You and your people leave *me* alone and I'll stay out of *your* way. No trouble from either end, ok?" He closed his eyes and eased back in the deck chair.

"Mr. Vemish," Booth began, "I don't think you understand. My job on this cruise is to serve you, to make you as comfortable . . . ."

"Fine," Vemish interrupted him. "Fine! Exactly! Good! Serve me by leaving me alone!" He closed his eyes again. Booth changed his voice a little.

"Mr. Vemish, running a cruise is a complicated thing. You don't have to participate but there are certain details about life on a cruise ship that you *do* have to be made . . . ."

"Screw!" Vemish said chomping down on his cigar, this time without opening his eyes. Clifton Booth turned to Vemish's silent wife.

"Mrs. Vemish," he began, all but unaware of his tone, the patronizing whine in which he spoke to wives about their childish husbands. But Sara Vemish cut him off.

"You heard him," she said.

Director Booth stalked away, surprised at the motion of the ship.

So *that's* the way it was going to be, Booth thought as he moved sightlessly through the ship's familiar corridors to his office-cabin. So the Vemishes didn't want to play the game by the rules. Well, he'd see about that. He'd just see about *that.* Why in hell, he wondered, did they take the cruise? To make misery? to bring gloom and trouble instead of happiness? It comforted him to think that people who took cruises that they didn't want were just those kinds of oddballs who required the most dealing with, but that it equaled out because the hard-heads were always easiest to handle if they didn't come around, if they didn't *shape-up*: he could always throw them out. In five years (four years of his own command) he had done it fifteen times, sent couples home. He would give them a letter of refund credit and arrange a flight out from the next island that a plane could land on. A few times he had to get them space on a returning boat because they wouldn't fly, but he had managed even that.

Fifteen times! Which was about fifteen times more than any other Tour Director had done it. At first the Home Office was disturbed and then appalled, but when the letters from the other passengers, some of them, particularly the older ones, started to mount up, letters praising Booth for his decisiveness in removing the "spoilers" (for he would always make it publicly clear to his cruise why he had taken such a drastic step), his actions took on the stature of policy and Booth found his geriatric *metier.* The Lootens Line discovered that it could guarantee your shipboard ease and pleasure (what didn't fit, throw out), and its advertising began to reflect that. So Martin Vemish had just better watch out. On the last call, if it went to that, the Director always would hold all the top cards.

Clifton Booth sat at his desk with the Vemish dossier in his hand. He read over the bland particulars: Martin Vemish . . . Sara . . . Ogahala Park . . . business . . . . Down at the bottom of the page-long form, in the Activities and Interests Section, none of the numerous boxes was checked.

"We've got us a problem case," Booth said over to the other side of the cabin where Joseph Crenshaw, the second of Booth's assistants, sat recording into the Tour Log the events of the mid-watch, twelve to four, his responsibility.

Joseph Crenshaw had been a Tour Director himself, once, but he had been caught by a husband performing a duty beyond his call. The Lootens Line was a humane one, and it demoted Crenshaw instead of firing him, but it demoted him for good. He had worked for them for sixteen years now, ashore and aboard ship, and he would never be a Tour Director again. But he liked the life; he was obliged to no one but himself and his own pleasures, of which there were many in the April islands of the azure Caribbean.

"Who's that?" Crenshaw asked not looking up, not caring. He had sailed with Clifton Booth frequently in the past and preferred it: Booth took so much of the work upon himself and to his heart that the Assistant Directors had little more to do than relax and enjoy the cruise, not that there was that much to enjoy with the "gerries." Joseph Crenshaw knew, then, what was going on in his superior; he could imagine, then, what the outcome would be. He didn't permit himself the luxury of judgment nor that expense of energy. What energy he had he used to pursue his own interests. Let Booth pursue his own.

"This Martin Vemish," Booth said. "Apparently he thinks we're going to turn this boat around for him. Well, he's got another think coming, I'd say." Joseph Crenshaw nodded his head and wrote on. Booth flipped the dossier down on his desk and settled back to think the situation through. He didn't want to lose perspective.

So far nothing disturbing to the others had actually happened and that was the important thing. As long as Vemish could keep it that way, then Booth *would,* in fact, he promised to himself, leave him alone.

There had been others, after all, on every cruise. On every cruise there had been those whom you couldn't really think of as a part of things: singles who had been sent on the cruise to recover from some grief, or to meet someone new; newly married old people oddly shy as they had not been the first time forty or fifty years before; and there were those touched by a sudden, morbid depression. Booth left them. Their sympathy-evoking presence didn't help the gay *tone* of the cruise, but they were no threat to it.

But Vemish was. At the end of it all, Booth knew that finally there would be no way that either of them could leave the other alone. And even if there had been, Booth knew that with a Vemish it would have to come to more than that because he looked at his job in creative terms: he imagined that he was a craftsman.

Booth saw each of his cruises as a separate object, as a made thing, like a sculpture or a painting or a good piece of furniture. It wasn't enough for him just to float his tour safely and comfortably from New York to the Caribbean and back again; he wanted the cruise to be, as every artist wants his work to be, memorable. *He* wanted to remember; he wanted *his passengers* to remember. He kept the collective gift that almost all his cruises had given him as an athlete keeps his trophies, the date of the cruise noted on a tag gummed to the bottom of the gift. He Xeroxed the Tour Log. He had innumerable pictures. At the end of a good cruise he was high; at the end of a bad one, low. And there had been bad ones, at least by his lofty estimation. Every time they had been the result of blighters like the Vemishes, who like dark fists of clouds on the clear horizon, could become in less than an hour black and fearful storms.

In the face of their clear threat to his accomplishment and personal happiness, Booth girded. None of his successes were sweeter than those he had had to struggle for, wresting his shining victory with skill, ingenuity, and courage from the maw of blackness. He mounted, gathered up his thunderbolts, and rode forth.

Bradford Bates stood on the half deck overlooking the chlorine-blue swimming pool set into the stern of the S.S. Solar. Around the pool shroud-white bodies lay variously reposed in files and ranks of deckchairs. Most of the flesh that Bradford Bates looked down upon was nearly formless, like the globs of lard he remembered his whole life-time ago from the cook greasing a baking pan for biscuits. The amorphic streak in the third chair, second row on the east side of the pool, was the woman to whom he had remained married for thirty-five years. Her name was Charlotte. She wore a two piece bathing suit of which each half of the halter was a different tone—a deep green fading into a dull red; like traffic lights flickering out.

In the pool a portly but solid, shiningly bald man swam, cavorted. He splashed and dived, squirted water out of his mouth while floating on his back like a whale, whooped loudly, and now and again raced across the width of the pool in a frothing channel like that made by an erratic torpedo. No one else was in the pool. Nor had anyone else been in it that day before the bald man. Bradford Bates knew because he had been standing in the shadows of the higher deck for nearly two hours hiding, which was what he usually did.

No one had gone into the pool. Very few people walked about. It was nothing at all like the gay pictures Charlotte and he had looked at in the magazine section of the *New York Times*. It was nothing like what his daughter, a younger Charlotte, had told them. Only the one man in the pool and the waiters moving about bringing liquids and fruit. But Bradford Bates didn't mind.

Off to the opposite side of the boat from him he saw the first of Porto Rico. Minutes before it hadn't been there and now it was. He quivered at the solidness of it as all who have ever been at sea do at a landfall. He wanted to shout out as if he had been high up in a crow's-nest. He moved. He stepped forward out of his shadow. He stepped to the railing as the island became each instant more and more detailed, a place of trees and huts and hovering but transparent clouds, diving and wheeling seabirds against the dark green of the humped-up hills.

"Bradford," Charlotte Bates called up at him. "Bradford," she called, light and swift, the practised refinement of her voice hissing through the air like a tamer's whip, certain and sure. She waved him to come to her. He sank.

In their cabin Charlotte Bates held forth.

"Once, once in my lifetime we go on a cruise and you desert me, run away. Two days and I only see you when we eat, and not always then. Where have you been? Where do you go?" He knew that he wasn't expected to answer. He stood by patiently as his wife stepped out of her bathing suit as if she hadn't been wearing it. She walked into the bathroom as he watched her clear, etched skeleton articulate without reference to the merest sheath of flesh that slid over it. Before the shower drowned her out she called, "And that man in the pool! Puffing and snorting like an animal! What does he think, that he's the only one on the boat? Who is he, that . . . that *vulgarian*?" The water pounded upon her chest.

Bates felt defensive for the man. What had *he* done? For himself he felt nothing; at least, after battering years, he couldn't think of what he felt as being something in the definite way that he felt something for the bald man enjoying his lively swimming in the pool. He couldn't permit himself to think of himself feeling. He might have liked to swim himself except that he knew Charlotte. He could imagine: "You've come a thousand miles from home, more, for a *swim?* You needn't think of yourself as a . . . a *youngster,* that you must make a spectacle of yourself. Think. Who else is in the pool?" And now that the one person in the pool was someone whom Charlotte had decided against once and for all time, her resistance to his own going into the pool would be glacial. He wanted for her to finish her shower and to dress. It was the story of his life.

"When does the ship dock?" she asked him over her shoulder as he zipped her completely into her dress. There was so little of her to hold it.

"I don't know," he said. "Soon, I think. Now, maybe."

"Now? NOW?" She was alarmed. She had not come to San Juan, Porto Rico, to stand around in a cabin explaining to him how he should conduct himself. "Let's go," she said. "Let's *go.*" She hurried out of the cabin leaving him to scuttle after her. Everything in her world was always his fault.

The S.S. Solar had almost docked. The enormous brown hawsers like incredibly long snails in a surreal dream were tightened around the giant black cleats on the wharf below by thick-shouldered men sweating in the Caribbean sun. The gangplank deck of the ship was busy with crew members preparing to disembark the "cruisers." (Clifton Booth had initiated the idea of calling the tour passengers "cruisers" and not "tourists.") And the "cruisers" were gathered and crowded. What noise and excitement they were capable of, they made. It wasn't much.

Individually none of the passengers was so old as to be actually infirm. And what black grief any one of them might at any moment have begun to discover in his body was not revealed in a personal meeting. Everyone, alone, walked vitally enough, had his single—if fragile—strength. It was their collective agedness that oppressed them, all of it together bearing down upon them that silenced them, frightened them. Standing as a group upon the shaded deck about the kaleidoscope of San Juan was like standing in a hall of mirrors: there was no where you could look without being reflected, unless you closed your eyes, and that would have been most terrible of all.

Clifton Booth addressed them over the gently loud speaker system. They came to even quieter attention.

"Well, folks. This is it. First port and a beautiful day. Now let me go over some of the things we talked about earlier." He told them about the guided tours, the free hours, the "better" restaurants if they wanted to eat ashore, to watch out for the drinking water, the places to look for bargains, and lots else, like where the police station was and what to do if you thought you were being taken advantage of by a native and what to say if you weren't feeling well (*"Señor, estoy enfermo. Traigame al barco, por favor."*) Many of the "cruisers" were taking notes. He also told them that although the ship would not sail until two o'clock that morning, he hoped that they would all be back on board no later than ten o'clock that evening.

"Now one last thing." His voice became cautious and serious and they leaned forward toward him. Then he quickly changed. "Don't spend all your money today. Tomorrow is St. Thomas, *duty free!* Two hundred will get you four hundred every time." They laughed. A few clapped.

The grate and snap of the section of railing swinging out of place before the incline of the gangplank turned them away from Booth and into the slow funnel that they began to drip down and through on to Porto Rico. From the south rim of the funneling deck Charlotte Bates and her husband moved toward the gangplank. And from the north rim came the late-arriving Vemishes. Near to the gangplank entry Martin Vemish said to his wife, "Well, let's see what it's all about. Maybe there are guides or something we can get to show us around." Sara nodded.

Twice now Vemish had not heard about the pains the Lootens Line had gone to to provide an intricate and interesting guided tour for its "cruisers," for him. And if he didn't know that then he probably didn't know what to do if he got sick or when to absolutely get back to the ship. He might even spend all his money before St. Thomas, not to mention Martinique or Barbados or the rest. Resentment stirred through those around Martin Vemish like brief eddies through anemones in a tidal pool when the tide begins to rise. Who was *he!*

Charlotte Bates heard and balanced her anger at Vemish against the satisfaction of confirmation in her first dislike; he was the man in the pool. She had *known* what he would be like. She hurried to reach the gangplank before him as if his arriving first in Porto Rico would defile it for her. They reached the entry almost together, but not quite. Vemish moved in a half-step before her, Sara on his arm. Charlotte Bates had to stop abruptly; she was not used to having people step in front of her. And Bradford Bates was not using to having his wife stop suddenly once she had begun to move where she decided she would go. He banged into her and started her off again, this time into Vemish. She bumped him.

"Easy lady," he said back through his contrail of cigar smoke hanging in the still afternoon air, hardly looking at her. "There's plenty of island for us all. Plenty." It was Vemish's kind of pleasantry.

"Some people," Charlotte whispered loudly to her husband and to all the rest. Some of those who heard her nodded the way some always nod before the sibilances of the Charlotte Bateses, as if they dared not. She marched down into San Juan, which had now gone all red before her.

Clifton Booth leaned back against the white plates of the bulkhead hearing and seeing. It won't be long now, he thought.

Robert Clark, the third of Clifton Booth's assistants and the one closest to becoming a Tour Director on his own, sat at the little table near the gangplank reading by the sharp, round light of a hi-intensity lamp. An occasional moth would flutter up from the city to dance in the white cone. If it did not go soon, Robert Clark would snap it out of the air with his hand and cast the crumpled thing away. Since he came on to his watch at eight o'clock, he had been sitting at this table reading and marking off in the Leave and Return Book those returning. It was 9:45. Then Clifton Booth was at his shoulder asking,

"Have the Vemishes returned yet?"

"No, not yet," Clark told him.

"Let me know when they do," Booth said and walked away, but not far, not so far that, minutes later, he didn't see the Vemishes when they reported in. Clark didn't bother to ask who they were. They were the only couple of the cruise left to be accounted for.

"Pleasant evening," Clark said as they passed him.

"Wonderful," Vemish said. "Wonderful. Look!" He had stopped and turned. He took from under his arm a box of cigars. "Havanas," he said. "Corona Corona. The real thing. I haven't smoked a real Havana for I can't remember how long. The trip's worth it already." He put the cigars back under his arm, put his lighted cigar back in his mouth, and turned into Clifton Booth, who had come up on them.

"I'm glad to see you folks made it back in time," he said.

"Ah, it's Mr. Ruth," Vemish said.

"Booth," Clifton Booth corrected him. "Booth, not Ruth."

"Have a cigar," Vemish opened the box and held it out. Three cigars were gone.

"Thank you, but I don't smoke," Booth declined.

"A shame, a shame," Vemish nodded his head. "All this tobacco and you don't smoke." He gestured out at all the islands of the Carribbean. "A shame."

"You know, you can't bring Cuban products back into the states," Booth informed them.

"So I'll smoke fast," Vemish said and with his silent wife passed on.

But in St. Thomas it was different. The S.S. Solar and its cruise was scheduled to leave St. Thomas for St. Croix at six in the evening. Passengers were to be on board by five in the afternoon at the latest. At 6:15 the Vemishes were not to be found.

In his cabin-office Booth sat drumming his fingers on his desk when the intraship phone rang. Joseph Crenshaw answered it. "It's for you," he said to Booth holding his hand over the mouthpiece. "The Captain." Booth took the phone quickly.

"Captain Harley here. Where are your sheep, Booth? I've got tides to consider and weather, and docking schedules."

"Yes, Captain. I can appreciate the inconvenience. In ten more minutes I will initiate our search procedure by calling the police, the hospitals, and the tour guide office. I suppose all we can do for now is wait."

"Why don't you start looking for them right away? Why didn't you start earlier?"

"Yes, sir," Booth said. "The Lootens Line procedure is to wait an hour and a half before alerting the authorities." Booth felt how white he was, how all of him that lived had coalesced into his stomach, and there it lurched.

"Well, let me know as soon as you hear something," Captain Harley grumphed.

"Yes, Captain. Yes, I will. And Captain," Booth caught him before he hung up. "I can promise you this: it won't happen again. No, Captain. Oh, no. *It won't happen again.*" Saying it, thinking about how it was true, gave him back his blood.

The Vemishes returned by seven o'clock on their own. Booth called the Captain and in fifteen minutes the ship swung away from its berth and into the still light evening. For an hour Booth left the Vemishes alone. And then he called upon them in their cabin.

"Have you eaten?" was what he asked them first. "If you would rather, I'll come back after your supper. It's a matter of some importance." And there was no hurry. He had all the way to St. Croix to tell them and for them to pack.

"Not yet," Vemish told him. "We haven't eaten yet, no. I need time to recover." At which Vemish sank down heavily upon the bed.

"Recover?" Booth asked.

"From the excitement. What a day." Vemish swung his legs onto the bed and lay back. "Let me tell you Mr. Ruth . . . Booth. I'm not such a young man anymore. This kind of thing can take it out of you."

"What happened?" Booth asked.

"Sara," Martin Vemish said, his eyes closed now. "Tell him." Booth turned to her.

"No," Sara said. "You tell him."

"No, no." Vemish said, "I'm resting. You tell him."

"No," Sara Vemish said.

"WHAT?" Clifton Booth shouted. "TELL ME!" Martin Vemish said:

"A little boy fell into a deep hole with water in it and I jumped in and saved him. From the water in the hole I got wet, so the boy's mother took us to her house and cleaned up my clothes and dried them. That's why we're late, so help me God. But it's all right, it's all right. Don't worry about me." His eyes were still closed. "They wanted to throw us a big dinner. They wanted to give me some kind of medal, you know. But I told them. 'Look,' I said, 'I got a whole ship of people waiting for me. As soon as my pants are dry, I got to go.' They pleaded, but I was firm. So here I am. Offf. What a day. What did you want to talk to us about?"

"NEVER MIND," Booth continued to shout. "NEVER MIND."

Outside, even in the liquid air of Caribbean dusk, Clifton Booth was dizzy near to fainting.

About ten-thirty, well after supper but not after the food, quiet and unused tables of it placed here and there in the great forward Lounge of the enclosed Promenade Deck, Bradford Bates did the third bravest thing of his life. Giddy, almost giggling with his daring, he stole away from his wife, deep in her gesticulating story to her circle, walked up to the smoking Vemish and Sara, and introduced himself. It must have been the salt air.

Vemish looked up at the frail Bates for a moment and then asked him to sit down. He did, and then they told where they lived (as it turned out, not far from each other), what they did (Bates had a small accounting business), how they were enjoying the trip.

"Eeeeh," Vemish said. Bates smiled.

"What about this?" Bates asked indicating, with a small circling of his thin head, the Lounge.

They were sitting in the middle of what looked like a giant bazaar. Everywhere there was the booty of the day, the treasure of the fabled St. Thomas. Floating about on the sea of old people, many awake beyond their ordinary hour, bobbing about everywhere between the blue-haired heads of excited grandmothers and their husbands, were the various, colorful trinkets of the tourists' lust. It was as if, after three or four hundred years, the Caribbean natives were turning the game around and buying back their land and soul with the same humiliating, gaudy baubles and eye-bashing colors that the earlier Spanish masters had raped them with.

"Terrible," Vemish said loudly out of a burst of emphatic smoke. "Terrible." His eyes were hot but not angry. "You ask me, it's expensive crap, even for bargains. Still, it's their money. What do I care."

All day he and Sara had wandered slowly through the inescapable market place that was St. Thomas, annoyed and embarrassed by the ugly squeal flickering at them where ever they went, an animal call sent up by their own "cruisers" as well as from the passengers from the six more cruise ships in the port, for they were not alone on the Spanish Main. All day he and Sara had heard the passionate yelps of pleasure from the stalls around them everywhere as if the women were being serviced by an obscene substitution of wooden bowls and French China and roughly-dyed table cloths. Still in Vemish's ears were the growls of satisfaction of the men as then fondled duty-free cameras and tax-less Scotch. He remembered the whistle of the ship ordering the orgiastic climax, the frantic push and drive to conclude the business, giver and taker alike hearing Time's 14,000 ton winged chariot pursuing them; the climax and then the peaceful exhaustion. And later, now, the leering recall of conquest.

"Tell me, Bates," Vemish said leaning towards the little man. He removed his cigar and used it as a blunt pointer, aiming it like a gun just fired. "What do you see here that you couldn't buy exactly the same in the city? Eh?" Bates nodded yes.

"Nothing," Bates agreed, delighted in his friend and in himself. Delighted to be asked a question. "Not a thing."

"Right," Vemish said, loudly enough for any near to hear him. He laughed. "What they don't sell here, in the off season they ship up to Gimbel's. Ha! For *LESS!*" People heard. Vemish picked up the ashtray next to him and examined its bottom as though it was something he had bought. "Made in Japan," he shouted. He and Bates roared. The others, more of them, heard. "Why do they do it, Bates?"

"I don't know," Bates said. He felt a little drunk.

"I'll tell you." Those near to him didn't want to hear, but he spoke so that they had to, that or leave, though he didn't care if they did.

"Nothing to do. We get shoved out of our beds away from family, business, friends, and we're told to *enjoy* ourselves. Have a big time. Chance of your life. Yeah, yeah. God forbid we don't come back with our arms loaded to prove it!"

Bates nodded his head rapidly and giggled at last. A couple nearest to Vemish got up and hurried away. Some others rewrapped their packages.

Bates saw Charlotte see him and start toward him. He hung on. From the other side of the lounge, behind him, he didn't see Clifton Booth. Both of them arrived in time to hear Vemish proclaim loudly something about getting sick of being dragged from one Caribbean shopping center to another Caribbean shopping center.

"Bradford," Charlotte Bates commanded. For an instant Bates's wrinkled throat was jammed with his desire, but he bit down, swallowed hard, and stood up.

"My wife, Charlotte," he said to Vemish. To his wife he said, "Charlotte, this is . . . ," but Charlotte Bates wasn't about to be introduced to Martin Vemish *ever,* and certainly not in front of two-thirds of the "cruisers." And would her husband hear about *that.* She stood draped about by four yards of a bolt of native cotton cloth, mainly orange with a purple thread design; she held the rest of the column of the material almost as thick as herself in her arms like an artillery shell.

"Ah, Mr. Booth," Vemish said, muffled a little from his cigar but still plenty clear enough to be heard far into the quieted Lounge. "Do you ever buy anything?"

"Frequently," Booth said like an announcement. "Every trip, in fact. It's one of the best things about the cruises.

Friends are always asking me to bring things back for them."

"Tell them to try Gimbel's, right Bates?" Vemish snorted to his friend, reaching out to poke his knee. But now Bradford Bates was afraid as he considered how the knife of his wife's vision of social rectitude would cut him through the night and the days—and the days.

"I'm sorry Mr. Vemish, but there is no smoking in this lounge. The smoking lounge is aft." He pointed aft. "If you want to smoke you'll have to smoke there or on deck. You can't smoke here." It was clearly an order.

"So why are there ashtrays?" Vemish asked.

"For when the ship is not . . . ," but Booth stopped quickly.

"A floating hospital? Is not full of old people with rotten lungs?" Vemish finished for him.

"*Extinguish the Cigar,* Mr. Vemish, or else smoke it where you're *permitted* to." All of the other "cruisers" were watching and listening now. Charlotte Bates, like a Victory, stood thin, orange, and smiling. Bradford Bates was white, tight-lipped, eyes closed. Booth was the total Presence in the Lounge, everybody's son. Vemish ground his Corona Corona into the glass ashtray. Then Sara Vemish said to Booth, like quiet thunder,

"Get out. Get out." Then she screamed like lightning, "*GET OUT!*"

Although it was three o'clock in the morning, Clifton Booth had assembled all his assistants. He was nervous, drawn, and queasy even with the long, lulling yaw of the ship. He doubted that he would sleep until he saw this thing through. Still, he wanted them to be appraised of his decision to send the Vemishes home, which, unfortunately, could not be tomorrow because, instead of scheduled Guadeloupe, the ship was going to Barbados. There had been a small ramming in the Guadeloupe harbor and for at least two days the only possible dockage would be either at anchor or at a hardly accessible wharf, both situations too difficult for the old people to manage with comfort and safety. They would make Guadeloupe on the return.

Tomorrow, then, would be a day at sea. And tomorrow he would tell the Vemishes that once they left the ship in Barbardos, that was it. He read to his assistants the report that he had written so far which, when completed, he would send to the Lootens Line home office. He wanted them, the assistants, to hear it now in case later any of his procedures should be questioned. There was always the chance of a court case.

Arthur Lewis, eager to learn and to please as a new, young man on a job always is, carefully watched Booth pace bloodlessly back and forth before them. It was as if he were back in college, poised to take precious notes. Joseph Crenshaw and Robert Clark, however, were curious, and pleased.

Both had sailed with Booth before and knew much about him and his methods from others who knew him too. Crenshaw even had been with Booth when, twice before, he had sent people home: a psychopathically belligerent eighty-year-old who had taken to hitting people with his cane, and an old alcoholic who almost went overboard twice. But Booth was acting altogether differently now than he had then or before or was legended to. He seemed frightened of the Vemishes, as if it were he who was being stalked. As far as Crenshaw could see or could comprehend, Booth's charges and actions were unfounded. The Vemishes might be giving Booth pain, but they were hardly disruptive in any direct way. Not that he cared.

Crenshaw looked on and listened to Booth's tension with bemused interest, with the ironical amusement of a raffish beachcomber on this, his floating island. Robert Clark, however, looked at the spectacle of Booth's pain with ambition's delight. He couldn't see where Booth had a case against the Vemishes, and he would be damned if, later, it was necessary to support Booth, if he would. Neither Clark nor Crenshaw were going to help him very much.

"When will you tell them, sir?" young Lewis asked.

"I don't know," Booth said. "Have any of you suggestions?" They were silent. It was the first time Booth had ever asked them anything. "Never mind," he said and started to pace again. He rubbed his thumb against his fingers in a noiseless snap. "It will come. The time will come." He made it sound mystical. "Besides, *they* don't matter. I can tell *them* anytime, even when we're docking, for that matter. There's a flight out of the island at twelve noon. I've booked them on it already." He stopped. "No, no. It's what they'll do to the others that I've got to think about. They've done enough damage as it is. I've got a job to do. We *all* have. And the Vemishes are trying to stop us. *Don't you see that?*" He turned from their silent faces and over his shoulder asked them to leave.

In the morning Booth, showered but wan, made the announcement that the ship would be going straight on to Barbados because of the accident in the Guadeloupe harbor. They would be at sea the entire day and into the evening. To keep them occupied Booth had organized the S.S. Solar Sweepstakes, a kind of ship-board decathlon of modified deck games designed more to be looked at than participated in. He could always count on twenty or so passengers healthy enough to have a gentle go at the rocking horse races, the deck tennis (with a lowered net), the shuffleboard, and the rest. Most of the excitement for the observers would be in the moderate betting that Booth encouraged but strictly limited. At a table off of the main dining room Arthur Lewis set up an entry desk and a manual pari-mutuel, where the "cruisers" could place their bets on their favorites either before or after they saw them. It was all to begin at two o'clock.

After the Sweepstakes, at the height of the "cruisers' " friendly and unified gaiety, Clifton Booth would tell the Vemishes that they didn't belong, that they were going home. Indeed, he imagined that that prospect would even please them.

Now, at ten o'clock, his battle plans arranged, he lay down to try and sleep a little. He could never have dreamed that Martin Vemish would have entered the Games.

Martin Vemish entered the Games and played them with destroying vigor, relentlessly, aggressive like in a rage but without malice. If he threw a quoit, he threw it hard (into the face of his slower opponent and cut his nose). In the horse races he rode down a rider who had staggered a little and veered into him (sprawling the man out of the contest). In the dart throwing he heckled the others like they were the Mets in Shea Stadium, unnervingly loud and jeering ("Get thicker glasses, grandpa"), and when he himself threw, it was like the javelin. In the golf ball driving contest, though not a golfer, his rushing, dangerous presence threw off those who were. He lost points there, but not many.

And now instead of gaiety in the "cruisers" a slow, fine panic started up out of the confusion between what they were expected to do and what they were doing. In place of light, leisurely time-passing laughter upon the emerald sea, there was instead a grim silence sharpened by the huffing of the struggling men, fighting surprisingly once more in their lives, the wheeze and rattle dry in their throats as they fought. They fought with Vemish. He alone laughed. And Sara.

The Shuffleboard began like rifle fire and the men had begun to shout back at Vemish and at each other. Here and there in the crowd a tightly strung woman cracked and sobbed. A participant collapsed and was borne off to the infirmary. The games went on. Vemish cracked his shuffle into his opponent's so hard that the wooded disk flew spinning fifty feet off a deck stanchion for thirty feet more into the ankle of a woman who screamed and fell, and like the man was borne away. A low moaning fluttered through the crowd. Vemish slammed and slammed again. Old women implored their old husbands to stop. By twos and sixes people fled while others came and pressed in closer.

Clifton Booth spun in his nightmare. "Mr. Booth," Lewis, as soaked by perspiration as the players, implored, "What'll I do? Lots of them are coming back to bet. They demand to bet. On Mr. Vemish. I *told* them the betting was closed. I *told* them it was just a fun thing anyway. They won't listen. They won't listen, Mr. Booth. Mr. Booth, they've gone *crazy*."

"Booth," Captain Harley's voice shouted through the telephone. "You've got two people in sickbay in fifteen minutes. What are you running down there, a war? What's happening, Booth? What the hell is happening?"

"I'll sue. I'll sue you and the whole shipping line," Mr. Robert Phillips shouted at Booth, nearly shaking his clawed fist in the Tour Director's white, blank face. "It's broken! You broke Lydia's ankle, you and your asinine games. You'll hear from me. You'll hear from *me!*"

Topside again Booth staggered toward the crowded game deck, the moaning growing louder as he neared. He worked his way through the "cruisers" to the edge of the playing area. The moaning was loud now, but he could not believe that he was in the middle of it, that it was outside of him. He thought that it was in his own head. Vemish was before him, fifteen feet away, his sunburnt head peeling already, glistening, his cigar, a new cigar, in his mouth, bent, in motion, and the accurate crack of the wood on wood.

"Eighteen to eleven, Vemish leads Morrisey," a scorekeeping voice said.

Booth stood as still as he could. For him the ship was heaving like in a hurricane. The old woman next to him grasped his arm, though she did not know it was he—she was staring at Vemish before her—and said,

"Oh! Oh my! Oh look!"

Vemish's opponent, Morrisey, was bleeding from the nose, from one nostril, slowly but clearly. Nothing had hit him or bumped him to cause it. He simply bled. Now Booth stepped forward just as Morrisey bent to shoot.

"Mr. Morrisey," Booth straightened him up.

"What?" Morrisey said, his concentration broken. "What do you want?"

"I think you had better stop, Mr. Morrisey," Booth said.

"What? What for? What are you talking about?" Morrisey looked around, amazed, impatient, his sweat beaded on his eyebrows.

"You're bleeding," Booth said. "Your nose."

"Huh?" Morrisey said. He looked a little like Vemish, only with more hair, smaller, and no cigar. He rubbed under his nose and then looked at his hand.

"It's nothing," he said. "Nothing," and turned to play.

"But Mr. Morrisey . . . ."

"Come on, come on," Vemish said.

"It's nothing, I said," Morrisey said. "Nothing. Now leave me alone." Morrisey's sparrow wife pushed forward.

"Albert. Oh Albert, please. Stop this."

"Go away," Morrisey snapped. "All of you, go away and leave me alone. Go *AWAY!*" Booth and Mrs. Morrisey backed off.

The game continued. Vemish smashed. Morrisey bled.

"Twenty-one. Vemish."

And now Booth took the last of his strength and moved forward again. He would wait for nothing now. He would tell Vemish. He didn't care who heard. He hoped they would. He would tell him *now.* He knew his duty and his responsibility. If anything, he had let it go too long. But five paces away from Vemish, Vemish took his shuffleboard stick, his lance, and flung it cartwheeling into the Caribbean and walked out of the games into the crowd which shrank, cringed, back from him. The S.S. Solar Sweepstakes were over.

Booth stopped only for an instant and then started after him through the still open sea of spectators like Pharaoh after Moses. But he would get him now. Now he would have him. He was his arm's length away and reaching. But what did stop him was the sound of Bradford Bates clapping. And then the tiny many cheered. Alone. And the waters closed up over the Director.

"Shut *up,*" Charlotte Bates smashed at her husband through her clenched teeth, making as though no one would hear, though they did. "Shut up!" She had him gripped by the boney curve of his small shoulder and started to shake him so that his head bobbed. "Shut up!" she ordered.

But he would not.

Clifton Booth rushed to the railing and vomited.

The ship arrived in Barbados around midnight and quietly docked. Only a few, those whose cabins were near to where the men were working at securing the ship, might have been awakened slowly, partly, in the near tropic night. The rest of the cruise slept, except Joseph Crenshaw, whose watch it was, and Clifton Booth. The two men sat in the office part of Booth's cabin.

"Is there anything I can get you?" Crenshaw asked his gray superior.

"Nothing," the suffering man said. "Nothing." They were silent. Then he said, "I can't get rid of them now, can I? The Vemishes? It's too late now, isn't it?"

"I'm afraid so," Crenshaw said, not quite sure of, and not quite interested in his Director's demon.

"He's won, hasn't he?"

"Won what?" Crenshaw asked. "The Sweekpstakes, well, they just . . . ."

"The cruise! The cruise is a shambles, isn't it?" Booth pointed out.

"Oh, I don't know," Crenshaw considered. He started to light a cigarette, but looking at Booth's color made him reconsider. "There has been a lot of excitement, after all. I don't think the people are that displeased. And anyway, there are days and days to go. *Days!*"

Booth shuddered.

But in the morning when, immediately after their breakfast, Booth appeared on the gangplank deck to give his Barbados talk and instructions to the "cruisers," less than a third of the usual number were there. During the day, however, it was reported to him that most of the passengers did leave the boat but mainly by two's or four's. Hardly any took guides or tours. Also it was reported that few were returning with anything, with any packages.

At six-thirty Mr. Elliot Newly, a representative of the Barbados Visitors Trade Commission, came on board the S.S. Solar and asked for the Tour Director. Directly and simply he complained that this cruise ship had probably spent less money than any cruise ship that had ever docked in Barbados in recent times. For it to be a Lootens Line ship was rather amazing. For it to be a Clifton Booth directed ship was almost beyond belief.

"What do you want me to do?" Booth snapped. "Order them to buy? What do you want me to do? Threaten them? Beat them?"

"It's not what I want you to *do,*" Mr. Elliot Newly said, rising before the spectral, gaunt, and strident Tour Director. "It's a little late for *that,* after all." He backed toward the cabin door away from Booth's glazed eyes. "It's what you've *done,* I was interested in." And then he was quickly gone.

More important trouble came in Martinique. The cruise arrived there at eight in the morning and was scheduled to leave at six that same evening. It was the tightest day of the tour, leaving the "cruisers" between nine and five to "do" the island, just a working day. But by as late as nine o'clock, 118 "cruisers" were still ashore somewhere.

Captain Harley, never a reasonable man, ranted at the stunned Booth from six o'clock until sometime after eleven, when the last passenger was aboard and the unhappy ship was moving off to St. Croix. By that time Booth found some peace, some rest, not in sleep but stretched out on his bed in catatonic rigidity, stiffened the way a man is just after he is hit and before he crumbles. Lewis, Crenshaw, and Clark were disturbed enough by their leader's condition to keep from him the increasing reports coming up from the infirmary of indispositions and near-illnesses. And then illness. Every cruise ship had its normal health and well-being problems; a geriatric cruise would naturally have more. But the S.S. Solar, this time out, approaching St. Croix, was something else again.

The ship arrived in St. Croix three hours off its schedule. The day was five degrees cooler than the more constant Caribbean seventy-eight and, though lovely as day can be, felt chilly to most of the "cruisers." Few left the ship at all, and on board they were mostly hidden in books sullenly read or in slow but ceaseless, bleak walking around the Open and Enclosed Promenade Decks, guilt or defiance by turns their companion. Many wore sweaters. The heated, chlorinated pool-side was deserted. Little of any of the food was eaten. The chefs and their helpers looked with puzzlement at the unordered services on the waiting trays, at the untouched portions on the returned plates. They shrugged and shoveled the food into garbage cans from which it would be dumped in the night (to discourage the noisy, screeching seagulls) into the furrow of the dark ship.

Captain Harley called a council that evening. He and his first two mates and the ship's doctor, Doctor Goff, met with Booth and his three assistants. They were all in uniform. It was all very military.

"It's not my business to meddle with the cruises," Captain Harley shouted, though he was only talking. "To me a ship is for carrying things over water, that's all—people, crates, bags of coffee, it makes no difference to me. And whatever has happened to this cruise I'll never know." Booth's stomach lurched. "But as Captain I've got two responsibilities, safety and, as near as I can make it, schedule." He paused a long moment. "To get to the point. I think when we leave St. Croix we should skip Guadeloupe and head straight in to New York." Booth almost came out of his chair. He waited for more, but it was the doctor who spoke next.

"You've got a sick cruise this time, Booth," he said.

"Sick?" Booth said. "Sick?"

"Well, as I mentioned in the reports, there are . . . ."

"Reports? *What reports?*" He looked around to his assistants. They looked elsewhere. Finally Arthur Lewis said, "When you were . . . sleeping, sir. The doctor reported some illness and . . . ."

"You didn't tell me." He looked at each of them. His eyes were yellow. Rapidly he added new, darker dimensions to his suffering. "You . . . you . . . none of you told me."

"We thought it best at the moment not to," Robert Clark was pleased to say.

"But *later?*" Booth's voice was drying up, his throat crusting.

"Mr. Booth," the Captain demanded. The doctor went on at the Captain's direction.

"You've got God knows how many cardiac possibilities in your troupe, Booth, and right now I've got four suspicious disturbances under observation."

"Four? *FOUR?*"

"And I've got a woman who went into insulin shock. I've got *twelve* cases of acute diarrhea."

"I told them. I *TOLD* them about the water," Booth insisted, pleaded. What more could he do for them?

"I've got one woman on pretty heavy sedation for her nerves," the doctor continued. "And three cases of what I guess you'd just have to call exhaustion. And, of course, Lydia Phillips with the broken ankle. Mr. Booth, there's no more *room* down there."

"Exhaustion?" he asked in a whisper. "Exhaustion?" Tears were in his blood-veined yellow eyes. "But they haven't *done* anything." The corners of his mouth were tight like little knots and white as polished ivory. "Dr. Goff, this is a *pleasure* cruise. It's especially designed for the old. Exhaustion?" At which something broke in Clifton Booth; there was not a cell left in him capable of protest.

"Mr. Booth," Dr. Goff said gently, "For whatever reasons, this is not a happy cruise."

"So let's go home before it gets worse," Captain Harley boomed, not gentle at all. "We've done it before, shortened a cruise, when there's been serious illness or trouble with the ship or the weather. I remember once we thought we had typhoid," he started to reminisce.

Booth nodded yes. Yes.

"I'll send something up for you to take," the doctor said to him.

When he left the cabin of the meeting, he leaned a little on Arthur Lewis, although he didn't know it.

But things did get worse.

Edward Clanton of Lambertville, New Jersey, aged sixty-eight, one of the four heart condition suspects in the infirmary, died that night.

By nine in the morning three more "cruisers" reported in with pains here or there in their body. More beds were moved into the infirmary.

If the death made his job harder, it made it, that morning, easier, too, as Director Booth called together all those people whom he had brought out on the sea so far from their homes. They did look tired, unhappy, and very old. White. Transparent.

He announced the death of Edward Clanton of Lambertville, New Jersey. It doused them, the cruise, like a spray from the icy sea.

And he announced that the ship was heading back to New York now and would by-pass Guadeloupe. No one complained. Subdued, he promised them a full slate of entertainments and activities for the pleasant days at sea that lay before them. No one seemed to care particularly, at first, but by noon, adjusting without clearly knowing it to the sun riding on their starboard side instead of port, the spirits of the "cruisers" shifted cautiously.

They were going home. There was nothing more they *had* to do, at least for the next three days. Then, on the fourth, they would have to face their children. They tried not to think about that.

The days and the nights at sea were not good for any of them. The weather was less than it was supposed to be and grew colder as they moved north. Sometimes the day was cloudy for an hour or two or three. They seemed to be moving into a front. There was nothing they wanted to do on the ship, nothing but sit in their cabins or in the lounges or on the decks and think, if they did, about the cinders of their voyage. Nothing had gone smoothly, they could remember little of anything they had seen or done, they were too old for new friendships and none came anyway. And what would they do with what they had bought? How many pictures were there left to them to take with their new cameras? On what table would the rioting table cloth go in their lifetime-full and arranged houses? More and more they felt that they had spent all their days, and many of them, at sea—the day before, yesterday, today.

In the evenings, after a supper that they might have eaten at home—tight, limited, precise, unmindful now of the cornucopia they dined in, most went to their cabins and early to bed if not to sleep. Or there were nightly movies. There was even some TV, fluttery and white. There were nightclub acts: singers, dancers, magicians. There were slide lectures on subjects ranging from Caribbean history to home gardening. There was a five-piece dance band (circa 1940) in one of the smaller lounges playing slow waltzes and squared foxtrots to the gleaming, empty oak floor.

The "cruisers" partook of very little of what was available to them, and even of that little, they touched it heavily, clumsily. They were quiet, sodden. When they spoke amongst themselves it was often about the sick down below. A few, like Charlotte Bates, pushed on after gaiety as advertised. But the determined whine from her bridge table or the orderly insistence about the exciting food hung in the dining room or lounge like the snuff of smoke from a taper in the gray, late light of a winter afternoon, her parodic graciousness and culture muffled in the hollowing of the rooms her sound ever beat in. The S.S. Solar, encapsuled in its own environment and time, steamed northward through the roiled sea into a storm.

It was not a great storm as storms go, but for the "cruisers" it was like a spark to a powdery anger that their journey had ground in them: To be here.

As the ship plunged forward into the heightening waves, the stabilizers to aft slapped about helplessly in the water like the flukes of a shoaled whale. The ship swung back and forth across its center in great arcs like an upside-down pendulum. Or else it lurched in an unpredictable zig-zag that could knock a person down or throw him into a table or against a wall.

That they were here. To have come so uselessly far to be here.

All the rankling ironies of the cruise rose in them and drew them from about the ship to the large, non-smoker's Lounge. And there, in the black storm, they found the communion falsely promised them by the sunny, gaudy brochures, the effusive travel clerk, and by their children. They found another kind.

With dignity they complained. They had not slept well since they left their own beds. They had forgotten to leave a tender for their African Violets and Impatiens at home. They had missed the wedding of a favorite niece, the annual affair of a club they had belonged to for thirty years, more than a week (unrecoverable) of a TV afternoon serial, the close letters from far-off kin.

That they were here, in the terrible night, with green water booming over the bow of the pitching ship.

"What a laugh," Martin Vemish said to Bradford Bates, enjoying what he could not change. "Come on," he said cuffing his companion on the back. "I'll buy you a drink."

In the empty bar adjoining the Lounge, Vemish bought his friend a drink, scotch and water.

"You know," Bates told him. "It's been years since I've drunk in a bar." He lifted his glass to Vemish.

"With me too," Vemish said, returning the salute. "How do you like it?"

"Not so much," Bates said. "I'd rather drink at home."

"Your wife lets you?"

"Charlotte's not so bad," Bradford Bates said, squinting down into his glass with one eye. Vemish said nothing, willing to leave any man alone with whatever accommodation he has managed. He lit a new cigar and ordered another two drinks.

Then others, many for the first time since the cruise began, came into the bar, swaying with the ship or crawling along the walls, at times impaled upon them by a sudden severe list. They drank and talked, sometimes fiercely and loud. Men left, others came. All were gray or white-haired, neat, in the main frail, but younger now than in their actual years, refreshed by their outrage.

That they were here.

Vemish grabbed Bradford Bates and, swayed in addition now by storm and scotch, wandered a little until they found the wide-lapeled dance band and bribed them back to the Main Lounge. The two of them led the band back into the larger room to the trumpeter's fanfare and the cheers of the crowd. There looked to be present a good part of the "cruisers," nearly 150.

The band began to play and Martin Vemish began a bounding dance with his Sara. Others joined. The band played loud and faster following the whirling Vemish. The party had begun. The dancers shifted about between the card tables and sofas and the writing desks and reading chairs and lamps. The bucking ship shifted the dancers in exotic movements against the music, forcing them into bizaare but expressive gestures. Comic bumps and staggers. Tittering pratfalls. Puffing guffaws as couples collapsed against each other. Bottles were ordered into the Lounge. Ice, glasses. The great Lounge slid and tumbled about—people, music, glasses floated about in enormously slowed motion, arms grabbed out for balance, hips swung against the turning fall-line of the ship, heads, bellies, knees, old bones angled about free, order gone.

That they were here.

Then the laughter, the assailing laughter, rose up and over them, a saving benison.

At eleven Joseph Crenshaw shook Clifton Booth out of his wet, clenched, but tranquillized sleep.

"You had better come at once. The Main Lounge."

"What? *What now?*" Booth screamed, half certain that he was in a nightmare until he felt the tilting ship and his nausea swirl up in him. He tasted his bile and knew that he was awake. "What? *WHAT?*" But his assistant had left him to return to where he was needed.

As Booth, barely dressed, hurried through the inner passageways of the ship to the Main Lounge, bouncing from wall to wall, running, sometimes careening, downhill, sometimes struggling slowly up, he fought against the centrefuge that was pulling his mind apart. Running through the twisting, snaking tunnels of the ship was too much like the terrible dreams he had been having for him to get it straight now. He didn't know, as when he had first been awakened, if he was still inside the terror of a dreamscape or was really awake and running toward (from?) the terror of fact. When he turned, at last, into the broad passageway leading directly to the Main Lounge, he knew it was the latter.

Three crew men, large and muscular, stood at the entrance to the lounge and every ten seconds or so one of them would reach out to an emerging "cruiser" and easy but certainly shove him back into the howling room. Booth watched for a minute from twenty feet away, unbelieving; then he rushed forward.

"What are you doing?" he demanded, facing the three sailors. A highball glass lofted through the doorway and crashed against the back of Booth's head, the water and ice running quickly down his back.

"Aggh," he uttered and tripped forward, like a man shot, into the hard arms of one of the crew. Behind his dizziness he heard the other two men move at the door.

"Oh no you don't," he heard one of them say. And then he heard the little grunt and the light, quick scuffle.

He stood up out of the line of the open doorway.

"What's happening? Oh for God's sake, what's happening?" It was a question and a prayer.

"Them old geezers' flipped out," one of the men said, grinning.

"The Captain said to keep 'em from bustin' up the rest of the ship," another offered.

"Hey, hey," said the third. "Lookit him go! Will you just *look* at that old rooster go!" The other two pushed in to see, Booth ran past them into the Lounge.

Chaos had come again.

Everywhere the old people were dancing madly to a music they may have heard or not. Some danced together, many alone. They sang or hummed; old voices—harsh, granulated, reedy—babbled pieces of Charlestons, Lindies, WPA work songs, songs from various wars, forgotten Hit Parades. Glass, liquids, overturned furniture, clothing, food, people mixed about above and on the deck of the heaving ship. A ribald crone, bones in a dress, lifted one foot high across her knee, put it down, and lifted the other, threw her head from left to right, and clapped out her personal, stuttering tempo.

Across the room Booth saw Clark and Lewis shouldering their way through the rolling people toward the entrance of the bar. Between them they supported a rag-doll man, his legs bent under him, his feet dragging, his chin upon his chest. At that doorway he could see three more crew men knocking mad revelers back into the room. At every moment something was breaking.

Near the center of the room the head of Charlotte Bates was shouting. She reached out again and again to grab at the little man moving easily beyond and around her. As she reached for him some motion of the ship would prevent her, while he, as though in demonic league with the sea, anticipated every lurch. She screamed and clawed at him as he rhumba-ed around her in an eyes-shut caricature of grinning passion.

In one corner Booth saw two people passed out (dead?) on a sofa. In another corner he saw a man retch and retch into a rubber plant until the chords in his skinny neck would snap. Booth closed his eyes against it all. A sharp, breaking pain on his forehead woke him again. Someone had thrown a glass.

"There he is. Our Director." Another glass was thrown against his chest. Booth bolted for the small stage, knocking three, four, five "cruisers" down as he went.

"*STOP IT!*" he screamed from the stage. "*STOP IT! ACT YOUR AGE!*" But they rained him with anything they could throw. He ran through them again and out of the room, knocking down more as he went.

He ran out of the lounge and away. He was wet with whiskey and water and blood and his own tears. He ran, he felt, forever, turning through passage after passage until he could not. In a dim alcove off of a promenade deck he fell back against a bulkhead and gasped. Only when he could breathe enough to ease the explosions going off in his gashed and battered head did he smell the cigar. Not ten feet away Martin Vemish sat quietly smoking watching him.

"You!" Booth said, straightening himself off of the cold bulkhead with what was left of his strength. "*You!*"

"Me," Vemish said with his cigar in his mouth. What could he say?

"*You!*" was all Booth could say, appalled.

"Me," Vemish said, tracing the word with almost a giggle.

"*Why?*" Booth suddenly shouted, but it took too much from him. "Why?" he whispered.

"Why what? What are you talking about?"

"You . . . you know. This. All of this." Booth fluttered with his hand behind him.

"This is all yours," Vemish said. "None of this is mine."

"Why did you do this to me? What have I . . . why did . . . ."

"Nothing. I've done nothing. *You?* You don't even exist. None of this does." Vemish waved his hand more largely than had Booth. "It's all a . . . a big . . . a *little* dirty nothing." He waved his hand in the dark, erasing it.

"I . . . I . . . ." Booth stiff-legged the ten feet to Vemish, his arms outstretched as in a monster movie, and grabbed the thick Vemish by the throat. But he could do nothing. He held him and moaned. Vemish sat smoking.

"Get away. Get! You crazy nut, you," Sara Vemish said out of the dark.

"Ahhwk," Booth squeaked, surprised by her. His hands flew up from his shock and he fell down at Vemish's feet, into a puddle more than a shape, and sobbed. "I'll . . . I'll get you," he wept.

"You should live so long," Vemish said and got up and stepped over him. Sara rose. Together they walked off. The sea was subsiding.

By the time the S.S. Solar secured its last mooring at Pier 62 on the western shore of Manhattan, the storm was over and the day showed settling promise but still, like April, was capable of anything. Thronged about at the foot of the gangplank were the children of the "cruisers," quiet and frightened. Near the gangplank five ambulances awaited. And a hearse. Soon the railing creaked open and official men, some in uniforms—Port Authority people and Lootens Line people—swiftly ascended, grim-faced. They were followed by the white-suited ambulance crews. And these by the dark morticians.

In time the ship gave up its cargo. Bleary, haggard, unshaven old men came slowly down. Frazzled, wild-haired old women. Some limped. Some rolled down in wheel-chairs. Their children waited like stone.

"Daddy. My God, Daddy, what happened?" a woman asked of an old man who was shaking slightly in the morning chill. She hugged him and tightened his coat around him and rushed him toward a waiting car.

"Storm," he mumbled.

All about amazed children reclaimed their loved ones.

Charlotte Bates rushed down the gangplank into the arms of her duplicate daughter. "Your father," she gagged, overwrought, pointing behind her at the ship. "Your father," she tried to explain as her voice broke.

"What, Mama? What's happened? Has something happened to Papa? Mother? *Tell me!*" She shook her mother. Her mother swung her head no.

"Your father," was all she could say through her streaming face. Her daughter helped her away. The younger woman turned to her husband.

"I'm going to take her home now. You wait for him," she ordered.

When Bradford Bates finally came down the gangplank he came like Sir Christopher Columbus to the New World.

"What happened, Dad?" his son-in-law asked, awed. "What's going on?"

Bradford Bates paused and smiled up at the Westside Highway. He smelled in deeply New York. "Well, Nelson," he said. "I'll tell you." And taking the younger man by the arm he directed him toward a taxi and began.

In another, later cab, Herbert Vemish asked his father and mother, "How was it? How did you like it?"

"Not much," his father said. His mother nodded to agree.

The Man Who Lived

For as old age is that period of life most remote from infancy, who does not see that old age in this universal man ought not to be sought in the times nearest his birth, but in those most remote from it?
Blaise Pascal

ON THE NIGHT General William Tecumseh Sherman burned Atlanta (that was November 15, 1864), Frederick Kappel, junior, was born. He was born in Pittsfield, Massachusetts, and his father, Frederick Kappel, senior, who was with Sherman, would ever after celebrate the two major events of his life with his yearly reflection upon the ironies: that a city should die in part by the hand of him whose son should come to live at the same moment. "It makes you think that maybe there *are* reasons for it all," his father would say, waving his hand out over the universe.

Frederick Kappel the elder did not believe in God—not after Georgia. Only on November 15 he would come a little close. Then he would stand on the ornate wooden scrolled porch of the substantial house his father had built on Nye Avenue in Pittsfield and say to the autumn street, "It makes you think that maybe there *are* reasons for it all."

But that yearly remission did not convince the son. And in the years, all the years that came to him, he never thought that there were reasons for any of it.

His own war came in 1898 when the U.S.S. *Maine* exploded in Havana Harbor.

He was thirty-four but he enlisted, though out of no patriotic fervor or intent. Enlistment seemed to him as good a way as any of the others he had considered and subsided from to leave Pittsfield and the Berkshires, at least for a while, although he never came back. There was nothing to come back to even as there was nothing very much to leave from. But he thought that he was near to the middle of his life; he thought it to be half over, and although he was hardly a restless man, the idea that he had never been out of the state, not even across the near New York and Vermont borders, seemed to him improper. Enlistment had the simple urgency that could commit him to leaving, so he did it.

He spent his war in Florida watching railroad cars of meat cook themselves into seeping lakes of rancid grease widening under the cars while in a parallel siding, carloads of ice weathered unused back to vapor. In the end the ice and meat wasted, and so, Frederick Kappel supposed, did he. But not for long. He was in and out of the army in about eight months altogether.

He was by craft and trade a bookbinder, a good skill to move about with as long as you stayed near a printer of books. Not that Frederick Kappel thought about that when, at fourteen, he had been put to apprenticeship in Pittsfield. That or anything else. In 1898, at war's end, at thirty-five years of age, he got as far back north as Philadelphia (to visit an acquaintance from the army) and settled down, taking a job on Race and 4th Street in the firm of Bauch and Brinker which he never left. Which he came to own.

And he took a wife, a cousin of one of the many Bauches, a heavy woman, near to thirty, who bore him four children—three girls and a male—in seven years, and died. He married a cousin of hers, who bore him two more children, both male, and then she died in the diphtheria epidemic of 1910. Kappel's third wife, a widow of a customer (Oswald, the founder of what became World Publishers), bore him no children and lasted until 1930 when she too died. His fourth and last wife, whom he married in 1932 when he was sixty-six, was fifty-seven, but he outlasted her too, healthy though she was and strong.

Frederick Kappel did not venture much beyond the bindery. His children grew up and had their children as he went on folding great creamy sheets of double crown or foolscap or royal into folios and octavos and sixteenmos and more. Wars came and went, the Wright brothers flew and then Lindbergh flew the Atlantic and then men were on the moon. Nap Lajoie and Honus Wagner gave way to Babe Ruth and to Joe Dimaggio and to Willie Mays. He became a great-grandfather and a great-great-grandfather. Most of what little he knew of his world he found in newspapers (which he increasingly ignored), but mainly he learned from what he caught out of the books that passed into their rich clothing under his fingers. As he would sort and arrange the signatures to be sewn, his eyes would fix upon a paragraph or a stanza or a sentence but sometimes a page. He might never have read a book entire, but he was loyal to his fragments like a good Miscellany, and held them tightly, well bound in him.

When Frederick Kappel began his apprenticeship in 1879, all books were made by hand, everything even to the mixing of the pastes and glues; but his firm, under him, was one of the first to accept the rapidly developed bookbinding machinery—the stitching machines, the automatic folders, the jiggers, the conveyor belt pasters and casers, the stiff vinyl-impregnated fabrics, and even eventually the glue-backed paper-covered books which Kappel could never think of as bound. But he did it, or rather Bauch and Brinker did it as the printers came with their demands.

Kappel himself kept at the art of his craft and specialized in the restoration of fine texts. He became well known for his skill, the authority to whom the rare and the beautiful were brought for his exquisite ministrations—the damaged first editions of the Nineteenth Century, Dr. Johnson's dictionary and his *Lives of the Poets,* a copy of Roger Ascham's *The Schoolemaster,* which was said to have been Queen Elizabeth's personal copy as well as a copy of Lord North's translation of *Plutarch's Lives* which he bound in a soft, floppy suede.

And once a nearly perfectly conditioned but uncovered First Folio. The famous bibliophile Rosenbach had gotten it (in his ways) in mystery and had sold it enormously to Theodore Hyde who wanted it bound in leather. There had been argument. The Folger people had come up from Washington to protest and had marshaled pointless arguments from Shakespeareans all around. But there was nothing they could do and Kappel bound it in a leather so fine it made the senses ache from the sight of it, bound it in the old manner with cords rising through the leather of the spine.

It was about then and because of that that he became known beyond professional circles. About once a year thereafter someone would write a feature article on him and his business and personal workshop for one of the area newspapers, the Sunday sections. Mostly he bound expensively for those who could afford that last of elegances, whether they read or not.

Kappel stretched and dried his leathers and mixed his special pastes and glues and sharpened the blades for his cutters and waxed his linen threads, stitching and pressing together the world's history and its words, though he had none, history or words, of his own. Only in time, he did, as time which he had taken for granted for so long at last occurred to him.

In October of his eighty-fourth year—1949 (in a month he would be eighty-five), Frederick Kappel sat in his private workroom and looked out of its one large window at the small square courtyard of garden that he had maintained in back of the bindery as it had grown up and outward and factory-ish over the decades. His workroom was as smooth and well rubbed as any of his other tools, abraded and formed into the fit of his hands and their own tasks: boxwood and pearwood folder ribs, light but firm as his own fingers; a mahogany sewing frame (a gift) swirlingly carved and turned in elaborate counterpoint to the simplicity of its stiff function; the trim paste pots stationed strategically along the workbench; pressure devices all about—nipping press, drying press, lying press, cutting press, pins and clips and pure sluggish steel ingot weights—until the warm-wooded, life-stained room became itself the mold and form of union, of boundness, the tight, secure domain of the artificer, order immanent.

He looked out at the trees which he had watched grow up from saplings and though he had seen them, the four maples, arch up to their mature height (as much as a city air would allow), he had not until the moment thought of what they measured, of the enormous tick of accumulation that they were, of fifty years. He sat gently looking out and thought back to a rememberable condition somewhere between the saplings and now, but he could not find any. That was when time occurred to Frederick Kappel, in the month before he would be eighty-five.

He looked out at October and the trees yellowing down into autumn, the day darkening into night. Neat plots of still-green grass surrounded each tree and between the green plots the right-angled walks were paved with faded, salt-stained red bricks in the old Philadelphia manner. Late purple asters bordered the walks and yellow chrysanthemums burst up at each corner. Behind him on his worktable desk lay Blaise Pascal's *Treatise on Vacuum.* He had finished the binding of it that afternoon and had finished just now his final approving inspection, and what he had read, as it was his nature to do, still was before him. He saw the trees through the elegance and dignity of the ten-point unmodified Baskerville type on the marvelous beige Amalfi paper, the paragraph superimposed upon the trees, upon the season.

> *From the Preface:*
> *For as old age is that period of life most remote from infancy, who does not see that old age in this universal man ought not to be sought in the times nearest his birth, but in those most remote from it?*

He was not at all sure what that meant, but it would not go out of his head. The words hung there like odd, spiky fruit on the maples. Frederick Kappel eased back in his chair and waited. What came to him was this:

Oh would I were a boy again,
When life seemed formed of sunny years,
And all the heart knew of pain
Was wept away in transient tears!
When every tale Hope whispered then,
My fancy deemed was only truth.
Oh, would that I could know again,
The happy visions of my youth.
Oh Would I Were a Boy Again
Forth we went, a gallant band—
Youth, Love, Gold and Pleasure.

But he didn't know what that meant either. He knew what the words, the sentences, meant; he understood the idea of the poem. What he didn't know was what it meant to him. What happy visions were there in his youth? What hopes, disappointed or realized? Had there ever been pain or transient tears? How had he come to be here? Who was Gretta? Why, suddenly, this train of thoughts? After eighty-five years? He turned in his mind the page that the poem was on, a heavy Chatham buff-colored sheet with a laid design on it. He had read the poem thirty years before, but his fingers felt the stiffness of the paper and the granular surface.

Gretta was his first wife, the mother of Frederick III, Anna, Elizabeth, and Clara. The light was going out of the garden square, the maples silhouetting now, dark against darkness. He sought for more of Gretta but that was all he could find. He could not even see her face. He had last seen it thirty-nine years ago, when he had buried her, when it was even then already too late in a life to remember things.

It was hard to have memories when all there seemed to be was future, when one wife came along to crowd out the other, when entire structures came and went and with them whatever certainties and truths, calamities and triumphs attached. So that in this October, in this strange moment, it seemed incredible to him that he had grown up—smoked a first cigar, made love, learned a trade—before Theodore Roosevelt was president, had married and raised children while coal was still carried in sailing ships, and had built as with other men a life. He had been—was still—a voyager in time passing through galaxies of blurred existences. But what had any of it meant to him? His second wife's name was Martha. He rose up before the black night in his window.

A memory broke over him like the chill, thrilling cascade of wind on the cutting edge of a summer storm. He and his brother and a friend were climbing up through the almost dry river gorge of October Mountain ten miles south of Pittsfield, where the frogs live in their season by the tens of thousands, when the rain drove down like a wedge into the rocky creek bed. The three of them had scrambled up onto a ledge protected by an overhang. In thirty minutes the water of the creek, now white and swift, slid onto their platform. They crawled from under the ledge and up the muddy bank to higher ground. Safe. A little adventure. Seventy years ago. Now he shivered in the rainy clothes and in the bite of the newly wetted green. Now.

He left his workroom office and then the building as a night shift was entering. The men knew him and gestured soft greetings which he nodded to. He went by cab to the apartment he lived in in the Broadwood Hotel off of Rittenhouse Square since the death of his final wife two years before. There he washed and changed his clothing and went nearby to the Triangle, his club, where he dined, as usual, in his place upon his Wednesday fare: braised vegetables, cold sliced duck with apples, baked potatoes, and a half bottle of an unknown Beaujolais which he seldom finished. He read his Philadelphia *Bulletin* at supper, although the news and the rest always seemed the same to him, always had. Tonight in a feature section he saw

> *Much on earth is hidden from us, but to make up for that we have been given a precious mystic sense of our living bond with the other world, with the higher heavenly world,*

but before he had finished reading it, he knew what the rest would say, *and the roots of our thoughts and feelings are not here but in other worlds. That is why the philosophers say that we cannot comprehend the reality of things on earth.*

He had bound that years ago in a stiff, heavy, hollowback fashion with dazzling Bertini end papers. He read and remembered it now in and from the newspaper. There was an exhibit of Dostoyevsky memorabilia at the Art Alliance. The excerpt was from a letter which later became part of the novel.

That night, for the first time in twenty years, Frederick Kappel dreamed—distinctly and clearly once again; what had he had to dream to anyway? What he dreamed that night was paper, typefaces, bindings, and fragments—the particles he had cemented into whatever dimensions he possessed.

It has been a thousand times observed, and I must observe it once more, that the hours we pass with happy prospects in view, are more pleasing than those crowned with fruition.

The words were in his head as sharp and glowing as the gilded and embossed letters of the titles he had worked into leather with his hot punches and roulettes.

It is notorious that the memory strengthens as you lay burdens upon it, and becomes trustworthy as you trust it.

But then:

A great memory does not make a philosopher, any more than a dictionary can be called a grammar.

He turned in his sleep; there was nothing but the words in his dreams.

In nature's infinite book of secrecy
A little I can read.

He twisted:

I have entered on a performance which is without precedent, and will have no imitator. I propose to show my fellow-mortals a man in all the integrity of nature; and this man shall be myself.

At last:

O Boys, the times I've seen!
The things I've done and know!
If you knew where I have been
Or half the joys I've had,
You never would leave me alone;
But pester me to tell,
Swearing to keep it dark,
What . . . but I know quite well:
Every solicitor's clerk
Would break out and go mad;
And all the dogs would bark!
O Boys! O Boys!

He awoke in the morning convinced that he had been mocked through the night—what times, indeed, had *he* seen? But by whom? By what agency?

He was in his workroom by nine o'clock, as ever. Whatever else he was starting, unbidden, to remember, he could not remember ever not being at his craft and task by nine o'clock. He speculated that perhaps he never missed a day. His son, Frederick Kappel III, Gretta's, came in. The business, Bauch and Brinker, was his to run though the ownership of it was divided into various parts among the other children. Where were they, the father thought as the son explained the meaning of some papers he was laying out before him.

"Where is William?"

"What, father? William? My brother?"

"Yes."

"In Chicago, I suppose." He looked at his watch. "Getting ready to drive to his office." William, though he had been taught the book-binder's skills, had elected the law. "Why do you ask, father?" It was, after all, a strange question. Where, after all, should his second son, William, be? Where should his father expect him to be?

"Never mind," Frederick Kappel said. "It's nothing. Never mind." He turned to the business before him. "What is this?" And after Frederick had explained again, he nodded and signed at various places and was, again, alone for the day. As he preferred.

But that day he bound nothing. He sat before his window instead leafing through his fragments, as his fragments came before him. Dreaming or awake, it made no difference now, as though all that he had ever known, regardless of how little, had determined to a last appearance, a summation.

For that was the construction that Frederick Kappel put upon what was happening to him. It was all, he accepted, the final consequence of age, of dying: this slow-motion spin of his life before his eyes. To the young swimmer caught beyond his depths and weakening, or to the old, drowning in years, it was the same. That is what it was, and perfect though his body and mind still were, or seemed to him to be at nearly eighty-five, death was not to be unexpected; and if that, death, was what was happening, then he was absolute.

But at what pace, for surely all men were dying:

To every man upon this earth
Death cometh soon or late;
And how can man die better
Than facing fearful odds
For the ashes of his father,
And the temples of his gods?

Soon or late, that was the question. But at eighty-five, how late was late? How late could be late? Not very, Frederick Kappel decided and settled down for it.

The years seem to rush by now, and I think of death as a fast approaching end of a journey—a double and treble reason for loving as well as working while it is day.

But he did no work that day, nor the next nor the next. Not the old work anyway. If he worked at anything now it was on appraising the journey, or discovering it. If what he was fast approaching was the end of his, then where had he been? What had he traveled through?

He had been married longest to Hanna, twenty years, and though they had conceived no children, it was she who had been most mother to his progeny. Certainly for William and Martin, infants when Martha had died, Hanna was their mother. When she died in 1930, Frederick Kappel was sixty-six years old, all his children were out of the house or almost, the great depression was descending upon all, and the tremors of the war had not altogether concluded. He remembered now in this October that that was when he had first thought of death, thought that sixty-six was close to seventy, which was enough. He had had enough; all he could expect. Now, as then, he felt completed, or at least sufficient to his universal fate. He had begun, achieved, and now was ending: life's lucid parabola. But what had he achieved? Honor among book-binders? Wealth? Substantial sons? But when he came to the hard, squinting perusal of it, the craftsman's close attention to scrupulous detail, he could find little. He could not reach back easily for faces and Christmas parties or sharp pleasure or colors or triumph or occasions or failures. For a week now he had been looking at the maples, but all he could see was the striated bark and the burnishing leaves beginning to fall rapidly.

In the second week, close to November, his son asked after his health. And about his work. Without discussing it the father told him that he was well but that he would not accept new projects. He would complete what was at hand but no more. And he went back to his window and waiting.

By the end of November his trees were bare as too were the closets and bureau drawers of memories. He had waited for them like a host for guests; he had expected them soon to flood up and over him; and then he had nervously rummaged, and then he ransacked like a man running frantically through the empty house he has returned to, but too late. Gretta, Hanna, Martha, Betty, the children and grandchildren, his own parents, his bland war, Pittsfield and childhood, his century itself—all like tiny argent specks upon the broad black absorbing velvet of his past, tiny winking glints in the darkness. He stood on the needle point with nothing behind him and no time left for anything before. All that remained were the words that he had hooked out of the stream he had fished in; they were nearly all of whatever was of him. As the first snows of the winter began, he knew that. He added himself up.

Of Family:

> *It is not observed in history that families improve with time. It is rather discovered that the whole matter is like a comet, of which the brightest part is the head; and the tail, although long and luminous, is gradually shaded into obscurity.*

Children:

> *He that hath wife and children hath given hostages to fortune; for they are impediments to great enterprises, either of virtue or mischief.*

Of Fame:

> *Oh, who shall say that fame*
> *Is nothing but an empty name,*
> *When but for those, our mighty dead,*
> *All ages past a blank would be.*

Of Wives:

> *King David and King Solomon*
> *Led merry, merry, lives*
> *With many, many lady friends*
> *And many, many wives;*
> *But when old age crept over them—*
> *With many, many qualms,*
> *King Solomon wrote the Proverbs*
> *And King David wrote the Psalms.*

And even of death, all he had for it was

> *Is there beyond the silent night*
> *An endless day?*
> *Is death a door that leads to light?*
> *We cannot say,*

and other such remnants. Comets, hostages to forture, great enterprises, mighty dead, David and Solomon, Proverbs and Psalms—what had he to do even with the flotsam of his reading? Through the winter he sat in his window and fingered the rags of his life.

On February 18 he woke up with a cold. Even as he dressed he knew it would worsen. By the time he got to the office he was slightly feverish, only enough so that the flush beneath his white, smoothed flesh shone up through it, as sometimes pink will in the finest marble come up suffusingly out of depths. He sat in his chair and coughed and sneezed a little.

When his son saw him he wanted him to go home, to *his* home, so that he could be attended to.

"I've had colds before," Frederick Kappel told him. "Worse by far than this one." But you weren't eighty-five his son wanted to say but couldn't. Precisely, his father would have answered. At last he had his way. Of course death must have its agent. I approach my climacteric.

He had a startling genius, but somehow
It didn't emerge;
Always on the evolution of things
That didn't evolve;
Always verging toward some climax,
But he never reached the verge;
Always nearing the solution
Of some theme he could not solve.

Frederick Kappel laughed so hard at that, howled, that the secretary (for twenty years) in the outer office ran in to him; she had never heard him laugh, that way or any other. He laughed on, gasping and coughing and sneezing. Between his own tears squeezed out by the irony of the fragment, he saw her own tears, of pity, but what did she know? Then she ran for his son.

Still, after he had calmed down, he would not leave. He heard them mumbling in the outer office and soon Dr. Freed came. Dr. Freed examined him more thoroughly than for a cold, wrote two prescriptions, told him to go to his son's house till he recovered, and then told him to go to Florida for the rest of the winter and more. He thanked Dr. Freed and went back to looking out his window. Later he consented only to take the medicine. It wouldn't be long now, he thought. There isn't anything left to wait for. Death's predictive ambience of the past five months had turned assertive.

But he did not die. He did not even miss a day at his window.

Nature's first green is gold,
Her hardest hue to hold.
Her early leaf's a flower.
But only so an hour.

He watched as his maples blew out again, flinging their netting leaves out once more to entrap the sky. Birds came back. The tulips that he had ordered planted bloomed where the asters had been and would be. By the end of June he had never felt better, but different. He was lighter, as if his bones were hollowing; he felt himself floating, hardly feeling his own weight upon his foot when he stepped. And he *looked* lighter, more transluscent, like a thin parchment held against the light, like Moriki paper from Japan, like the spring leaf before it hardens against the summer heat. Thin and thinner he became until at the top of August, sitting now under his maples, he became like the subtlest of membranes, the thickness of a mere cell, so that he could not tell easily what was outside of him or inside. When a leaf fluttered, he fluttered; when a bird sang, he resonated; when the heavy summer raindrops pocked the dirt, he took the impress too.

There was no knowable joy to this, no express pleasure, only a great subsumptive neutrality, as though the long, nearly perfect vacuity which was his life had prepared him, or opened him, or by obliterating him had absorbed him. In mid-September, when the roses were coming back, he remembered a monument, the volumes of it he had bound, the veiny, calendered, burnt-umberish leather, the waxed threads, the sewing, the endsheets, the pressing, the carving, all of it. He had worked a long time on it a long time ago.

> *Only that day dawns to which we are awake*
> *There is more day to dawn. The sun is*
> *but a morning star.*

and

> *September 19, 1860: the temperature unseasonable. The foxes fur is thick. Birch buds seem longer than I remember.*

And then he was wholly clean.

And he lived on, lightening and lightening until at last he quavered in the particles of sound and pulsed along the frequencies of the photons in and out of the spectrum; until in his one hundred and sixth year, when it seemed to him increasingly, even against all of the reasonableness that he still possessed, that his life would not, would never leave him, he relinquished it.

Leave My Mother Alone

AT SEVEN O'CLOCK on the morning of April 29, in a recently sown alfalfa field about sixteen miles southwest of Rochester, New York, after a restless night, Altaina Rhonda, the *Phui dai,* Queen of all the Romany of the Quinda, the Zolaly, and the Athusian tribes, died. She was eighty-five and had ruled from the age of fifteen, when she ascended the throne, about two years after Grover Cleveland was elected President for the second time. She had been a great and a gracious queen. Because of that, and because it would be the first royal burial in this century, and because of the coronation of her successor (already named), the Council of Ten, which had sat for the week of her dying in the sleek fifty-foot aluminum trailer home of their queen, decided that the time for an entire assembly of all the Romany of the three tribes (virtually all of the gypsies in the United States and Canada) had come. By noon of the fourth day the word had been sent out.

Betty Hoffman, her arms around her groceries, leaned, for all her lightness, heavily against the door of her third floor apartment and inserted the key in the difficult lock. She shouldered at the door like a miniature TV detective. After the merest resistance, a symbol more than a fact, the door popped open. "It's weakening," Betty Hoffman thought. And then. "But so am I." Twenty years takes from locks and people. "Ah," she sighed, releasing the groceries onto the kitchen table and sinking down. She was weary from her day of selling dresses. And she was weary from missing Ellis, her husband, who had died two years ago. She gave herself five minutes of giving in and then got up easier in her spirits and brighter in her life and started to make supper for Paul, her fine son, who by six o'clock would be returning from his accountant's job downtown. It was while she was taking the celery out of the bags that she noticed that one of the letters in the fist of mail she had clutched up the stairs with her was not like almost all of the things she usually got—buy this, buy that, free-offer kinds of things—but was a letter postmarked Rochester, New York. She stopped with the celery, opened the letter, and read it:

> *Dear Mrs. Hoffman:*
>
> *Altaina Rhonda, our queen, is dead, having passed to her eternal rest on April 29. The Council of Ten, in the name of Janice Sola, our new queen-to-be, request your attendance at the Funeral (May 11) and the Coronation (May 12).*
>
> *Enclosed is a list of hotel and motel accommodations available in the Rochester area. If you have your own accommodations, provisions have been made to camp on the farms indicated below. Registration will be at the intersections of route 44 and Townline Road, indicated on the enclosed map by the X.*
>
> *Eastern members of the Quinda tribe have been alocated zones a, b, c, d, and e on the map.*

There was no signature.

When Paul came home he looked at his mother and said, "What's the matter?"

"So what should be the matter?" she answered him with a weak shrug in her voice.

"That's what I'm asking. That's what I want to know. Come on. Tell."

"I'm telling you. Nothing's the matter. Go wash. Supper's ready." She turned to her pots, rattling them, evading him behind the steam of her cooking.

Paul let it go through supper and talked instead about the usual and the close, the things in which his mother took such delight—his job, his progress, his fiancée Sandra and their plans.

Their meal finished, he stood beside her at the sink wiping the dishes she washed and rinsed. For almost all of his life he had done that, at first as a boy with recalcitrant self-pity, but now with love. And now, as the big, the important dislocations of a life were about to happen to him—his imminent marriage, his own home, soon his children—the comforting certainty of this ritual meant a lot. The jabs and flicks of tough affection which they exchanged at the kitchen sink were the constants he needed with which to measure all the exciting rest that was happening. But this night Betty Hoffman said nothing to her son, and he, though growing anxious, abided her.

Paul was in his bedroom changing before going over to Sandra's when the telephone rang. He went into the hallway and stood there listening to his mother say, as softly as possible, "I . . . I really don't know . . . yet. Please, please. Call back some other time," and then hang up. Paul confronted her at once. She was white as he had never seen her, even at his father's death, and she trembled, badly, totally.

"Mother," he demanded from her, "What is it?"

"Please, please," she said, trying to wave him away, not looking at him. "Don't ask. Don't know."

"Mother. For God's sake," he shouted at her. He went down upon his knees and grasped her a little below the shoulders. "You've *got* to tell me what it is. MOTHER!" he shouted, giving her the slightest shake.

"Oh, Paul," she said turning to his straining face, herself about to weep, "the gypsies. The gypsies have come," and dropped her head upon his shoulder and quietly and drily sobbed. It took him about ten seconds to recover. And then he jumped up and stepped back.

"The GYPSIES? THE GYPSIES? What are you talking about? Will you please tell me what is going on?" And so she told him.

After he had read the letter and heard about the telephone call (would she be interested in the chartered buses?), he made what he thought was the obvious and solving statement.

"So," he said with dismissal in his gesture, "tell them you're not interested. Tell them you're not a gypsy." He wanted to smile at the idiocy of the whole thing, but he could see that his mother was not at all relieved.

"Listen," she said to him in a desperate seriousness which itself more pained him even than what she said. "If they say I'm a gypsy, they know. What do you think? They'd let me attend the secret ceremonies—the funeral? the coronation?—if they weren't certain? They keep records, you know. Forever and ever. In their heads they keep them. See, they knew I was married. Even where I lived. It's no use."

"But they didn't invite me," Paul countered. "And why haven't they ever contacted you before?" But she wasn't hearing. He went on to argue with that eyes-shut patience and restraint affected by the maddeningly frustrated. He pleaded with her to consider the sanity of what she was saying. And he said more. The telephone rang and he leaped for it, but it was Sandra wondering where he was. He told her as best he could, without telling her, that his mother was upset about something and that he was calming her down. He'd explain it later. He'd be over soon.

"Listen, Mother," he said turning from the phone with the confidence of a man who has quietly drawn to an inside straight in a game no one remembers he is still in, "who ever heard of a Jewish gypsy? I mean there just isn't such a thing." So that's that, he thought. But without even looking up or out of her gloom, she said.

"That's what you think. Besides, religion's got nothing to do with it. It's all a matter of blood." Paul bellowed.

"YOU ARE NOT A GYPSY. DO YOU HEAR ME? YOU . . . ARE . . . NOT . . . A . . . GYPSY!" He came down off his toes breathing heavily, his brows, even in this cool Spring, damp. Then Betty Hoffman did look up and, even though tightly, smiled a little.

"Paul, baby," she said to him, reaching out a hand not yet altogether stilled, "I think I *am* a gypsy, a little bit," and explained.

Years ago when she was a little girl attending daily the after regular school Hebrew school and had heard the stories upon stories of Hebrew suffering and triumph, her class had come finally to the period of the Jew in Spain. The young rabbinical student from Yeshiva had explained to them that the Jews of Spain were called the Sephardim while those of Central and Northern Europe were call Ashkenazim. You could tell the one from the other, he went on, because the Sephardim were darker. "Like Elizabeth," he had said to them, and had asked her to stand up in evidence. That evening she had asked her grandfather, who lived with them, what it all meant, and he had told her as his grandfather had undoubtedly told him, the story of many of the Sephardic Jews, but more than that, he went on and told particularly the story of her own family. Simply, the legend was that when the inevitable dispersion of the Jews came, some of the poorest ones moved in with the gypsies. In time the two groups, persecuted by Spaniard and Turk alike, had, high in the white caves of Andalusia, melded together.

"So you see," Betty Hoffman said to her son, "they're probably right."

"Nonsense. At best it's only a folk legend," Paul fought back, neither disturbed nor impressed by the possiblity of its truth.

"Look at yourself," she said. "Do you look like a legend?"

Walking the four blocks to Sandra's Paul hunted for whatever it was that was bothering him. Beyond the obvious, beyond the pain of his mother's tears, there was yet the unsettling annoyance of trying to work a puzzle without all the pieces. Even that isn't so bad if you know what pieces are missing, but Paul didn't, at least not until he got to Sandra's, kissed her hello, and told her briefly the story. In telling her he found what was missing. He realized that he didn't really know why his mother had taken the gypsies so badly. In the blur of his own feeling at her distraughtness, he had simply forgotton to consider or ask, "So what?" He kissed his love goodbye, ran the four blocks home, and asked his mother,

"So what? So even if you are a gypsy, so what? I mean so what's the big deal? Why should you be upset? They think you're a gypsy and they invite you to a gypsy affair. So what? Every year my college fraternity invites me to the annual convention. I don't even bother to refuse." And then he laughed broadly and happily out of his ease and release. "And listen, my gypsy baby," he said to her, slipping into the idiom and tone of their affection, "with me your secret is safe." He concluded with an open mouth, burlesque-clown wink. Betty Hoffman said, stonily and without humor, "But Paul, I don't want to go."

He felt dizzy like to music he knew played too fast. He sat down before her onto the ancient, cracked imitation leather ottoman, the fort, stage coach, and jet fighter of his childhood, and took her hands.

"Mother," he said. "That's just what I've been trying to tell you." There was a sigh in his voice. "Don't go. You don't have to go. That's the point. They invite you, you don't go. So now just forget it. It's all over. It is all over." But it wasn't.

"I've *got* to go," she told him, the fear coming back into her again a little. "They won't let you say no. They're gypsies, Paul." She reached out to him a conspiratorial hand. "With them you've got to obey the rules . . . or else."

"No Mother," he said slowly, patiently against her melodrama. "This is America, a free country. This is the middle of the Twentieth Century."

"For you, for me, maybe. But not for *them,*" she answered him. "For *them* nothing has changed. I'm telling you, it's dangerous to cross *them.*"

He could have asked her how she knew that, or why she assumed that, but he knew that she wasn't arguing to a conclusion now but rather out of a fear. He got up from the ottoman, kissed her goodnight, and walked back slowly through the late streets to his Sandra's, ruminating upon his mother's fear and what to do about it.

Supper was unusually silent, but his mother, Paul noticed, though nervous and brittle, was yet contained. Supper finished, the dishes washed, Betty Hoffman then said:

"Well, I'm going. Monday. For three days. I told Min at the dress shop. It's ok." Through her statement she hadn't looked directly at him. Now she did, and smiled, at least as best she could. "Besides," she said, "it could be very interesting. It's not everyday you get to see such things. And . . . and who knows, I might even meet a . . . a nice man. What? I'm such an old bag?" At which she half leaped clumsily into a dimly remembered Carmen pose, one arm up, the other down, a rose stem ground between her flashing teeth. She stamped her heels *a flamenco*. Paul said nothing, hurt badly and quietly at his mother's absurb posturing facade of gypsy cliches. For what?

"What?" he asked. And then she rushed back into Betty Hoffman and into her son's arms suddenly.

"For you," she answered him. "For Sandra. If I go then they won't be mad. Then they'll have no reason to hurt you or even maybe to even find out about you. You'll see. Three days and it'll be all right." She said it bravely but she held him hard.

Out of her wide love for him her fear for him had driven her to her fine gesture, and out of his love for her in her pitiful falling and in her glory of courage, his own love for her and that gesture had snapped through him like an obliterating spasm so that he could not see and he could not hear for a time, but when shortly he could again, he saw his mother opening the apartment door to a small dark man, neatly but just a degree unstylishly dressed, who lifted his hat politely. Paul heard him say,

"Mrs. Hoffman? Good evening. My name is Alva Seguin. I called yesterday to see if you wanted to go on one of the chartered buses?"

"Oh," Betty Hoffman said, falling back a little. "Oh." Fear moved quickly up and down in her at once. The gypsies were here! At her door!

But it was only one gypsy, a little, stooped one, with no gold in his ears, no knife scars on his pallid face, and in his slightly watery eyes, nothing deeper than the message he came to bring about Greyhound buses. "Come . . . come in," she finally said to Alva Seguin, and stepped away from the door to allow him. He hesitated a moment, looked cautiously about, and then went into her apartment even as Paul walked brusquely forward.

"Listen," Paul said, loud. "Let's get this straight right away. My mother is not a gypsy. I don't care what any of you think, she is no gypsy. *Leave my mother alone!*" At Paul's sudden appearance, and at the first cut of his sharp tone, Alva Seguin caught his breath in frightened surprise, took an involuntary backward step, and bumped into Betty Hoffman closing the door behind him.

"Excuse. Excuse me," he begged of her shrilly, trying to speak to her and to look at Paul at the same time. He heard the door click shut; his eyes flickered and he sank. He almost groaned.

"Paul!" his mother said, not sure if she was reminding him of his manners or pleading with him not to anger "*them,*" him, but Paul, knowing what he was doing, continued.

"It's ok, Mother. I'm just going to straighten this out once and for all. For me, for you, for *them.*" He said to Alva Seguin, pointing a teaching finger at him, "I mean you no harm, but you have got to leave us alone. We are *not* gypsies!"

Alva Seguin appraised them both quickly as though he had his doubts, but what he said in a little voice, almost a whine, was, "Why do you tell *me* this, this way? Even if it is true, why do you tell me?" His hand was on his chest, open across it. Paul frowned, suspicion rising up now for the first time out of Alva Seguin's strange question. He answered.

"Why do you think I tell you? You invite my mother to the gypsy funeral and coronation obviously because for some wrong reason you think she is a gypsy. Well, she isn't. That's what I'm telling you for. And what I'm also telling you is . . . ."

"No, no!" Alva Seguin interrupted, sputtering in relief. "Not her. Not *her!* The *husband!*" he fluttered with his two hands up near his ears. "The *husband* was the Romany, the gypsy. We invite her because of him. *Him!*" he screeched a little to emphasize the point.

"Ellis!" Betty Hoffman said. "Ellis a gypsy?" She said it calmly, quietly, like a disinterested spectator quizzically removed, held, for that one moment, by perfect equanimity in the balanced tension sometimes possible between the truth and the preposterous. And then she laughed so fully, her *delight* at the absurdity so great, that even Alva Seguin was not proof against her. Even he smiled to hear such roaring laughter; whatever else, laughter such as that was worth hearing.

Paul smiled at the ridiculous idea of his fragile, proper little father as a gypsy, and, too, at the realization that his mother's anxieties were over now absolutely. It wasn't *her* who was the gypsy. And nothing would ever convince her that it was Ellis Hoffman who was. Nothing.

"If he was a gypsy, why didn't he tell me?" she giggled out at Alva Seguin, who by now had remembered the purpose of his visit and had stopped smiling.

"Sometimes, now so many of us live in the cities, men don't tell," he muttered, unconvinced himself. She fell down into the sofa.

"I'm sorry," she said trying to say more, and then buried herself in laughter. Memories of her endearingly bland husband in all his un-gypsy-ness, thirty years a shoe salesman, swept through her and collided with visions of him playing a sobbing violin to the serpentine shimmer of a gypsy maiden as she danced about a campfire somewhere upon a plain in Hungary. She shook until the muscles beneath her ribs convulsed into knots of pain, but still she shook.

Just before Alva Seguin left the apartment Paul asked, "So there's really no reason at all for her to go to the funeral, right? I mean even if Ellis Hoffman *had* been a gypsy, she wouldn't have *had* to go? Isn't that right?" Betty Hoffman on the sofa snorted and gasped under the talk like an accompanying line in music.

"Yes," Alva Seguin said, nodding, looking down. "That is right," and left.

Even with the little gypsy gone, Betty Hoffman could not stop laughing—about Ellis, about the whole silly thing with the gypsies from its beginning to this end, about her general relief—so Paul made her get dressed and he took her with him to Sandra's to tell her the wonderful story. Through the streets, Paul's hugging arm about her, Betty Hoffman howled, and at Sandra's some more. Only later, back in the apartment, his mother finally quiet in her sleep, Paul wondered why anyone had thought that Ellis Hoffman could have been a gypsy.

Paul had decided to shave before going to Sandra's, and so it was over the water running hot and steamy in the bathroom sink that he heard his mother scream, yelp rather than scream. He bounded into the living room, half his face still lathered. Betty Hoffman, her hands to her cheeks, stood looking across the threshold of the door at three men, Alva Seguin and two others.

"What is this?" Paul shouted, advancing on them. "What's going on? Yesterday we settled everything. What do you want?" The two new men looked even further down than they had been, x-raying the toes in their shoes.

Alva Seguin said, "Please, I ask you. Only a moment or two. It does not concern your mother, but *us*. The Romany, the gypsy. Please?" Paul watched his mother lower her hands from her face, and he remembered last night. She would be all right.

"Come in," he said.

When they were seated in the living room, and Paul had wiped off the lather and put on a shirt, Alva Seguin began.

"It is about your father, the departed Ellis Hoffman." The gypsy to Alva Seguin's left crossed himself. The gypsy on the right spoke. He looked much like Alva Seguin, a little darker, a touch more of the inappropriate about him, and his voice had a cracked, reedy quality.

"Sir," he began, "Our problem is this. If your father was a . . . a gypsy,"—he said 'gypsy' without liking the word —"then your mother should attend the funeral and the coronation, for she becomes of his flesh and he continues in hers. But if he was not a gypsy, then how did it come that he was thought one? That is a strange thing. And then, if your mother does not attend the funeral and the coronation, *in what manner does she not attend?* To us these are important matters." All three of them nodded vigorously at that.

Paul started to try to unravel in his own mind what all that had meant, but then he decided not to. It was all too bizarre, and it looked as though it would become even more so; and, finally, it was irrelevant to his life. Enough was enough, and that limit had been reached last night. Tonight, now, he wanted to finish shaving and go to his Sandra, his betrothed. He began to say so, to dismiss them, when the third gypsy said, only not to him nor to his mother but to the other gypsies.

"Unless, of course, she *is* Romany. Maybe Gitanos?"

"Spanish," Alva Seguin interpreted for Betty Hoffman and Paul.

"Ah," the gypsy who had been speaking first answered, "But even if she is *Gitanos,* but the husband is nothing, as they claim, then the situation becomes the same."

"No," the other argued back. "The blood of a woman is stronger."

"Only if it is pure," the first rejoined.

"No," said the other shaking his head. "Even the female blood of a *posh-rati* is binding."

"*Posh-rati,* the child of only one pure-blooded gypsy parent," again Alva Seguin interpreted for them, but quickly now, as under an imposition, now anxious himself to enter into this elaborating contention with his partners. Soon the three of them disappeared into the swirls of ever fining distinctions and the strange, lovely lilt of the Romany language. Betty Hoffman and Paul were left alone, aliens in their own apartment.

At one point, however, the reedy-voiced gypsy said something that sounded like "nich gefiddle," and Betty Hoffman could not help interrupting.

"What did you say?" she asked him. "Did you say 'Nich gefiddle?"

"Ja," he answered. "Yes."

"But that's Yiddish," she said, amused and amazed. " 'Nich gefiddle' is Yiddish."

"There is much Yiddish in *Yenische,*" Alva Seguin explained. "It is the dialect of the gypsies who journeyed mainly in Germany. There is a kind of Yiddish also in *Calo,* the dialect of the *Gitanos.* Sometimes more, sometimes less. It depends." But before she could say anything, the three of them were back into their intricate fretwork, unmindful that Paul went into the bathroom and finished shaving and dressing, or that Betty Hoffman made for them hot tea with lemon.

When Paul came out, bright, neat, smelling nice, he went up to his mother, sitting at the kitchen table, smiled and shrugged.

"What'll we do?" he asked, the humor of it all too rich to disturb.

"I don't know," she said. "Let them go on, I guess. What's the harm. Go," she said to Paul, standing up, straightening his tie, kissing him. "Don't worry about me. I'll be all right."

So he left, and she continued to watch them rattling at each other like the old men who sat about downstairs in the synagogue arguing needle-sharp points of Talmudic law over sponge cake and sweet wine, consuming themselves in the pursuit of an abstraction, battling for law, and traditions, rituals and rites, the truths and deeper strengths of Jew and Romany alike.

Only once did she say anything. At a moment of high, tense pitch in their considerations, anxious to save them from whatever precipice they seemed to be lurching towards, she had blurted out,

"I'll go, I'll go. I'll make it easy and go, already." But Alva Seguin had said, shaking his head to thank and reject at the same time,

"It is not that simple anymore." He sighed and went back to his work.

They left at quarter to eleven, apparently not having resolved anything. Indeed, they had created dimensions and complexities that they had not earlier dreamed of, issues, the threads of which ran into the cloth of their existence. She did not seem to matter very much to them anymore. She had watched them all the while, and though she hadn't understood anything, except for a little Yiddish here and there, she felt more and better entertained than by anything she had seen on TV for ages. She would miss them.

The next night there were four; Alva Seguin, his two companions, and a man as old as the kind you only see in art photographs. His white mustache was as wide as his face and hung lower than his chin. His face and hands were like an ancient hide. He wore a crumpled, double-breasted blue, pin-striped suit that once, maybe thirty years ago, had been costly. None of its buttons matched. Four or five gold chains strung back and forth across his paunch, and there were diamonds, sapphires, rubies, and topaz on every finger. The three lesser gypsies were deeply obeisant, and both Paul and his mother knew instinctively that they were in the presence of a gypsy lord, almost the last of any nobility in the modern world still possessed of personal power. His visit was an honor to her home.

The three began where they had left off on the previous night as though time had not happened. Then, after fifteen minutes, the old man spoke. He had not been introduced to Betty Hoffman or Paul, and he did not address himself to them. In the infinite folds of his face, it was not ever certain that he looked at them or that he even saw them. He spoke in Romany. He spoke for near to half an hour, like a song, phrasing, pausing, rising and dying. And then he was silent. And then Alva Seguin said to Betty Hoffman, solemnly:

"It is decided. You cannot come to the funeral and coronation because you are a *didakai*—one who is much less than ever a quarter Romany. Whatever of Romany there may have been in you will be gone in your son's son." But Betty Hoffman could not accept her gypsy fate with a good grace.

"What about Ellis?" she asked.

"A mistake," Alva Seguin went on. "He has told us that there have been many." He indicated with a slight nod of his head the old man.

The three younger men rose, and then slowly the old man. His gold chains jingled.

"But what about me?" Betty Hoffman implored strangely. "What about the funeral? The coronation?" The men heard nothing. They did not see her. They walked to the door. Betty Hoffman ran in front of them. "Don't I get to see something? *Any* of it?" The men waited like for an elevator. "I mean . . . I mean it doesn't seem fair." Finally she stood aside and opened the door for them. "What about my quarter of the blood?" she asked softly, failingly, as the men filed past, the old man first. "My eighth?" she said after them, a concession.

None answered. They turned down the hallway. She heard them descend the stairs. And then they were gone, all of the gypsies were gone forever.

Natural As Can Be

"He said *WHAT?*" Caleb asked again, for emphasis not information.

"That's right," Barbara said. She was peeling supper potatoes. "That's just what happened." She giggled. "Isn't that ridiculous?"

"God damn it," he said. His lower intestines clenched a little, creaked. "Sooner or later every lousy Eden ends up with its god damn snake in it, doesn't it?" Caleb Goddard was a poet by craft and a teacher of literature by profession, so metaphors, good or bad, fresh or old, came about naturally and most of the time. He didn't count on them; they were just there.

Caleb taught at an oafish little college tucked into some hills in upstate New York and away from all of the world. The students of the school were academically poor but, like the universal young, generous in the spending of their spirit and alive to their own bodies and interests. As far as Caleb was concerned, which was not much, they were all right. The faculty of Loughton College, however, was petty and dull as only a faculty of failed academics can be. Caleb had nothing to do with them.

It was only to live where he did that he continued on at Loughton. Where he lived was twenty-five miles north of Loughton, in Broomsville, beyond Broomsville back a dirt road which opened up on a small lake formed in the glacial valley of two cliffs. The lake was so lonely, so hidden, that many of the inhabitants of the nearby village had never seen it. Some didn't even know that it was there. The lake was so lonely that large rafts of Canada geese rested upon it summer and fall; loons rose and sank in it in their season; beaver ate down the trees upon its boggy margin; fox and deer short-cutted across it in frozen winter.

The lake was so alone that it could have been two hundred miles further north in the high Adirondacks, but it wasn't. It was twenty-five miles from Loughton College where Caleb could supplement his middling inheritance by teaching, and it was only four hours from New York City, where he and Barbara and the two boys could go to supplement their lives. It was an arrangement, and it suited the Goddards perfectly. But now trouble had come to the Happy Valley. Not big trouble. Not the trouble of calamity and desperation, but the trouble of stupidity and annoyance. Just the kind that Caleb Goddard hated most.

"But he's seventy," Caleb said, as if that would matter now or change things. "No, seventy-one. He just got out of the *hospital,* for christ's sake. He almost *died.* I mean he almost *DIED!* Doesn't he *know* that?"

"I told him," Barbara said. "I reminded him. When he started to feel me up he began trembling and shaking so much I thought he was going to have another attack, or whatever it was. I sat him down and then I gave him a good lecture. I told him it could kill him and that *I* certainly didn't want him dying in *my* bed. But he had all the answers. Boy, he must have worked it all out." She quartered the potatoes.

In a thin band, about an inch wide, the skin over Caleb's eyebrows tightened. It was a strange feeling to him, a new one. He had never felt it before, and he was a man precisely aware of his body. The tightening and stretching worked its way across his forehead around to his ears. The idea of the old man touching his wife's breasts cinched at the band around his head. Her talking about it, her saying "in my bed," her talking to the old man about sex at all, *his* talking about it to *her,* his "propositioning" her—it all drew the belt in another notch.

But that was absurb. That was stupid on his part. It wasn't the sex part of it, it was the disloyalty of the old man that angered him. It was the injustice of having to be made angry now by someone whom he had never hurt, by someone to whom he had been especially friendly. He thought about how he and Barbara had helped out the old man's wife while he was in the hospital, and the anger buzzed in him like electric.

"The son of a bitch," he said. "The ungrateful, lousy, miserable, dirty old son of a bitch." He hated to be disappointed in people. He stared out in front of him looking into human failure and hopelessness. As deep as his anger was his sorrow.

"Oh come on now," Barbara said. "Take it easy." She put her hand out and on his. "Look at the forsythia," she said, looking out of the large wall-window in the kitchen out over the lake. "It's not going to bloom again this year." She laughed for them both. It was one of the things that she did for him. He understood that and loved her.

"But to do something like that," Caleb persisted. "Well, you know. It has to qualify, to affect, our whole relationship. How can he expect to be friends with us now? Didn't he think of that?"

"What he was thinking about was Nature," she explained. "That was his justification. It was the natural thing to do."

"*That's* what he said? You're kidding. *He* was kidding."

"No," Barbara shook her head. "I told you, he had it all worked out. When he was in the hospital his nephew and the nephew's girl friend visited him. He was feeling pretty low, sorry for himself and all, and they tried to cheer him up. 'Give the nurses a pinch,' they told him. So he did and the nurses laughed and they started to flirt with him. You can imagine—'Look out for the old geezer in 309.' One of them, he even claims, kept trying to expose her panties to him. Anyway, whatever, it made him feel better. It made him feel good. He started to think about the meaning of existence, about the Beatles and their guru and the freedom of the young people today with their mini-skirts and 'pot' and their dancing and . . . ."

"The *Beatles?* Good grief," Caleb Goddard said. He asked his wife, seriously, "Is he getting hard in the head? Is he getting senile?"

"No," she said. "I really don't think so. He's just 'hard-up.' He's just all sexed-up with no place to go."

"What about his wife? What about Betty?"

"I asked him that. She's packed it away." Barbara went to the sink and turned the water on into the potatoes. " 'You can do it if you want' is what she tells him. 'It's more than a man can stand,' he tells me." Barbara mimicked him, making her voice high, squeaky, mouse-like, single-toned. " 'It ain't natural. Natural's what's important. Like the animals. Free. No problems.' "

"Good god almighty," Caleb said. "A seventy-two year old flower child."

"Seventy-one," Barbara reminded him coming back to the table from the stove where she had put the potatoes.

"You noticed?" he said to her taking her hand, finally.

"Well, seventy-one is only six years older than Cary Grant." She leaned over and put her free arm around his shoulder, bent further, and kissed him on the temple. The stricture that he had worn like an Indian head band disappeared. "Look," she said. "It wasn't as though he actually—you know—*did* anything to me. And it isn't even as though he could. He's so frail anyway I could pick him up and carry him home if he got . . . *naughty*. And I set him unmistakably straight. We ended by talking about apple trees blooming so well this year. It's over. Finished. He won't try anything again." Barbara was wrong.

The next day, Thursday, nothing happened, but Friday, after Caleb had driven home and put the car in the garage and sat in the kitchen with a glass of scotch, letting Loughton College dissolve in the alcohol, Barbara told him.

"I was working in the garden, high up on the bank where the rocks are," she described it. "And he came and stood at the bottom right by the retaining wall. He said he was looking for his dog. Then he spread his arms and said, 'Have you got a little kiss for me today?"

"He was kidding. He *must* be kidding," Caleb urged.

"Well, he is and he isn't. Anyway, there he was."

"And you said?"

"What do you *think* I said? What do you *think* I did?" Barbara paused now. She just waited for a few moments for the flush to go out of her. " 'No,' I said. 'No. Not now and not ever. Now go away and leave me alone.' "

"And?"

"And? And what? He went away, of course. What do you *think* he did?"

Hearing her now was worse than the first time. Then he could accept Barbara's idea, as she could herself, that the old man had tried and failed and would let it go at that. Her sternness with him then had stopped it, both of them believed. But his persistence now meant that Caleb was going to have to do the stopping.

His evening was ruined. He drank too much wine at supper to blunt his furious edge and then fell asleep after supper for too long. He awoke at eleven bloated and nauseous. His head ached from the rope of anger wound around it. He read in two books. He read *Life.* He listened to Mozart. But all he saw or heard was the situation: what it was most likely to be in the morning when he talked to the old man, and the more deadly situations of anticipation ("Maybe he's flipped. Maybe he'll panic and go for a gun. Maybe he'll deny it all or get huffy or belligerent as a defense. Maybe. Maybe.") By two o'clock Caleb fell asleep but awoke at six wishing it was nine. He hammered away at some wooden project in his workshop until it was.

His plan was to drive down to his neighbor's with Barbara and the boys on their usual Saturday trip to the dump and simply tell the old man to cut it out. That part was easy. But Caleb also wanted to restore, or maintain, the peaceful and friendly context in which all of them had lived for the past six years. At least as much of it as he could. He wanted to tell the old man to stay away from Barbara *as a woman* even as he wanted to re-establish the woods-wise, crinkly-eyed, secure, uncle-ish structure of plants and roots talked and traded, gardening implements or household tools lent, Christmas gifts exchanged that they had all lived in pleasantly for so long.

"If only he'll let me make it easy for him," Caleb sighed as they drove the two hundred yards down the dirt road to the old man's place and got out of the car. The boys scattered. Caleb walked toward the splendor of tulips lining the long inclined driveway and started taking pictures of them. Barbara followed two paces behind. The old man saw them from his high porch and came toward them, rolling toward them on his amazingly bowed legs.

"Hi," he shouted ten yards away. He looked for all the world at ease enough. Caleb crouched and clicked at the tulips. "Mighty nice of you," the old man shouted into Caleb's ear. He was getting deaf quickly and shouted almost all the time now.

"Don't mention it," Caleb shouted back. "It's what good neighbors are for." In the past the old man had often asked Caleb to take color pictures of his place, his various gardens and plantings, the variegated ducks and the chickens he crossed and raised, and Caleb had always been particularly pleased to oblige him. Nothing made better for friendships than the gifts of things and skills. Now he used the pictures to remind the old man. He used them to prepare a base of friendliness for what he had to say. "Don't mention it," Caleb said again, but suddenly different and not how he had intended.

He saw the old man stiffen a little and not look at Barbara, whom he had always greeted gaily. Caleb was sorry for what his tone had too soon revealed, but he was relieved, too, to see that the old man was alert, aware, and sensitive to nuances. He was far from being senile, and he wasn't going to be huffy, to "act up." Caleb, shaking a little inside, felt the relief coming in, filling him up and out. The hell with it, he thought. Get it over with.

"Listen, Alex," he said, straightening up and looking at the old man directly for the first time. Their heads were close. "Just stay away from my wife, ok? We've been friends and good neighbors for six years, right? So let's just keep it that way, ok?"

The old man nodded once, quick, and stuck out his hand to shake on the agreement with Caleb. Caleb took his hand. That was that. He crouched back to the flowers. It had gone off better than he had hoped for or expected.

Then the old man said, "Them bees don't ask permission of the flowers. The rain don't ask to fall. It just *does* fall." Caleb froze. Nothing was settled at all. He stood up again slowly and faced the old man. He was going to ask his neighbor now, and as a challenge, what he was trying to say, what he was driving at, but the old man needed no bidding; he was in the thrall of his vision.

"Life is all that's real," he proclaimed. "That's the truth. There is only one truth and that truth is *life.* What lives is good, what doesn't is bad. Look at them birds. Look at them flowers. The woodchucks dig where Nature makes them. What Nature makes you do is *TRUE LIFE!*" He screeched a little on the high note. He would have gone on. He prepared to.

"Glory be to god above, halleluiah," Caleb shouted back at him waving his arms and hands over his head.

"Huh?" the old man said.

"Glooo-oooor-oooor-ria, in excelsis de-ea-OOOOO." Caleb had let go of the camera and it swung like an amulet now from the strap around his neck. He sang to all the woods and the birds stilled for a moment. Down by the meadowy verge of the lake his sons looked up from their stone-throwing to see if the sound was for them, and then turned back. The old man startled.

"What? Wha . . . what?"

"This is what," Caleb said, hard and teeth-clenched. "You don't know crap about what you're talking. You're just trying to justify your own dirty itch. You're . . . ."

"No, no," the old man squawked. "A man's got needs like the birds. He . . . he . . . he . . . he got life in him and the life needs . . . needs . . .

needs . . . ." When he was worked up about something the old man stuttered. He stuttered now and was trembling. The color was gone from him and the skull-tight skin of his face, tightened by his illness, tightened more now to nothing. Only the droop of welt-like cords under his eyes reminded that there was any skin at all.

"Listen you stupid son of a bitch," Caleb shouted at him to drive his words into the old man and not just so he could hear. "A man is not a bird, he is not a beaver or a woodchuck or a bee or a god damn flower. It would be good if he were, BUT HE ISN'T. He's got duties and loyalties and friendships. One flower doesn't help another flower when he's in the hospital. MEN do that." The old man winced. He was spinning but he held on.

"Caleb," Barbara said. She wanted to draw him off.

"But I didn't die," the old man said. "I need to . . . to . . . to . . . to go *on.* A man can't stop. He's got to go . . . go . . . go ON." Spittle flecked the air in front of his mouth. "I didn't die in the hospital. I . . . I . . . I didn't *die.* I got to go on." Caught in his Revelation, he stumbled about. He couldn't give it up, nor it him, and he couldn't flee from Caleb.

"Fine. Fine. Live. Go on. What's stopping you? But 'going on' means more than getting 'layed.' Listen you hypocritical old bastard, listen closely."

"Caleb," Barbara said.

"You're talking about a simple piece of ass and you're making it sound like a mission of the Lord's. You've got a wife. Use *her.* Doesn't she suit you? Is *that* your Nature? Yeah? Well why don't you ask your nephew's wife? Why don't you put the question to the young fellow's girlfriend in the hospital? Sure. Why not? You go in there and get on the phone and call up the young thing and tell her that you feel like a bee today and you'd like to buzz her a little. Go on. Call *her.* Or go to the city. You need two bucks? Here." He gestured at his wallet. "WHY MY WIFE? What is she, a slut on the street?"

"Oh," the old man groaned. "Oh." Tears rimmed his old man's eyes, some spilled. "Oh," he said.

"Caleb," Barbara said. "Caleb, please."

"What about justice, Alex? Bees don't have it. Come on," he said to Barbara. "Kids," he shouted to the lake. They ran up.

In the car over the rutted roads that were drying out now from the Spring run off and dusting up Caleb drove too fast. He drove to the pace of the spasms in him and against the pain in his head. Barbara said nothing; she sat watching the road snake before her as Caleb twisted the car in a slalom around the pot-holes. The boys whooped. At the dump he emptied the station wagon quickly and only once punted a bag of refuse, exploding it like a *pinata* at a Mexican Christmas. He drove back more slowly. By his neighbor's he could see the old man far down near the edge of the lake sickling down the high grass.

"Three weeks ago he was almost dead, and now look at him," Barbara said. Caleb said nothing.

Back in the house Barbara asked him if he wanted a cup of coffee with her. He told her yes. They sat together in the kitchen looking at the late Spring turn to the heaviness of Summer, the black jabbing lines of trees against the snow having softened into the returning earth and then disappearing under the slow-motion of the green billowing up like a rolling cloud over everything. In the living room the boys were at the Saturday cartoons. Caleb drank his coffee and suffered. Nothing had come out right. There could be no old friendship now and he wasn't even sure if he had stopped the old man from annoying Barbara. Or if he had done that, had he done it so that the old man understood and could control himself?

He said to his wife, "I really brutalized him, didn't I?" He looked out the window at the widening V of a beaver arrowing across the lake. And then he said, "he's not really wrong, is he? I mean altogether?" He finished his coffee in a swallow and stood up.

"Where are you going?" Barbara asked, for it was clear by his body that he was going somewhere, whether he wanted to or not.

"I forgot to tell him about Mercy." Caleb left the house. He was swept out of the house and down the road to the old man's. He walked strong across the clipped field toward the old man down by the lake. The old man saw him coming and stood up waiting for him. When Caleb got close he saw that the old man wasn't trembling nor weeping and what color there was to him was back.

Caleb said, "I'm sorry for my words." And then he said, as if the two men had encountered for the first time, "Stay the hell away from my wife." And then he swung on the old man even as the old man chopped at him with the sickle. Caleb caught the sickle hand by the wrist and his fist flattened the old man's nose. He twisted slightly and the sickle dropped. Blood spurted from the old man's nose. Caleb hit him again in the stomach and the old man dropped to the ground on to his knees retching for air. Caleb stood above him with his fists clenched and felt solid, firm in the calves of his leg and in his intestines and all around his head. Wind blew off the lake and he shivered in it but only with his skin. The old man got his breath back and sat back on his heels and look up at Caleb. He said through his bloody moustache, "Ok."

The Clay War

—all things fall and are built again
and those that build them again are gay.
William Butler Yeats

IN A SMALL alcove, or perhaps it is merely a niche, on the west side of the New York Metropolitan Museum of Art, behind the rooms of dusty colored Egyptian vases and urns and amphora-type vessels standing quietly as doom and as forlorn, behind all those rooms to which few come and in which no one lingers long, there is a smallish glass display case, about three feet high by five feet wide, which is sometimes lighted and sometimes not. It is as if the case were there by accident; unlike the Egyptian pottery and the more popular halls of French Impressionists and Titians and Tintorettos and the great fake Etruscan Warrior threatening forever, high up in the ether of the museum, which get lighted by an automated and computerized central control panel in the museum's deeps, the small glass display case is illuminated only when a guard, accidentally passing by it, notices that it is darkened and stops to attend to it.

The guard flicks the ordinary light switch on the side of the case and the three flourescent bulbs stutter on slowly. They are old bulbs with antique starters. Not an art historian, he is yet familiar enough through his years of peripheral rounds to see that these objects are different from the Egyptians nearby or from the Greeks beyond.

In the glass case is a teapot with six cups surrounding it, a low bowl about twenty inches wide at the rim, a pitcher about twelve inches high, and then, taking up almost a third of the case, a great glowing metallic red bubble of a lidded porcelain bottle as wide as it is high. It looks as if, freed from the case, it would float pulsingly upward. All the other pieces are muted, earthy, and matte like stone, glistening like stones after a rain has dampened them. The tones of the pieces shift about on the surfaces, mottled hue blending into hue so that each inch is different, although one can never tell when they become different. The pieces are like fire itself, definable but amorphous, present and gone in the same instant. The guard reaches out his hand to touch the pieces and bumps his hand against the glass. Do not touch. Do not lean on the glass. But his hand is on the glass and he thinks that if the glass were not there, he would touch the pieces regardless, that he would daringly pick them up and try them, and if, unimaginably, he could, he would eat and drink from them.

The glass case is sealed, locked by a concealed lock in the base to which the key is misplaced or unrecorded. Someday the bulbs in the case will burn out, one by one. Perhaps then the case will be dismantled and relit or even repositioned in the museum. Or perhaps the case will come to be accepted that way, finally to be lighted only for a few hours each day from the reflected light of the Egyptian Room as the sun passes over the glassed, transepted roof, the vessels in the case quietly hidden in the New York Metropolitan Museum of Art like a solemn and honorable promise of silence, though with no grandeur lost in the keeping of it nor beauty dimmed.

Ephron Gherst came from Poland to this country in 1878 when he was twenty-three years old. He came with a wife his own age whom he insisted on calling, in this country, Fanny (in Poland it had been Fanaela), for he determined that that was the American style and he would, now that he was here, practice it. English, he declared, was all they would speak as soon as they learned it. He came, too, with a son, Aerrie, age five. And he came with a skill. He was a potter. Besides one hundred dollars after the passage, that was all he came with: strong youth, responsibility, a craft. But what more was there? And this was America, so what more did he need?

He put in his greenhorn year in New York City. It wasn't bad. The leap from the weeping muddy hovel of his birth and rearing, with its slow realities of seasons and its relentless poverty and mad danger, into the sharp, paved, artificial clatter and angular brightness of the quick and growing city, was just right for Ephron Gherst just then. He was a learner, an adapter to possibilities, more concerned to eat whatever life served up rather than to judge and select, a man of appetite before taste, though not without taste. An adventurer, perhaps. Perhaps, too, he was enchanted, either victim or source—or both—of a fine and potent magic. Had he not already done the impossible, learned a highly skilled craft in a country that explicitly and threateningly prohibited him from doing so? Had he not married on nothing, less than nothing, on the wage the cheating bastard in Fremlen paid him for the platters and baking dishes and cups that he turned out, for the killing labor of mixing the clay, of cutting the wood, of firing the kiln, of walking the ten miles to the work?

So what was there to be afraid of? Not the pale, collapsed timorous elders of the village who despaired at his labor, that he should work with his hands rather than mumbling into toothlessness with them over the scrolls, and who feared for themselves through him, that he should enrage the Governor or, worse, the rabble of Fremlen, by his audacity. And not the leering bastard shop owner in Fremlen who sold Ephron's work as his own and held the threat of exposure at Ephron's butt like a white-hot drawing iron ready to brand him before the world. He had learned despite them all and had married Fanny when he needed her. (And what a crying out there had been at that!) And he had made a son and had earned and saved and even stolen to come away to here to form and pursue his dream.

His dream was simple enough: to live without fear and to live by what he was able and pleased to do. He was a craftsman. He wanted a place to make his wares, a kiln to fire them in, a chance to sell them, a house to live, a garden to grow his potatoes for the winter. Beyond that, what? More sons? A gold piece or two to bury against hard times? For once a fine dress and boots of the softest leather for Fanny? And that was all.

"All," Kollowitz said. "All?" He came around from the heavy desk in his tumbled, strewn office and sat down next to Ephron and took the glass of half-drunk tea out of his hand. "Aren't you forgetting something? Aren't you forgetting the fancy brownstone on Twenty-third Street, the one with the servants? Aren't you forgetting the carriage with the two matched horses? And what about the summer house by the ocean? Tell me, Ephron, why are you forgetting all these things?"

"Speak in English," Ephron said.

"Aiii," Kollowitz said, slapping his forehead and getting up and going back behind the desk where he felt safer. "You don't know English, Ephron Gherst," he said in English, "so how can I speak to you in it? All right, all right," Kollowitz raised his hands. What he had to say, even in English, wouldn't be too difficult for Ephron to understand. What he had to say was *no*.

Kollowitz was a cousin to Ephron Gherst, so distant that it was impossible for either of them to establish or deny the connection. In the puddle of a village, less than a crossroads, in which Ephron had spent most of his life, Kollowitz was the one thread-thin bond that any of them had to the New World. Not *this* Kollowitz, who was not much older than Ephron, but to a grandfather or perhaps even a great-grandfather. When the village would speak of America, it meant not a place but a single declarative statement: Kollowitz went there. It was all they had to say about so arcane a subject as America, until the expression came to mean nothing at all. When some stray breeze over the marshes brought with it America, someone would say, "Kollowitz went there," and that would be that.

There were many Kollowitzes in New York, and it took Ephron two months of daily searching to find the only Kollowitz who remembered Fremlen, if only vague and muffled mentions of it. But that had been enough. Kollowitz liked Ephron, admired his odd history, his rare skill, his easy courage, and accepted the obligation to help. He got Ephron a job at once in a small leather-goods factory at the river end of Canal Street, sweeping up, moving material, and slowly learning a little about cutting the hides into straps and belts. There were no potteries in New York for him to work in.

And Kollowitz reestablished Ephron's family in a tenement better than the one they had been led to that first day off of the boat by the landlord agents who came to feed on their helplessness like gulls hovering in a ship's wake. And although Kollowitz could not see the Ghersts socially—he was too well established for that—yet he visited them each month, laden with food and clothing and a toy for Aerrie. Then they would sit for a few hours over glasses of strong orange-colored tea and tell each other about what each lacked, Kollowitz his Polish past, Ephron his American future.

But this that Ephron asked for now—*wanted*—was impossible.

Since the early spring, since April, Ephron had been going by himself into New Jersey, to the capital, Trenton, on the train, and then from Trenton, by wagon when he could beg a ride but mostly by foot, into the edges of the pine woods which was most of the state. He had heard about this New Jersey and its endless and mysterious stretches of pine at about the same time that he had learned that Trenton was the pottery center of the East, of probably all of America. At once, even before he knew anything, he imagined this to be his place. Effortlessly available quantities of wood to fire his kilns, and pine wood at that, the long and quick flame of pine so perfect for *his* kind of pottery. The clays that he would find and buy from the Trenton mills. The closeness to cities where he could someday sell—Philadelphia,

Trenton, New York, and more. It was everything. And surely, if there was a pottery industry already, it was a sufficient sign that the conditions were right for a one-man operation. His trips to the region confirmed him. His mind made up, he walked about in that countryside to find his place on earth.

It took most of the summer. First only using the long Sunday, leaving New York in the dark on the rattling milk train and arriving at Trenton still in the dark. Then he would steal a Saturday from work, then more and more of them, until he was warned by his boss at the leather factory. But by then he had found it: a shack for a house, a shallow well, and acres of scrubby pine. In two creek beds nearby he had found some promising clay deposits, rough fire-clay that he could use to build the kiln and some good earthenware clay which might get him started with some low-fire things until he got settled enough to move on. Best, he found the owner, and learned that the property could be bought: two hundred dollars.

"Ephron. Friend. How can I give you five hundred dollars?"

"Lend," Ephron corrected him. "Two hundred for the property, the rest for nails, wood, tools, things, food for the winter."

"Lend, give, is not the point. I'm talking about the risk. To start this way . . . ." Kollowitz shook his head back and forth, weighty with his knowledge of business ways and the world, a pendulum swinging from doubt to doubt. "What I'm saying is you would be taking on all the problems at once—the making, the selling, the building, the . . . the . . . everything. If anything went wrong anywhere along the line . . . buuum." Kollowitz threw his arms wide, leveling Ephron's life. "Go a step at a time. Get a job in the factories in Trenton. Then get the land. Then build. Get the feel of the market. You see what I mean? Aiii," he slapped at his forehead again, seeing from Ephron's face that he had indeed considered steps but had already decided on leaping. Then he would have to be tougher.

"Five hundred I can't lend you, Ephron, so that is that." He settled back. He glanced at his watch. He was a busy man and Ephron had had enough of his time. Clients were waiting in the outer room.

"Four hundred, then," was what Ephron said.

"Four hundred? If you needed absolutely five, so now how come suddenly you can do it on four?"

"I can't," Ephron laughed, roared. "But I will."

They settled finally at three hundred. With a weary shrug Kollowitz had given in, but not without hope. For when he asked, with a businessman's reflex to a troubled agreement, but in softening humor, what Ephron had to offer for collateral, after first explaining what collateral meant, Ephron held up his two hands to him and said, "These."

It was better than Kollowitz had gotten from many another.

By the time the first snows of early December came, Ephron, Fanny, and the boy were home. Ephron had sawed, hammered, and patched against time and had won. Each fresh and sound timber replacing a rotted one shored up his life, each nail driven into each firm, shaven board sang to him the descant more ancient than man of home, of place. Door jambs, headers, shingles, shelves, post, two rafters, three joists, and an entire sill on one side of the building. Pushing in a bellying wall, twisting straight a canted corner of the building, he beat his shack into a house and comfort in eighteen-hour hosannas, in flower bursts of energy like the sudden autumn asters all about him. The weather stayed good. It kissed him and he kissed it back. Besides his potter's craft, this was the first of anything he had ever owned. Already it was superior to all he had left in the mud ten miles from Fremlen.

Fanny gathered herbs and late berries and fruits and then mushrooms, scouring the fields and nearby roads with a thoroughness the already abundant Americans could not comprehend. And established chickens. And acquired a goat, the start of a flock of geese, a cat. She sewed and mended and arranged. Nothing ended but that it began. To Aerrie the work was play. So when the snow was higher than they could fight through out to the clogged road, they were ready. Wood, food, Aerrie, the preparations for spring—the garden, the kiln, the workshop—all, all of it a sustaining gaiety, a reliable pledge that life had its reasons and its ways.

Only once, in October, before the earth froze up, Ephron had paused for a week to dig clay from the nearby creek beds and to go the difficult twenty miles to Trenton to seek out additional clays and other supplies. He had returned late at night in a rented wagon with what clay he needed, but with a worry too. Or the shadow of a worry perhaps. It was hard to tell, as it is hard to tell if we hear or if we think we hear a twig snap behind us in the tangled woods we sometimes plunge through in dreams.

He had gotten most of what he needed in Trenton, and if it had been hard bodily work, yet it hadn't been too difficult to transact. The large potteries were not very interested in selling raw materials, certainly not in the small amounts that Ephron wanted and could afford, or could carry away. Still, a precious dollar here and here and there and there and a yard man at one mill and the chief mixer at another could be persuaded to look elsewhere for ten minutes or so. But what worked best for Ephron was the absurdity.

When asked what he wanted the clay for, he would say, to make pottery.

And the head man in the yard would laugh above the clamor of the efficient mill, the dray loads of clay, broken and unrefined mountains or powdered and sifted, shifting from mound and building to tanks and bins, the muffled roaring of the continuous fires in the building-high kilns and the monuments of streaming smokestacks a hundred feet high, the creak and screech of the compressors blending and mixing and extruding the clays, the slap and skitter of the leather belts on the rods and gears and pawls arranged as power take-offs for the wheels before which inconceivable rows of whitened men sat in hunched and productive array. The head man in the yard would open the black hole of his mouth in the clay-cloaked body and laugh and wave about like a lord to whatever Ephron wanted. It was worth the good joke. Anything to help a competitor, the ghostly yard man had said.

By three o'clock the steepsided wagon was full, but Ephron had not found one clay, one kind of clay, the ball clays from places called Tennessee and Kentucky, that he wanted to learn about, to explore, to use in time. In his year in America, Ephron had heard of new materials unknown to Fremlen, the wondrous kaolins from Georgia and Florida, strong stoneware clay from Ohio, refractory flints, dense feldspars, smooth fire-clays from Pennsylvania and even New Jersey, self-glazing clays from Albany in New York State. But particularly he had heard of the silky and plastic purity of the white ball clays from those places, Kentucky and Tennessee. Even in America they were just coming into use. So Ephron lugged out to the one mill he had been told might have this clay, flouring the road with sprinkles of his commoner clay through the cracks of the wagon sides at every jounce, the horses unhappy and a long way yet to go.

At the Mercer Clay Works, Ephron made his inquiries. The language of craftsmen, any crafts, are simple, basic, and direct, like the actions themselves. Few words are necessary to describe the nuances that the fingers achieve; to talk at length about the cleanness with which a well-formed pitcher lip cut off the fluid stream that poured over it was a waste of breath. Could describing the condition of clay accomplish the same thing as the feel of the clay in the hand of the man who would use it? Could fire be measured by equipment instead of by its color and the shimmering hold with which it grasped the ware in the kiln? So Ephron had little difficulty with language during the day, for it wasn't cracked English he spoke as much as it was the fundamental knowledges themselves, the immediate and intuitive current of truth to truth. By the time he was talking to the people at the Mercer Clay Works on the Bordentown side of Trenton, New Jersey, Ephron had come to know at the ending of this day that he had knowledges that none of the others had, that a man who knew about this didn't know as much about that. Was he the only potter in Trenton who fired the clay he himself shaped from the clay he himself mixed?

The Mercer Clay Works had the Tennessee ball clay, and it was safely stored, secured from weather and thieves, and unobtainable by any means. So Ephron begged.

"This much," he pleaded, making a bushel with his arms. Nothing. "A hatful," he implored, pulling off his hat and sinking to his knees. He laughed, to make his urgency acceptable. They gave him a hatful of the clay after he explained how he would test it. He told them about a type of shrinkage test for certain clays that they had never heard of, that he had developed himself. A hatful of clay for his useful discovery. A trade. The barter of craftsmen, uneven now, but the only trade in town.

At the special Tennessee ball clay storage shed, the men working there were quiet. They were shovelers, the lowest workers, the inept extra sons who knew nothing of craft, destined only for early disability and then death as their lungs calcified from the inescapable fume of clay they lived in.

As the Trenton potteries established and enlarged through the century, whole Irish villages were brought to America to be taught to work them, whole families and then generations stayed to live and die in them, scourged by silicosis, the potter's disease, too inevitable to be dreaded any longer, only one more penance they were taught to accept as a payment on the policy of the life to come, where they, with God, would breathe in the icy cool blue air and all would eat and drink from gold and silver plate and not off of the cursed clay.

So when one of the young shovelers upon receiving orders handed a hatful of the Tennessee dust to Ephron, he could hear nothing of Ephron's tremble of excitement, the flutter of imagining. He could hear only the strangeness of Ephron's accent, see only the difference of his clothing, the assurance of his walk, the hugging of his hat and the little dance of joy like it was gems he held. All he could see was this dark straight, strong man, no older than himself, claiming his terrific rights to walk away by the side of his wagon to . . . . But he could go no further, shape no more of his hate than that, just as with clay he could do no more than fling it dryly about. He spat whitely upon the ground and remembered.

Passing out through the gates to the Mercer Clay Works, Ephron felt Fremlen at his back, the cold, harrying wind that would blow him from the city to his hovel. In a spasm of panic he thought he was waking from a dream, that all that had been wonderful this year—the new city and Kollowitz and the home a-building in the woods and the plans and the future riding in the wagon he led and even the exquisite joy of his dirt-full hat—that all of it was dissolving into a murky, numbing morning, that he was waking up to his ordinary journey from his father's hut to Fremlen, and that all the rest had not been. He struck out at the horse to hurry it, to outrun the terror. And then the panic was gone. He sighed and laughed and patted the horse to soothe it. All that was good was still good. Trenton was not Fremlen.

Through the winter he prepared. In the lean-to of peeled logs that he had attached to the house, he dried and cleaned and mixed the clays he had dug himself in the nearby creeks. In a wooden mold he shaped the thousand special bricks he would fire in the spring and from which he would build his mighty kiln, already planned and drawn to the finest detail. Into other molds he pounded his densest mixture of clays to make the shelves for the kiln. Small amounts of the clays he had gotten from Trenton he mixed to special proportions and then rolled out into small rectangular slabs that he would thoroughly dry and fire and test to find all he would need to know about them.

He recorded his formulae and recipes and later his results like an alchemist possessed by the visions of what this and that clay body could achieve if they worked out to be what he struggled for in his imagination: the strength and the vitreous density and the color that the fired clay itself would bloom into and lend to whatever glaze he would devise, and to guess at whatever good accidents might spring out of the fire because he had prepared for them. It was all a glory of artistry to Ephron then, the freedom to work in the holy realm of his vision and his skill, to work only within the boundary of creation itself where there is no failure ever, for there even if the test tiles, carefully marked and numbered, should melt or crumble or burst or warp or die in all the ways that they can in the fire that must try them, so that the philosopher's stone or the great elixir eluded him this time, still they would not have gotten very far away.

What a glorious distance from Fremlen now, where he had been jesseled to his perch like a tame crow to do over and over again all of the old things, including the foolish errors and the tradition-bound faults, as though there was nothing more to know, or nothing further for a jug or a jar to be. Twice he had offered his improvements to his boss, each time to be rejected with scoffing and imprecations, so that he learned and found and imagined quietly and stored it up till his time would come—as it had now.

Why did he know all that he did? What was in him that he could rub a clay in his fingers or smell it or taste a little of it and comprehend how the clay would work, how it would likely fire and glaze? Perhaps it was in Ephron's will; perhaps it was the shapes in his head that called forth a clay body that would keep a daring curve or a clay that would sustain in the fire the arching handle Ephron's hands had stripped it into; perhaps his knowledge came out of the intimacy that love brings.

George Barton was the first person to befriend Ephron here. George Barton was the blacksmith for the Hightstown area. He lived three miles further in toward Hightstown than did Ephron but on the same coarse road. He was seventy-five years old, white-haired but as straight as he had ever been, all that was strong about him still strong, his skin thick and darkened like the crust on slow-baked bread by the decades of his forge's fire. Fire was what he and Ephron had first in common, the catalytic element both worked with, and thereby knew and cherished. They touched each other through it and discovered more.

Early Ephron had sought out the nearest blacksmith and had found George Barton. He would have need of certain special fabrications difficult to make. Ephron showed him sketches of the framing he would need for his kiln and of the rods he would need as he constructed his potter's wheel. And there would be other things too. Yes, George Barton could do all that. And then they talked, Ephron as best he could about his plans to build, to make, to sell, to live here.

George Barton listened, his great clubs of forearms twitching with their own memories of sixty years ago when he had come with his father from the middle of England to where they were now, this very place and land and smithy. The forge here was the forge he had built with his father, stone upon stone. He told Ephron that there wasn't a barn for miles about that didn't swing its doors on Barton hinges.

In the winter, when the snows of a storm had packed themselves down or been driven into opening canyons in the road, Ephron would bundle down to the smithy. Then the two men would sit for a time by the constant fires and drink tea together and George Barton would tell Ephron Gherst about this new country and his own old dreams and what it was all coming to anyway. And Ephron would come back full to his brim like one of his own bottles to pour out all of George Barton's history to Fanny and Aerrie.

To Ephron it was all a wonder that this land should be here now or that it had been as George Barton had found it. And George Barton was glad to speak to such a listener, for Ephron accepted impressions as quickly and perfectly as the clay he worked. George Barton had been silent too long with the scattering of his children, the death of his wife, the quickening all about that had sealed over him. It was good for him to find an Ephron, loud with life, boisterous with plans. And of course there was the fire and the clay and the iron, there was all of that to talk about.

Sometime before the spring George Barton dragged out of an unused stable stall a chest that only he could have moved alone, and opened it to Ephron. It was full of delicacies of drawn wire and tapered spikes, splatters and bursts of metal.

"Sometimes the iron would run so," George Barton touched a splayed teardrop of the dark cold metal. "Or here it would splatter or break in . . . a way. I used to save them. I couldn't melt them back. I took to throwing them into here. I even made some on purpose for a time. A long time ago." He dropped the lid to the chest and shoved it back again into the past. He didn't know what to think of it all, his doing that then or even his showing it to Ephron now, only that it didn't need to be explained. Iron or clay lived in fire. It took strong men to drive them and sometimes nothing at all could. Those were the moments George Barton had once saved and once even dared to imitate, to reach out to capture the fundamental dignity of elements when they spume and flare as in memorial of their own birth eonic distances ago.

"Yes," Ephron had said to George Barton, to himself. "Like throwing the clay into the air and firing it that way. To be able to do that."

"Yes," George Barton had said. He had gone back to horseshoes and scrollwork and iron banding and weathervanes, as Ephron Gherst prepared to go on to plates and jugs and bean pots. But Ephron thought that he would capture the flung clay yet.

Spring came quick and easily, the misty air not as soft as the winter-cleaned sunlight promised it would be, but soft enough for Ephron and Fanny and the boy to dance about in it. Ephron cut trees for a week, felling the thin pines, trimming the branches, and then, with no horse to do it, hauling the logs out in small trailing bundles, he and Fanny haltered together, giggling and stumbling through the damp needled matting of the forest floor.

He stacked the bricks of clay he had molded for the kiln through the winter and fired them like a brickmaker for three days. And when they were cool, or almost cool, he built his kiln like no kiln before it had ever been built, with intricate measurements for the flue placement and fireboxes and ash pits, bag walls, spy holes. As he mounted the bricks in interlocking patterns to eliminate all heat-losing chinks, mortaring them together only with wet clay, he shouted out to Fanny what he was doing, why this would do that, why it would work better than any kiln ever had, fire higher temperatures more evenly throughout, be precisely controllable, why it would do his will.

Fifty feet away Fanny dug in the loamy and sandy soil and laughed to herself to hear him. She would stop her work and grasp hands of the soil to watch it break apart softly and easily, to watch the rain sift down through it quickly, to kiss it for its goodness.

Ephron came back to her from the doorway; he was halfway through and sat down beside her and took her hands in his. "Listen," he said, "nothing bad can happen here." He raised her hands to his face. "Do you think I would let it?" Then he got up and went back to work.

The kiln fired as well as he had expected it to, demanded it would. The simple, low-fire wares—flowerpots, dishes, mugs—were excellent. And in Trenton they were more than acceptable, finely made and not expensive. He returned with money and some orders. It had all begun at last. The garden and his business grew. From his test tiles he selected the clay body that most suited him and mixed determined quantities of it, stoneware now, even some porcelains: high-firing, nearly translucent, bold. And in the midst of all his business he contrived with more formulae, blending and testing the precious Tennessee ball clay into amalgams fit to hold the arabesques and pavanes of shapes that pushed through him until he could not breathe with the pressure of them and until he would shout out the building joy of thinking that he would make what he would someday make.

He tramped about in nearby streams to discover pebbles that had trapped flickers of oxides, and then he would pulverize and grind them down in a machine that George Barton had devised for him. He hoarded those exotic colorants in small leather sacks like other men had held the gold dust they broke out of the rocks of another coast.

By September his life had begun to seat itself, diligence wearing away the obstructions, asserting the patterns, deepening the grooves that round and control our days. The orders for what he was making—the low-fire earthenware—were increasing steadily and were almost enough to sustain them, and even his blazing high-fire stoneware was, if not selling yet, at least being curiously appraised, people attracted by it but unnerved, uncertain as people always are before wonders.

Ephron Gherst, the potter from Hightstown, was beginning to be noticed, so much so that he had had to formalize his methods of procuring materials. To get his supplies now he had to go through the front office. And pay.

At the Mercer Clay Works it was not so easy. John Clough, the working owner, had heard about the successful advent of Ephron Gherst and took no competition, large or small, for granted. It was not, however, the daily low-fire production ware that John Clough was thinking about when he refused to sell the Tennessee ball clay to Ephron at any price; it was the special, occasional pieces of his that he had seen and that he had heard spoken of that bedeviled him. Those pieces were like nothing produced in any of the local factories or that could be produced there. John Clough understood that, but the pieces were not like anything produced by any of the other small native potters either, from any place or from any time that John Clough knew of. Ephron's special pieces were fired to as ringing a strength and density as the best bone china produced by the Mercer Clay Works, but the pieces looked like the fire, like the fire had been frozen, all the impurities of the clay burned into beauty. And the size of some of these pieces, and the balance and certainty of all of them were beyond anything the jigging and extruding and casting machines of the factories could match.

John Clough had no fear that these fine pieces of Ephron Gherst would establish a competing style or would challenge the main production lines as determined by him and the larger pottery manufacturers of Trenton or of Europe, but he saw no good reason to abet or to encourage the kind of skill and knowledge that Ephron's work represented. He would not sell Ephron Gherst the Tennessee ball clay: there was too much more that he might make out of it. But John Clough offered him a job. A good one. Which Ephron politely and absolutely refused. And that was to be the last he ever had to do with the Mercer Clay Works. At least officially.

On the way out of the office he passed by the shovelers he had seen the year before, or perhaps these were others. Who could tell beneath their shroud of clay dust? Only one, the one who spoke now. Ephron remembered him, remembered the terrible desperate glass-blue tinted eyes forever wet with a rage he could not comprehend.

"Hey, *yankle,*" the blue-eyed man shouted at Ephron as he passed by the group of cloudy men. Even sitting inactive they created a stratus of clay, a climate, a dry white weather of oblivion. "Hey, *yankle,*" was all he shouted. Or could even think to shout.

But it was enough. Ephron shuddered from history. Fremlen was following him after all.

Ephron got his Tennessee ball clay at last. He had to buy it directly from the Tennessee fields through a shipper in Philadelphia, and by the time it lay in burlap-bagged piles in the storehouse which he had added to the workshed, it had cost two hundred dollars, a breaking sum nearly thrice what it would have cost had he been able to buy it in larger loads or to have bought it locally. Still, he had plans for it that would make it worth emeralds.

He had gotten some of the money from Kollowitz, whom he had visited late in the summer. They had written frequently over the year, Ephron full of his bursting days, his inches of success, his ounces of gain, Kollowitz full of his encouragement and cautions. And of his pride in Ephron.

"Mad," Kollowitz said as they sat together in his summer-hot office. "What is it? The trip up here did this to you? The heat? Overwork?" Ephron had just explained to him his need. "You are getting on your feet, you are just about ready to meet your bills *and* your old debts, and now you are talking about a loan, about *new* debts? What's wrong with what you are doing? Making a living isn't enough?" But it was Kollowitz and not Ephron who was sweating. Ephron was used to heat and to living in the only day before him. Disasters were in the future; dreams were now. Ephron listened and smiled as Kollowitz dizzied himself in the tightening swirls of his practical fears, doubts evoking doubts. He was particularly upset by the foreboding refusal of John Clough. "Why?" he said at last, exhausted by the heavy black chimeras he had lifted up for Ephron to see. "What do you need this clay for? What more do you need to do than you've done?" He meant with Ephron's life, but he and Ephron defined that differently.

Ephron opened the box he had carried with him on the train up from Trenton and took out of it a large bottle, as round as it is possible to imagine roundness to be. At the precise top pole of it a neck and rim rose like an exquisite but defiant pronouncement, smaller than fingers could have formed but yet asserting that fingers had. Ephron put the bottle on the desk in front of Kollowitz. Kollowitz could only smile to see it, though it made him feel much more, the blood in his hot body lurch, the skin at his temples tighten.

"I made two of these," Ephron said. "Without the right amount of the ball clay I couldn't have done it. With the ball clay I can make more, and bigger. So that's why." But the bottle was sufficient argument for itself. Kollowitz looked upon it and relented.

The other bottle was for George Barton, who had lent Ephron fifty dollars toward the clay. He also build Ephron a pug mill for mixing his clays. Building it got George Barton back into some steelwork too, back into the elegant days when the finest axes and cutlery in this country were made by men like him and his father out of precious bar steel imported from England. George Barton remembered what it was to hunger at night for substances fit to compel. He found now that he had lost nothing of his skill, only the urgency to use it, and Ephron Gherst had given him some of that from his own great store. For two months George Barton welded and brazed, tempering and annealing through days and nights, and on the fifteenth of November, when the sandy road between them was frozen tight, the two strong men drew the heavy machine to Ephron's on a stoneboat behind a pair of borrowed drays. They skidded the mill into place and Ephron poured the dry mix and water into the hopper. Then, as he turned the heavy gearing that George Barton had made to mesh like a watch, all the substances binded together and emerged at the gate as workable clay. George Barton and Ephron and Fanny and the child, Aerrie, all took a turn. Then they drank strong tea and Fanny's dandelion wine. A ceremony.

The winter was again mild, and so there were days, even in February, when Ephron, with Fanny and Aerrie helping, could carefully stack the great kiln with the fragile ware. The child was old enough to learn useful things and to be truly helpful, and what needed to be done in the house or pottery was now finished, so Ephron fired the kiln more often and sold all he fired, and when the thinly crusted creeks that threaded the vast pine barrens broke back into spring water, he had a dollar more in his hand than he needed, although still much less than he owed. But better than money, the small store of oxides and pigments and colorants that he had ground out of the pebbles and rocks and dirt had accumulated to a usable amount. Soon he would stain and glaze and draw upon his pottery with earthly crystals none had ever seen before. For even he, even after his most recent tests, could not predict exactly what would happen in the kiln. But Ephron Gherst knew enough to accept mystery as a gift and not a challenge.

"Look at that," George Barton said showing him the handbill. "September the first to the fifth. A State Fair."

"What is a State Fair?" Ephron asked.

"Well, it's like a county fair, only bigger I guess. Like the fair we had last year in Allentown, remember, only this is for the whole state. The first New Jersey State Fair."

"Good," Ephron said. "We must go." The county fair had been a delight. He turned back to his work.

"But look," George Barton drew him back. "Look." He pointed to the small tightly packed lines filling the paper beneath the large blocky type. It was the usual list of exhibitions to be judged. But after livestock, foods, and quilts, and between tin-smithing and harness work, was pottery. There had been nothing like that at the county fair. Ephron took the paper and read on. At the bottom were the directions for submitting: all you had to do was show up at least a day before the fair was to open. And there were prizes too, ribbons blue and red and white.

"What about you?" Ephron asked. He pointed out to George Barton the blacksmithing.

"Sure," he said. "I'm going to work now," and left the shed, complications of weathervanes already turning in him.

One of Ephron's wheels was arranged so he could pull it ouside to work in the air in the good summer months. That was where the wheel was now, the second of the wheels he had built here, a refinement upon a refinement. The central shaft was machined steel, a bar that George Barton had ordered turned on a lathe. For the first time in his life Ephron had used true bearings instead of a simple tight hole drilled through a thick oak block. And when George Barton had welded to the shaft the flat round head upon which Ephron worked, he had leveled it to tolerances as fine as feathers, as certain as spider threads. There was no potter's wheel like it anywhere else. When Ephron sat upon it and spurred the great balanced flywheel up to its fullest thrumming speed, he rode it like an ancient charger, mounted, a bold knight after his grail.

Through the afternoon he worked out leisurely pieces that he would fire and from which he would select for exhibition. And there would be many more pieces. He had a month to go.

The month went quickly. Besides mixing quantities of the clay he would use for this performance, and aging it by quick devices he knew and others he invented, there was the wood that always had to be cut to dry a little to replace the wood that already waited to be burned. And there was the forming of the pots themselves. And when these were completely dried out in the sapping August heat, the bisque firing was loaded and completed. He and Fanny and Aerrie removed the still-warm bisque and spread out the rough, pinkish-white porous pieces in rows in the workyard.

"I leave them out overnight so the dew can coat them," he explained to the boy. "Then the pieces won't soak up too much glaze like a sponge. They'll be a little wet already." He taught the boy all that he could. It was all that Ephron would be able to give him.

They left the bisqued pots. Tomorrow Ephron would glaze all morning and dry the pieces in the afternoon sun, and in the evening they would stack for the glaze firing, and early in the morning after that Ephron would kindle the first soft flames in the kiln. But now, this day's work done, they walked off to George Barton's.

They returned home in the last of the August light. All of the bisqued pieces in the workyard were smashed, methodically and exactly, every one of them crushed where they had been placed as though an enormous claw had descended upon them through the unprotesting trees.

Fanny threw up her hands and covered her face. The boy whimpered.

"No," Ephron Gherst commanded them quickly. "No." Fanny lowered her hands to his voice. Aerrie stopped like a quivering, uncertain blade between them, and then he and his mother ran after Ephron as he strode heedless through the broken yard. He pulled a shovel away from the wall of the shed and dragged after him a clattering flatbed cart as he went. All that was left was now, and that was what he would work with. What hadn't failed him in the past shouldn't fail him here. At the perimeter of the cleared land around the house, just at the end where the pines thickened into an unbroken wave of forest across the state to the sea, he uncovered the pit in which he had buried a great mound of his thoroughly mixed prized clay.

"I was saving this for you," he explained to the boy, "preparing it. In ten years it would have aged like . . . ." He shrugged. Who could imagine a clay body so pure? "So we'll make more another time, yes?" He jumped down into the pit and began to shovel the fermenting clay up to the surface. "But now we will need it." He inhaled the clay like a soft cheese and nodded in approval.

"Ephron?" Fanny asked, pleaded. "Ephron, *what?*"

But he dug down. It would be easier to show her than to explain.

All night and into the morning the great wheel in the yard spun. Fanny wedging the clay, pushing and keading it like bread as Ephron had shown her; the boy, until he sagged down to sleep, carrying the clay loaves to his father, riding, riding.

Everything that clay could be made into, Ephron Gherst made that night, not simply the kinds of things but the *limits* of them, so that the merest unmeasureable fraction further and the high-bellying pitcher or bottle would collapse upon itself or the cantilevering lip of an incredibly wide platter would slump and crack at the impossibility of maintaining the mathematically perfect curve necessary for its strength. Freed by catastrophe, what could he not attempt or dare? Having already lost, what risky endeavors could threaten him? All the night long he flung the clay up into the sky and held it there.

The day was good, dry but not too hot. The vessels moved quickly into the leather hardness they had to have to be trimmed. Fanny slept for two hours but the boy woke up and moved pots into and out of the sun according to his father's explanations. "When the rims look dry, like nearly white, move them under the trees. When the bottom of the bowls lift off at the edges, bring them to me right away." He told the boy everything, singing out like it was a song, a canticle. As he finished trimming each pot—a casserole, perhaps, or a sugar bowl or a platter—he would sign his name sweepingly across the bottom—GHERST—large, biting into the leathery clay. What would they say when they saw that, his signature on a soup bowl as if it was a painting or a statue? He whooped at the thought. Fanny woke up to his laughter.

By that evening it was done. All of the broken bisque was gone, swept away into memory. In its place a new and grander kiln full of greenware waited.

"But there isn't time," Fanny said at the supper. And then she said what had been with her all along, what couldn't be swept out like the broken bisqueware. "And they may come back."

"I have a way," Ephron told them both, teaching the boy. "You can glaze and fire greenware all the way through to the glaze in one firing, but it is full of problems. It is very hard to glaze the unbisqued pieces, hard to stack them in the kiln, hard to handle them at all. One little nick and a piece is ruined. And the firing? Aaaaah. It takes forever. Slow? Feeeeh." He sighed out and shook his head at the weariness he could imagine from such a firing, at the hours, at the days. But that is the way that it would have to be.

About the other thing, those, or whatever it was, that might come back? What could he say? All he could do was what he could do, which was right now to glaze and stack and fire the most difficult kilnware in his life. That would have to be enough.

"Enough?" Fanny said. "But what is it?"

"It's all I've got," he said, getting up from the table and going into the workshed to modify his glazes so that they would adhere to the greenware instead of the bisque.

"Aerrie," he shouted out from the attached room after a while. "Come. I'll show you a trick with glazes." The boy looked up at his mother. Floating now with her, he moved in her current, in her tired, sad ebb, and hesitated.

But "Go," she said to him sharply. "Go. Quickly."

Ephron slept through the little of the night that was finally left for him after he had finished modifying the glazes. By early morning he was at the careful work of glazing the fragile greenware, first the driest smaller pieces and then, as the afternoon dried them out, he worked on the larger ones.

At last the stacking, like a ballet, the pots held from destruction against the kiln walls or other pieces by gesture and discipline. Piece after piece he offered up like a votary.

After midnight Ephron began the first small fire in one firebox. It burned that way, not much larger than a campfire, for a day and a night, the three of them taking turns that the barely smoldering fire should not go out or grow but only stay. On the second day the fire was enlarged and a second fire started at the diagonal firebox, and after twelve hours of that, with Ephron hovering from port to port, adjusting the damper, checking at spy-holes high up or low in the kiln walls, fires were started in the remaining two fireboxes. And at the beginning of the third day the kiln began to glow into visible internal life, the heaviest orange. And now the fire began, the upward drive for curing heat, the long drenching heat as the fire hourly clenched the now glassily swimming particles further and further into each other and into perdurable form. Now, when the kiln was unbearable to look into, when the flame roiled and licked about for air, Ephron drew yet one more test ring from a port.

"Soon," he said to Fanny. "Two hours, maybe three." He put his arm over her shoulder. What days had gone by! How they and the boy, like the ware in the kiln, had been tempered! "Soon," he said.

But in less than an hour he saw that what was left of the wood would not be enough. The huge store from which he had fired the bisque he had not had time to replenish. And now this endlessly long firing had outlasted his calculations and supply. He looked now at what was left of the former mountain and watched it dwindle even as he watched. At this point in the firing a four-inch-thick round of wood would break and twist into coals in less than a minute after it was thrown into a firebox. And there were four fireboxes circling the kiln from corner to corner to corner. He adjusted the damper one way and then another or pushed more heat through different fireboxes trying to drive the kiln more quickly. He drew more test rings and read them like augeries. Fire, they said. But there was nearly no more fire to feed them. He had come close. He had wagered and lost.

"Ephron," Fanny whispered, even through the rumble of the kiln, and looked to the edge of the barely lit circle of light glowing about them.

They had come back. Drawn at last by the two days of billowing smoke from his stack, amazed, perhaps, or furious, or merely come like creatures to carrion, whatever, they had come back. Ephron could not see how many. He did not know them. Only once he caught a remembered maddened blue glint of eyes in the flickering mantle between the kiln glow and the forest dark.

"Go to the boy," he said to Fanny, and she was gone.

He circled the kiln, stuffing its four mouths with the endings of the diminishing heap of pine logs. And then he circled it again and fed it again. He was a potter. By circumstance or destiny he didn't walk away from that. And what else was there to go to anyway? He circled and fed and the mantle flickered.

"Ephron," George Barton said. "I heard them come along the road and followed them," he explained. He pointed to them with a long staff, light and swift in his great arching arm like it was a staff of cleanly trimmed larch to walk with through the woods, but it was not a larch stick, it was an iron rod and he pointed it widely, roundly at them all.

Ephron told him about the wood. Already the kiln roared and bellowed.

"We could cut wood," George Barton said.

"Not fast enough, I think," Ephron said. "And not with them." He pointed with a toss of the head, the circle of grief undulated like an expectation. Soon.

So it had come at last to this, from Fremlen to Fremlen. Maybe Kollowitz had been right.

But maybe not.

"Come," Ephron Gherst said, pulling George Barton to the storage shed. "Here." He took George Barton's iron bar and smashed it into the corner of the building and a slab of wood pulled out an inch. He gave the bar back and George

Barton understood and rose up and hammered the slight shed apart and down, crushing it with learned strength as he had hammered at the harder iron all his long life. It was a nothing, siding, posts, and beams exploding into fuel in the late night.

Fanny ran out of the house at the noise and shrieked at the spectacle, the white-haired kiln-lit ancient giant flailing the shed to splinters. Ephron ran to the kiln with them. He motioned to her and she did the same.

In an hour they needed another hour. George Barton shouldered down the lean-to of peeled pine logs where the potter's wheels were kept, butting it flat and prying the logs apart with his hands. And now they were laughing, already triumphant beyond objects, safely beyond dread, as if they had drawn a sorcerer's circle in the sand about their wise making that nothing outside of itself could assail.

Some shelving, a few pieces of heavy furniture, the stairs to the upper loft in the house and part of the south wall, and it was done. At every spy hole the sun-bright trembling dazzle of the kiln pierced the last of the night evenly. Up and down, the kiln was equal. All the draw rings were eloquent.

Sometime toward dawn, unnoticed, they were gone, broken apart by what they had seen, if not forever, at least for now. Fremlens come and go.

In the brightening dew of morning Ephron and Fanny and George Barton and the boy, who could not tell if he had slept to dreams or had woken to dreams, tired, smoke-stained, pine-pitched as they had never been, sat and ate, ebullient as the spangling day coming quickly. Catbirds mewed in the trees. Brown thrashers sang back, doubling their cries.

It would take two days for that seething kiln to cool, just time enough to pack up for the first New Jersey State Fair. Ephron looked around. He would have to do a lot of rebuilding, but then, he had the rest of his life for that.

Charity Begins

DAVID LIPSON WAS a loving husband and a precisely considerate man, so, after his heart attack and then after retiring from active participation in his Baltimore law practice and after moving to quiet and softly elegant Crestwood in Florida, it was natural for him to be concerned about his wife, Hildreth. Not about money. Between what his father had left him, her father her, what he had earned in law, and what his firm would continue to earn for him, money, now as ever, did not matter as it must to most men. Nor was he concerned for his two daughters, both of whom had married decently—a professional man apiece. Nor was he obsessively concerned about death. What bothered him mainly was the thought of the inconvenience that his potentially sudden and probably early dying would cause for Hildreth. And, paradoxically, he became in time also concerned, though less urgently at first, about the effects upon her of living with him, a maimed man, should he live, by chance, too long. He was forty-seven, his wife forty-three. There were a lot of her years left to be dealt with. Living, dying—either way none of the important things were settled. After his eighteen months of successful convalescence, David Lipson set out to settle them.

He started with his estate. "Do you realize," he once asked Hildreth during the estate period, "what an advantage it is for you that I'm a lawyer?" And he went on to relate to her some of the "messes" men died and left their estates (and wives) in, the straightening out of which had helped to make him wealthy.

Bit by bit, piece by piece, from over the land and from across the seas, he assembled information, documents, laws into a legal instrument of such absolute strength, of such unchallengable certitude that he regretted only that he would not be around to see it work. That it would never have to work, that there were no imaginable reasons why anyone would attempt to confute it, that the simplest made-to-order stationary store Wills leaving everything to your wife (with a few bequests here and there added) would have worked as well, he had not allowed himself to think about. At least not for long or not seriously.

Once when Hildreth questioned the necessity of such complex, involuted precautions, he could only answer her with something like, "You can never tell," or, "Better safe than sorry." But second to his solicitous feelings for his wife was his pleasure, as with an elegant mathematical proof, in the extensive beauty of the thing. From the exact moment of his death his wife would glide, effortlessly, unknowingly, into total possession of all of his earthly goods that he intended to or could leave her. During his eulogy stock transfers would begin to take place. Even while being lowered into his grave corporate structures would be dissolving and reforming. On the long ride back from the cemetery bank accounts would be springing into being. In the exquisite marriage of his knowledge and his concern was born a legal masterpiece, but, alas, an artifact for its own sake.

"It's like a hobby for him," Hildreth had once explained to a friend. "It's what he's got instead of golf."

"Done," David Lipson said one morning at breakfast, presenting to his wife over his albumen-less egg a copy of his last Will and Testament, thick like the telephone directory of a rapidly growing town.

"David, please!" she responded. "Not at breakfast," and she tossed the bulky thing onto a nearby chair. Almost as his spirits sank, they rose. Of course, he reminded himself. You can't expect appreciation for these things now. It's later, afterwards, when they realize what you've done for them. He basked in that projected future imagining, fantasizing, the moment when Hildreth Lipson would know.

"So what's so funny?" she broke in on him.

"What?"

"What's so funny? You're sitting looking out the window, smiling like that. So what's so funny?" But he didn't tell her.

Every morning after breakfast David Lipson would walk the 573 yards to Crestview Park, where he would sit looking out at the Gulf of Mexico, at general peace in the immense warmth of unending sun. Florida weather was, indeed, "just what the doctor had ordered," and over the early, uneasy, tentative, gray-faced months, he had felt himself mend, his color brighten, and the fear subside. But it never wholly went away. Sometimes, on depressingly honest days, he would find himself reflecting upon what he would do if the fear ever did go away, entirely away. But that kind of thinking always led him as that kind always does, backwards to the time of our triumphs and our strength. He would put the brakes on as best he could before the vehicle of those thoughts gained a momentum which would rush him on and into an irrecoverable huddle of despair. What was gone was gone. Now, with his involvement in a future beyond his own, he had found another, pleasanter road out of the lurking present and away from the treacherous past.

That morning, sitting on his accustomed bench, the sound of the children in the playground on the far side of the park distant and lulling, the Gulf before him blue to glory, he reached into the inner pocket of his seersucker jacket and withdrew his black leather memorandum book. Opening it to his list, he drew a thick line through the first item, ESTATE. The second item was BURIAL.

Folded neatly into a small square and tucked into one of the pockets of the memorandum book was a newspaper advertisement which David had cut out and saved. He withdrew the paper and unfolded it. The top half of the ad showed within a black field the dramatically illuminated features in profile of a middle-aged man, just enough of him to see that he was thinking (distantly focused eyes) and that he was a little disturbed about *what* he was thinking (furrowed forehead; downturned, tightened mouth). In the area where his head would be was printed in large but sober type: WOULD YOUR FAMILY KNOW WHAT TO DO? In the middle of the ad was this paragraph:

> *Many families don't know what to do when bereavement occurs. Others are familiar with funeral procedure, but are too wrought with emotion to think logically and clearly. Your family, however, will be spared the necessity to make difficult decisions in time of need if you prearrange the funeral services. Such action costs you nothing, obligates you to no one, and provides the comforting reassurance that those you love will be guided through bereavement.*

At the bottom of the ad: Morrison Funeral Homes, Inc., some names, and an address. David sat on his bench for half an hour reading and rereading the paragraph. The irony, the absurdity of preparing your own funeral did not escape him. Still, it was Hildreth and not himself for whom he was concerned. He rose finally and walked slowly to the little house at the Park entrance which contained the rest rooms and a small office. He asked to use the phone and called a cab.

Once past the vast and pretentious facade of the Morrison Funeral Home, once past the too softly spoken (and too beautiful) receptionist, once he and Harold Morrison were seated across from each other with a desk between them, it wasn't so bad. And Harold Morrison was good at his work. He avoided every mortician stereotype, every undertaker cliche. In less than half an hour, under ordinary circumstances, David Lipson could have considered himself safely and efficiently buried. There were, however, a couple of special details in his case: he wanted to be buried "at home." Morrison had associates in all the larger American and Canadian cities. And a couple of long-distance phone calls secured for David Lipson a burial plot for two ("on approval") in one of Baltimore's most fashionable cemeteries. David signed some checks which would be deposited in an escrow account and was ready to leave. Almost. First Morrison presented him with his "kit," a little package of receipts, additional instructions and suggestions, and, prominently, the one telephone number the bereaved should call which would take care of everything. There was also one of those stickers which you put on the telephone and which provides a place for you to write in the number of the police, the fire department, the doctor. Printed on the bottom was the Morrison number.

"Could I have another one of these?" David asked. "Two phones," he explained.

"Certainly," Harold Morrison said, and reached into his desk.

"Oh, and one more for the car?" David remembered. Morrison paused imperceptibly and almost glanced up.

"Yes, yes. Of course." Morrison rummaged for a moment and then came up with four stickers. He handed them to David. And one for good luck, David could not help but think.

In the cab David Lipson drew another line.

Three days later, Thursday, at breakfast, Hildreth and he discussed the trip that they would leave on that afternoon. In recent months, from time to time, they would drive out over the Keys to a quiet, almost club-like resort called the Hideout. The break from their daily pace was refreshing, the new people they met there enjoyable, and the air, if possible, even purer than at home. The mail came and, before David could, Hildreth went and got it. Returning, she placed in front of him a thick letter from the Brandywine Arms, a luxury apartment house in Baltimore.

"What's that from Baltimore?" she asked. He opened it.

"It's the lease on an apartment I took. And the keys."

"An apartment? What do we need an apartment for?" she asked, pouring herself another cup of coffee. "Whenever we're in Baltimore we can stay with Alan and Jane or at a hotel." She looked at him closely. "You're not thinking of moving back to Baltimore, are you?"

"It's not for me," he explained. "It's for you."

"For *me?* What are you talking about? Will you please tell me what you are talking about?"

"For you," he said. "After." He looked down. Then she understood.

"Oh, David, really!" She put down her coffee cup, spilling some. "First it's the Will and now it's an apartment. Stop dying, will you! There's plenty of time." She stood up. "I've got to pack." Two steps away from the table she stopped and returned, softened. "Look, David. I appreciate your concern, but I'd really appreciate it a lot more if you would just put the whole thing out of your mind." She bent and kissed him on the forehead and walked into the bedroom. But in three minutes she was out in fury.

"What's this?" she demanded, flinging into the dishes before him an expensive leather legal paper folder. "Under your underwear I found it. What's this?" she shouted, pulling out and showing him a neat package of two thousand dollars in twenties. "And this and this and this?" Money, railroad ticket, Morrison's funeral arrangements, safety deposit box keys, passport, a list of names and telephone numbers—she had discovered package A. Damn, he thought. He had intended to tell her about it when, with the lease from the apartment, it would have been completed.

David and Hildreth Lipson seldom fought, and when they did, fortunately, never bitterly or for long. Their argument now, then, came quickly to a climax and subsided. "Think of living," she ended by pleading. "If you want to think of me, think of yourself." Without questioning the logic of that, he promised to change his ways. Still, he did not tell her about package B, a duplicate of the one scattered before him, which was taped to the top of the glove compartment in the car in case he should die on the road. Later there would be time. And that afternoon, spinning out over the blue water through the total light, he could not keep himself from thinking with satisfaction that dead, at home or abroad, all the final arrangements for Hildreth's convenience had been made.

But what, David found himself thinking suddenly, if he should live?

Not for eighteen months had he slept with his wife, nor would he, he discovered himself believing, ever again. Remembering back to the conjugal bed they had shared, remembering back to the capabilities of his still attractive wife, he realized, as the car whined over the concrete causeway leaping the Gulf, that his considerate preparations for Hildreth had not ended that morning, that perhaps they had only begun.

Early in his convalescense his doctor had told him that once he regained as much of his health as he could expect to (and he gave every indication of regaining most of it), that he would be able to live a normal sexual existence, "within reason," he had added. But what did that mean? David Lipson had quickly come to his own fixed and unwavering conclusion: if running up three flights of steep stairs was "unreasonable" for a man in his condition, then so was sex. And over eighteen months later, that's the way it still was. Hildreth, without discussion or any other sign—oneway or another—had quietly complied.

Within two hours the car ground over the crushed shell drive of the resort up to the cottage they had reserved. In twenty minutes Hildreth had unpacked and put on her bathing suit. "How about you?" she asked. "Are you going for a swim?"

"No," he said. "You go ahead. I think I'll take a nap." He lay down on the bed.

"OK," she said. "I'll be back in time for a cocktail." And then for the second time that day she came back to him. She knelt down beside him, her arms resting on the bed. "David," she said in tenderness. "Please, honey. Please, please, please. Don't think of the future, think about *now.*" Then she kissed him softly on the mouth and lightly rose and lightly left the room.

David Lipson spent his later afternoon thinking about *now.* Hildreth's slight perfume wove about his thoughts of the still youthful fullness of her bosom and how the flesh of her thighs was still trim and tight and not hanging and lumped, and how her stomach was still flat. He though about her swimming, even then, in the pool, without a bathing cap, her long yellow hair streaming sleekly as her taut arms leaped forward. He imagined her on the golf course tomorrow, bursting out in a gay, white laughter as she hooked a ball into the sea. Oh, God, he thought with shame and chagrin, what must my abstinence be costing her. He groaned. And then a plan formed, and though it had the taste of bitter wormwood lancing through the sweet wine of ease, yet he drank of it deeply as, at first, dry men always do.

As objectively as he could decide—given the nature of the decision, as objectively as any man could decide—David Lipson set out to cuckold himself. It was, he concluded, the only decent thing for him to do. What was important was Hildreth. She would not, he believed, seek a new sexual partner on her own. But in time the consequences of her not having one could lead her to look in that direction. What better sense, then, but that the direction be guided? Who could tell what she would end up with, and in what painful circumstances, if she had to go it alone? What a break for her, David comforted himself, that she's still got me around to look out for her.

He began looking out for her that evening.

That evening at supper in the dining room standing upon stilts in the ocean, Hildreth, her tan already deepening, buoyantly moved with larger gestures, spoke more quickly, higher pitched. Friends they had made at the Hideout previously sat here and there. Hildreth waved to them all and stopped at two tables to chatter for a moment. Clearly, David thought, she is making an entrance, and a good one, for others in the room, new people, turned or looked up to observe this handsome woman in the white sheath moving well and smiling among them. David, walking five paces behind, observed the observers. All the men were sitting with women, more than likely their wives. Disappointed, and yet pleased, he seated Hildreth and then himself, ordered a low-fat, salt-free meal and ate it in, compared to her animation, silence.

"Why so quiet?" she asked him as they left the dining room.

"Oh, no reason," he shrugged.

"Shall we go to the movie?" She paused on the narrow boardwalk which led to the small theater to her right.

"No," he said. She started to walk to her left, for "no" meant that he would take a prescribed hour's nap no later than by nine o'clock. For a movie he could stay up. "Let's go to the Bingo."

"The Bingo? But that starts at eight and your nap is at nine and I . . . ."

"It's all right, it's all right," he interrupted her. But still she stood waiting, tentative. "I'm doing what you told me," he explained. "I'm thinking about the present." She laughed and took his arm and they walked off to the Bingo game.

David hated Bingo—the thick, nervous smoke made by the players, the droning numbers, the mindless intensity, even the pattering clinking of the markers on the cards—but, better than the movies or the card room or (at this hour) the bar, it was the place to look for what he was looking for: a man for Hildreth. The idea struck him with the force of a physical blow. He felt hit all over, but he waded in.

He selected seats at the furthest end of the one long row of tables upon which the game was played. Here he could unobtrusively see everybody. He looked them up and down and quickly found two men who were alone. David settled down to evaluate them. For Hildreth he would accept nothing but the best.

Almost at once he discarded the man furthest from him—too loud, too vulgar. The second man, half way down the table, was soon joined by his wife. That's that, David thought. Trapped in the game, he played on blankly until 8:45, when a third unattached man came into the room and sat down at the table but two seats away. David watched him intensely. Twice in an hour Hildreth, who was playing a dozen cards at once, had to point out to David that he had a bingo. And after an hour, the man himself had become aware of David and uncomfortable under his scrutiny. But what David had observed interested him in the man very much.

First of all he was handsome in that fixed and durable way in which some men are who could be anywhere from fifty to sixty or even beyond. His flesh was tight upon him and his teeth were his own. His hair was thick and fell into a whorl which suggested, flickeringly, boyishness. And he was sparklingly clean. David also noted that, rapid though his movements in the game were, there was still a fundamental boredom, a listlessness. His smile at his occasional bingo had no pleasure in it. He was playing the game to kill time. There was nothing that he was expecting, no one for whom he was waiting, no where he had to go or be, no thought he had to think. David sensed the unnaturalness for this man, who in his easy bearing, his deft, poised gestures, suggested vigor, accomplishment, engagement, playing pointlessly and without enjoyment this witless game in the middle of the Gulf of Mexico alone. The golden wedding band on the man's finger, whatever its explanation, was at this juncture of circumstance, irrelevant.

The man got up and left the table. Telling Hildreth that he would see her later in the cottage, David rose to follow him. The hunt was on.

Outside, in the almost tropical night, David called out to the man as he walked off toward the cottage area. He paused under a flowering bougainvillea, glowingly red even in the darkness, and waited for David to come up to him. A striking figure indeed, David thought as he approached.

"What do you want?" the man said, a degree sharply but not in anger. "Why have you been watching me all evening?" Good, David thought, good. A man of some spirit!

"I thought I knew you," David answered quickly. "I thought I knew you from maybe five years ago. Is your name Martin Sears?"

"No, it's not," the man said. "But if you thought you knew me, then why didn't you ask? Why did you just sit there the whole night staring at me?"

"Well," David said, "if I did know you, if you were Martin Sears, then the conditions under which we met, well . . . ." He shifted a confidential inch closer to the man, who stood his ground. "Well, my wife being right there and all. I mean, it's not the kind of thing. On a business trip once? In Cleveland? A mutual client threw a party, a wild party? Remember?"

"I told you," the man said, now with an edge, "I'm not your friend. You've mistaken me for some . . . ."

"Of course, of course," David interrupted him, laughing. "Here I am doing it again. Forgive me, please. And please don't misunderstand me. It wasn't that something so terrible happened in Cleveland. It's just that I never mentioned it to my wife before, and if you *were* Martin Sears and if you *had* started . . . well, you know how wives can be. But look, what is the sense of all this? I'm sorry. Please, let me make amends. Let me buy you a drink, or is your wife waiting for you?"

"My wife is dead," the man said. And then, as though the saying it reminded him of something else, something which made his tense suspicion of David pointless, he softened. "OK," he said. "Buy me that drink." They walked off together, talking a little, amiable, toward the sea-fronting bar, David suddenly giddy in his role and in his success.

The man's name was William Taylor. He had an accounting firm in Worcester, Massachusetts, which was big enough to run itself. He had a married son on the West Coast. He had had a wife, Elaine, dead from cancer four years ago. He came to Florida often. He traded other introductory information with David over a weak scotch and water, but what David most wanted to hear was what in time he heard—that Taylor was staying at the Hideout for a week more. As they parted, he invited Taylor to lunch the next day with himself and Hildreth.

Back in the cottage Hildreth was in bed reading *Cosmopolitan,* waiting for David to return. He came in and while he was undressing explained to her how he had mistaken this man for someone else but in talking to him thought well of him and invited him to lunch. Soon they were both in bed. David turned out the light and, under the soft purr of the air-conditioning and the gentle weight of the day, they went to sleep. But who could sleep? And what, David wondered through the night, was this thing sitting on his stomach?

"What's the matter with you?" Hildreth asked the next morning at breakfast, which they always had delivered to the cottage. "Is something bothering you? You seem so nervous!"

"No, no," David said. "Nothing." But there was. "Let's take a drive . . . this morning," he all but shouted at her. And then quickly, more quietly, "We've never been further out on the Keys than here. How about if we ride out for a few hours, until lunch?"

"A drive?" Hildreth said looking at him narrowly. "Since when are you such a big traveler? Anyway, I've got a golf date with Marge Simmonds this morning."

"But what about lunch?" he demanded of her.

"Only nine holes," she said. "I'll be back in plenty of time. Why don't you look up your new boy friend?" She finished breakfast and left.

David didn't look up his new "boy friend." Instead, he spent the morning in misery. After checking at the dining room what the noon menu would offer—shrimp bisque, Pompano in paper, standing ribs (had he expected some aphrodisiac?)—he had come back to the cottage to ponder his actions. In the very front of his head he knew that all he could really do was to throw Hildreth and Taylor together and to provide, by his absence, their opportunity. His years of legal experience with cases of infidelity told him how often simple proximity was the culpable lever of adulterous action. It wasn't so much the traveling salesman after all as it was the next door neighbor. He could only assume that out of their mutual human need would arise mutual human affection. Thus clearly understood, he could then clearly and simply act: arrange them together and disappear. No need for elaborate plans or detailed plots; each day's opportunity would dictate the day's particular shape, and whatever its momentary form, ultimately the pattern would be the same.

All of that, or all of that which he could deal with, was easy. What was hard was what he found himself feeling about it. Why, from such a generous action, would such a dread come? Always in the past his considerateness had commended itself in the satisfaction and pleasure which it brought him. If, then, what he was doing was so good a thing, why, when he thought about it, did he always feel so bad? He came up with some answers. First of all, he reasoned—sensibly, limitedly, obviously—it's always a blow to a man's ego to think of his wife in another man's arms. So, he went on, my sense of pain is natural. But, he qualified, if I can no longer perform like the male, then I have no right to cater to the male ego, and so my pain is misplaced and the result of selfishness. Why feel pain for the loss of something I've already lost? Why not feel good, instead, for the giving of something I can give? Once I overcome my selfishness, he concluded, I'll feel terrific about all this. It was the best that he could do. We do what we can, he shrugged. He spent the rest of the morning thinking about Eskimos, Bantu tribesmen, Arab sheiks, nineteenth-century Mormons, and polygamy in general.

By twelve-thirty neither Hildreth nor Taylor had appeared. David, at first annoyed and then angry, became, at ten of one, apprehensive. Something must have happened. He started out of the screen door of the cottage to find out what, but there, walking toward him, was William Taylor, and there, leaning heavily upon him her golden arm over his broad shoulder, was Hildreth.

"Hi," she shouted, waving her free arm, her manicured nails flickering bits of light at him. By then he was to her, a solicitous but unnecessary arm extended. Taylor was support enough. "I met your friend," she said more quietly but still, David thought (hoped?), with exhilaration. "You might say I ran into him," at which both of them, Hildreth and Taylor, began to giggle. Like mischievous children.

"Well," David said, standing by. "Well, come on it out of the sun and tell me all about it. Then we'll get some lunch." They all entered the cottage. With a room-filling sigh Hildreth sank down upon the sofa, swinging her legs up on to it, her golfing dress fluttering well up above her knees. She gestured the dress down, but missed.

"What happened?" David asked. Again they began to giggle. David smiled. "So?" he asked as they quieted. But still their private, shared experience of whatever it was that had happened prevented them from including him in it just then. David waited, and felt the first hairline cracking of his glaze begin. Finally they told him. Hildreth had driven her golf cart into Taylor's.

On the eighth hole, splitting the fairway close to the green, a great piece of lemony coral, sixty feet long, thirty feet high, leaps suddenly out of the earth. The designers of the course had spared it, for besides the expense of removing it and the beauty of the thing, it was a geological wonder—the highest spot in all the Keys and unaccounted for by the usual explanations of natural oceanographic phenomena. Hildreth had driven around one side of the coral obtrusion precisely when Taylor had driven around the other. She had smashed into him and had, herself, been thrown out of her cart, spraining or bruising her ankle somewhat. The two of them went on gaily telling him and each other about how they recognized each other from the bingo the night before, from the planned luncheon engagement, and, time and again, how coincidental it all was.

"Kismet, you might say," David said, at which the other two laughed again and agreed. In their present state, what wouldn't they laugh at?

It hadn't happened as David had planned it, but then the apparent result was even better than he could have expected. Already they spoke and acted with the casual ease and intimacy earned, when earned formally, more slowly. Already they had touched each other, had felt their bodies pressed together. And, listening to their bright quick talk about golf, about accidents of the past, about all the things people talk about and in all the ways when they want to appear as in their best moments they imagine themselves, it was clear to David that already they had established "rights" to each other's company. It was going well. It was going very very well, David told himself with fierce determination. At one-thirty, Hildreth's ankle feeling better, they went to their belated, exuberant lunch.

And they met again for supper, after which Hildreth suggested that they take a ride on the nightly boat excursion, an easy two-hour cruise in the Gulf. Good, David thought, remembering his necessary after-dinner nap, and made his move.

"Not for me, I'm afraid. Too tired. Going to turn in early. Buy why don't you go?" sweeping a gallant hand at the two of them. And then at once he was asking himself why Hildreth made such a suggestion knowing that he wouldn't take her up on it. Was what he wanted to happen happening so quickly then? Is this the way it goes? Shut up, he said to himself.

But Taylor begged off as well. He claimed something about being busy until nine-thirty. And so they parted, but not until Hildreth and Taylor had made a golf date for the morning. Taylor invited David.

"No, no. I don't play," he said. "Anymore," he added.

Back in the cottage David undressed and lay down on the bed. Hildreth, in the front room, examined the TV listings.

"There's a good movie on at ten," she called in to him. "Do you want to see it?"

"To tell the truth," he called back, "I'm so tired I think I might just sleep through."

"OK," she called, "sleep tight." Over his already sinking consciousness, he heard her settle down into a book. For a fact, he was tired, and his body luxuriantly eased out of itself until it slept. But a trilling in some murky, imprecise region of him, a trilling higher than sound, felt not heard, was not stilled, and in a time grew into sound and grew until it exploded him and he was awake listening to Hildreth speak, *sotto voce.*

"Isn't that nice," she whispered. "Wonderful," she said. "I'll be right down," and hung up. She came to the door of the bedroom and looked in. David feigned sleep. And then she was gone.

In about two hours she returned, got undressed, got into bed, and in moments was asleep.

Tossing between his need to scream and his desire to weep, and balancing all of that against his frustrated, fruitless search for his rewarding joy, David Lipson arose from his bed of fire a haggard man.

"My god," Hildreth said to him in the morning. "You look awful. Is something wrong?" Inside of him his bowels clenched.

"I didn't sleep so good," he managed.

"I was afraid the phone would wake you last night. Bill called." Bill? BILL! So now it's *Bill.* Had he color, David would have blanched.

"The excursion boat lost its propeller or something at the dock and they didn't fix it until around ten. They had the cruise then. He called to ask if we knew and if we wanted to go. I went. It was beautiful. Even a moon. Pass me the cream, David, please."

What could he say? Thank you? Thank god?

After breakfast Hildreth left for the golf course and David sought the sleep that he had lost in the night. But first he came to new, better informed conclusions. He knew now that it would always hurt. No matter what rationalizations he might construct, his pleasure from providing for Hildreth would always be abstract and theoretical, never warmly felt and substantive as in the past. But if his reward would be less now than he had hoped, still the action was no less worthy than before. Ringed about now by the uncertainties which he had not fully anticipated, he realized that there were some more—and more complex—decisions to make, but that he had time and advantage. Nothing, after all, that he might not want to happen had happened, and nothing would unless he allowed it. It was important that he believed that and so he believed that and so he slept.

But when he awoke Hildreth was sitting on his bed asking, "David, when are we going home?" He looked up at her, his eyes coming to focus, and then his mind. He wondered at her asking.

"Why? Aren't you having a good time?"

"I didn't say that," she said. "All I did was ask." She got up and went into the bathroom and took a shower, leaving David wondering still why she should ask. Had Taylor made advances? Or had Hildreth found herself wishing that he would? Either way or right or wrong in his estimation, the future was his to determine, and the moment to determine it was now.

"Well," Hildreth asked as she came back into the room, a light cotton print dress straining graceful at all of her, her musk pervasive. "Well?" she asked him. He heard Taylor crunching up the broken sea-shell path to their door. What is important to her? he asked himself. What is important to me?

"I don't know," he answered her. Taylor knocked and called to them. And then they went to lunch at which Taylor, charmingly knowledgeable and ebullient, ordered for them an impressive wine. Hildreth, ever alive, drank hers with customary glitter and gaiety but, David was certain, with a darkness newly come. His he sipped slowly, drowsed by the fume of his own ambivalence.

After lunch, back in the cottage, preparatory to the three of them driving that afternoon further out upon the spine of the Keys, the phone rang. David answered.

"Hello, David? This is Alan."

"Alan who?" David said, even though he recognized the voice at once. With a sudden, dull fear he rejected it, fought the recognition of it down.

"Alan who? Alan your partner," the voice in surprise helped.

"Alan my partner?" Suspended, dislocated, David listened to himself floundering. The other voice changed, becoming cautious but slightly caustic as well.

"Hello, David? What's the matter? It's me, Alan Knopf. Your law partner? Baltimore? Remember?"

"Alan, Alan. Of course I remember. Why are you calling? Where are you?"

"Right now I'm in Crestwood. I'll explain when I see you how I found you, where you are. But what I need right away is your signature on some papers. I have to fly into New York and I leave at four-thirty. It's the Simpson business. Remember that?"

"But I'm retired," was all David could think to say, knowing at once what Alan would ask and in that same instant seeking an evasion. Not now, he thought. I can't go now. I can't leave her now. But is there any better time? he thought too. There was a long pause and then Alan said, his voice colored by resentment at this man who, after all, lived well upon his labors:

"David, I'm fully aware that you're retired. I'm not asking you to go back to work. All I'm asking is to come to the mainland for two minutes to sign some papers, *which* papers I might add are the result of your own doing. Four, five years ago you began with the deal and now it's coming off. Simpson is flying out of New York very early tomorrow. He's *got* to have the final papers to close the deal in Paris. Five other people are involved because of you. It's imper . . . ," but the voice stopped, suddenly angry at the absurdity of explaining the obvious and the simple. "Look, David. Are you coming or not? Leave now and you just make it in time so I can get the plane back. Say no and I can leave at once." He stopped talking.

"OK," David said. "OK. I'm coming. I'll meet you at my house." Putting the phone down he looked at Hildreth, who had come to stand beside him as he had been speaking.

"What is it?" she asked.

"Alan," David said. "A long time ago I got involved in a complicated business deal which just now is coming to its conclusion. I'll make a lot of money from it. But I've got to go to the mainland to sign some papers. It's very important. To tell the truth, I'd forgotten all about it."

"I'll drive you," she said matter-of-factly but quickly.

And then, at once, David was alive at every point of himself, each muscle, every thought, the furthest sense precise, illuminated. Not since before the heart-attack had he felt so—vivid? Indeed, had he ever felt so before, for what he felt now he knew was brave. He took a breath and said, "It isn't necessary. I'll have the limousine take me." He was looking away from her, casting about for his jacket. He wanted badly to know where she was looking, what she was seeing, but he would not turn.

"I know it isn't necessary," she said. "I know they've got a limousine service. Why bother? I'll drive you. Let's go." Had her voice risen?

"No," David said.

"No?"

"No," he said again. "Go for your drive like we planned."

"Listen, David, there's . . . ."

"Stop already, will you. Stop making such a big thing out of this." It was close to a shout.

"Yes," Hildreth said. She picked up her straw pocketbook and walked out of the cottage and kept walking. David listened to the last of her sound and then allowed his head to drop into his hands in histrionic sorrow, his decision finally made, time and advantage lost.

On the drive to the mainland David no longer felt brave and alive, but rather dead and fearful, a stumbler in swiftly come, unimaginedly bitter mists. What have I done? rattled in him as the great, soft air-conditioned vehicle drew him away. And lashing him to his fullest hurt was the certain knowledge that he did not know. What have I done to her? What have I done to me? Where does any of this end? Can it stop as easy as it starts? Is what is real only what is between our legs? Visions danced in upon him, kaleidoscoping doubts. Once even he imagined Hildreth and Taylor, after his own demise, married and honeymooning upon his thoughtfully prepared money in the Hideout. In my cottage even, he thought, and groaned so loudly that the driver turned around.

As the car left the Gulf and touched down upon land, slowing for the traffic circle and then accelerating up the highway to Crestwood, David Lipson descended into the depth of his tumult with the slow, langorous arcing of a heavy stone bouncing downward off of canyon walls until he came to rest upon a bedrock of a truth he had forgotten or perhaps had never know. The discovery of it now spasmed through him as once the pain of his cracked heart had, but there was no dying now.

Even as he lurched forward in his back seat to tell the driver to turn the car around, it stopped before his Crestwood home. Alan Knopf waved, rose from the aluminum lawn chair, and walked slowly toward the car. David stayed inside, rolled down the window, and shouted to his partner half-way to him:

"The papers. Hurry. The papers." Knopf, startled, paused a moment and then hurried forward. He reached the car angry.

"Listen, David. I don't know what's eating you but," but David cut him off.

"Quick, quick. The papers. I'll explain some other time. THE PAPERS!"

"OK!" Alan shouted back. He ripped a sheath from a portfolio and showed David where to sign. "Here," he said. "And here and here and here and here." David signed.

"Go," he said to the driver. "Back," he commanded. "QUICK," he yelled. The driver responded. The car turned, quivered against its own backward momentum, and then squealed forward. Alan Knopf, papers in hand, stood watching the car to the end of the long block turn to the right out of his vision.

"What in god's name?" he asked himself, more amazed than angry now.

Even as the limousine stopped, David was out of it, crunching his way breathlessly up the path to his cottage, and there he crashed noisily in. Hildreth and Taylor sat at a card table playing gin rummy. Taylor looked up to greet him. He ran past them to the bedroom, but before he got there he turned.

"I've changed my mind," he shouted at them but looking at his wife.

"Maybe it's too late," Hildreth shouted back.

"What?" he screamed. "What?"

"It's what you want, isn't it?"

"Yes," he said waving both his hands at her. "Yes. For *you!* BUT NOT NOW!"

"Say, what is this?" Taylor asked, unnerved at the sudden, hallucinated spectacle.

"Don't sleep with her," David turned on him, red from his exertion and his wrath. "I'm warning you. So help me god, I'm warning you—*don't sleep with her!* DID YOU?" Taylor went white.

"Wha . . . look here . . . I . . . . I didn't . . . . I . . . . look . . . . an attack . . . I . . . . two years ago . . . my heart . . . I . . . . ." His words stopped. His hand went up imploringly to his heart. He was trying to explain, but David knew what he meant. Instinctively, in sympathetic gesture, his hand went up to his own heart. He sank down upon the couch opposite to Taylor. The two men sat there mirroring each other, dumbly commiserate and draining, until Hildreth smashed the room to pieces with a laughter so highly hilarious and incisive that Taylor began to flush and David to redden more.

"I'd better leave," Taylor said, and was gone.

"Shut up," David said to her laughter flooding him. It subsided but would not go away. Hildreth staggered up and put on a sweater against the evening breeze. She started toward the door.

"Where are you going?" David asked.

"Out," she answered. "To the bar," she added pinking him with a snicker.

"To the *what?*" David said, getting to his feet.

"To the bar," Hildreth repeated, "to the bar." She was standing now at the door, her hands upon her hips, the lowering sun outlining her. "Where the ac . . . ."

"What the hell has gotten into you?" David demanded, approaching her.

"Nothing," she said at him, hard and level. "Nothing for a long time," and turned to leave.

"You BITCH!" David screeched at her back. "You . . . you little sexed-up BITCH!"

"That's right," she said. "That's right. Not always, not before. But now. Finally, NOW! It was your idea, not mine. But it's a good idea. See you later." She reached for the door.

Then David Lipson pushed, knocked, his wife down upon the couch and stripped her of her clothing and mounted her and lived again.

Leaving

I'M LEAVING MY wife," Blatt said to Reibner in whose office he was sitting.

"So who isn't?" Reibner said, even if he thought more.

"I mean it," Blatt, the younger man, insisted, shaking his head to himself as if he didn't believe his decision, or didn't want to. But there it was.

Alex Blatt worked for Joseph Reibner. He sold whatever Reibner bought a lot of: electric blankets, automobile seat covers, refrigerators, Chinese woks. After five years, at twenty-six, he was about where he had started (after two years in the Army) and, in forty years, would likely end: from his commissions just far enough ahead of his base salary to be earning slightly sufficient to his and Jane's needs, and to little Martin's. So money had nothing to do with it.

Reibner turned from the open merchandise catalogue on his scarred desk to Blatt, who was sitting with his hands clenched and vised between his knees. Whatever he could say would not matter, he knew; would not fix anything, not a marriage nor a heart. Still, who was he to say nothing for a friend, like Jane, who Reibner knew as well as he knew her husband. He liked them both and equally.

"What for?" he asked. At least it was a beginning. Blatt took time in answering, but what he said was,

"Because it's the most honest thing I've done to her in five years of marriage. We weren't meant for each other. Better we should be free now than miserable forever." By the last phrase the young man was up on his feet ready to chase the idea as if it were fleeing. "*I'm* not meant for *her.*"

Faah, Reibner thought. So?

"Who's meant for anything?" Reibner asked. "And what 'free'? 'Free' for what?"

"I don't know altogether," Blatt answered. "Free to find out maybe? Is that it? Free at least to not be something I'm not?" Reibner let that twistedness go; there were others worse than syntax to consider.

"What are you talking?" he said. "What are you trying to tell me? Don't I have eyes, ears? There was plenty of love between you, plenty. Where did all of that go so fast? You're two such good actors to fool the whole entire world for five years? Gowan?"

"There's love," Blatt protested. "There's plenty of love."

"And Martin? We just forget about Martin?" Reibner pushed in.

"Oh God no. No! What do you think I am? Do you think I sleep nights anymore thinking about the boy? It's none of that. Nothing. None of that." He rubbed it all away with his hand, smudging the past.

"Oh no?" Reibner said. "It's *all* of that." With his own hand he pulled back what Blatt had pushed away.

"What?" Blatt looked up from the toes of his shoes.

"Never mind." Then, "You've got a chippy, perhaps? A little something else you're working on?" But he didn't need to ask.

"There have been women," Blatt admitted. "But with me it's different," he said quickly. "I mean . . . I mean I don't get *involved.* They don't . . . you know . . . *count.* Anyway Jane knows. I've always been honest with her."

"But now? What about right now?"

"An incidental thing. It means nothing. It has nothing to do with the separation."

"You think so?" Reibner asked seriously.

"It's nothing. I'm telling you, Jane *understands.*"

"Which makes her very happy?" Reibner flipped a page in his catalogue.

"No, no. But happiness is what this is all about. There is no happiness for anyone with me around. She's young, pretty. Please god for *her* the next man is sane." He looked up, his palms out imploring.

Reibner looked beyond Blatt at the shelves and cupboards behind him in which were stacked and forgotten the remainders of unpopular small items: calendars that glowed in the dark (1958), plastic shoelaces that never wore out but which were too slippery to bind, tins of a pipe tobacco from Indonesia fit only to be burned in an asthmatic's vaporizer. You can't always be right.

"Sane, free—today you're filled with all the big words," Reibner said, "Let's hope tomorrow you'll be full of something else, huh?" He tapped with a finger at his temple.

"Joe," Blatt said, staring out at his future, not hearing any voice but his own. "Maybe all life is about is trying to find yourself. So maybe I'm finding myself. Is being who I am wrong?"

But Joseph Reibner said nothing to this even if, after fifty-three years, he had ideas. He turned back to his catalogue and considered the purchase of 1,000 gross of Japanese water flowers, whose buds of colored crepe paper bloomed in a slowed explosion when dropped into a glass of water. Sane, free—at sixty cents a dozen, 1,000 gross of Japanese water flowers was something to ponder with care. From now on Alex Blatt would have to be himself on his own time.

The Blatts were separated, informally (lawyers cost a fortune), in July. What plans there were, at first, were simple. Their new apartment (just four months old) was sublet to the end of the lease. Alex would move into a one-room kitchenette kind of thing near to the warehouse-office, and Jane and Martin would move to California, at first to a close cousin's and then, in September, to an apartment in lovely Cliveden on the Monterey peninsula. Jane would enroll in college courses that would lead to a teaching degree. She had already from before her marriage two years of college credit. At college she would grow. She would discover events and places. She would go to interesting parties. She would meet people, inevitably a man, that would be that. As for money, until she was working or married, he would support her nearly as well as he always had. He would pauperize himself, for it wasn't in anger or for her fault that he was leaving her, and he would not see her suffer. Nor his son. On his yearly vacations Alex would visit for two weeks with Martin. Put altogether this way it didn't look so bad or sound so bleak. Alex had made the package and the presentation. He threw in the car, a three-year old VW.

If anything, the whole affair was civil, except for the flaring occasions when Jane's frustration at not comprehending his reasons—his fuzzy gabble about freedom and searching for a life of instinct and impulse—would break her restraint and she would rise up in hurt and disappointment and descend in final tears.

But in the main it went quietly and quickly. Two months after his talk with Reibner he drove in a taxi with Jane and Martin to the airport. They talked about details—sending her furniture when she was settled, arranging for the car to be driven west, transferring the Blue Cross, and whatnot. Other than that there was nothing, except for Martin's twittering, who did not know what sword was soon to sever him.

At the airport he thought to kiss her, but did not. He said to her: "Be strong, Jane, and trust your heart." And she said, "I did that before, Alex," and turned with her son in an arm and walked forever away. It was a good line, Alex thought. Better than anything in any movie.

But in the endless bus ride back from the terminal, what he thought about was his feeling light, buoyant. He felt like a boxer in good condition on the exact edge of his training, able to go well in any direction, to hit hard with either hand, on balance or off, and to slip past anything that was thrown at him. He felt good and he thought about that as the bus passed slag heaps of unnameable refuse and blackened-brick factories and putrifying salt marshes heavy with the city's scum. And he thought about the little girl, Selene, who was waiting for him. Two hours after relieving himself of wife and child he was making slow love.

Thirty-seven days later Jane and Martin were back.

"What did you come back for?" He was nearly screaming. "Why didn't you give it a chance? How can you expect things to work out in a month?" He paced two steps back and two steps forth in the bedroom-living room he had been reduced to. Jane sat on the sofa bed. Martin clattered in the cupboard-size kitchen area.

"It was unbearable. Every woman there was divorced with one kid. The apartment was like a motel. It was so lonely. The only . . . ."

"But you could have waited for school to start. You should have figured it would have gotten better. What about all the reasons for why you went to California anyway? What about all the good weather?" He waved his arms.

"I didn't go, you *sent* me."

The club of his frustration battered at him two ways. He couldn't step back from his complaint, from his insisting that she *see* what a foolish thing she had done; yet nothing of what he said would by some quick magic transport her back to where he had, in a month, come to think of her as belonging. Being here, east, in the city, close, had brought back almost all of the old weight.

"What now?" It was nearly a shriek.

"What should it matter to you?"

He stopped. It was an important question. For him, not her. Why *not* remember that it was all over for them, that he had neither right nor need to demand from her anything at all? A huge check once a month. The price he paid. Wasn't that the agreement he had made with himself? So what was all of this?

"Maybe I don't," he said, cloudy. "Maybe it's just a habit, a reflex. Maybe it's thinking about the waste of all that money—the flying back and forth and everything else. Who knows, maybe it's even love." He laughed. He was suddenly manic.

Love remaining was something he had considered during her absence. Cooking a supper for himself. Looking for a sock. Alone. He had thought about her. Selene, the girl, was a plaything, fluff, like all the others. Jane, gone now, had been, at least, substantial in his life. But if he thought about her that way then, in his first loneliness, he had thought about what it was like before she was gone and he had put it all away. So he was surprised to have said what he just had, although saying it excited him to the entire unraveling prospect.

"Listen," he said. "Let's have supper together. I'll go get something fancy. I'll get wine. Maybe we'll go to a movie." He laughed and dropped to one comic knee. "How about a date?" He stirred in the groin.

"Alex, stop it. Just *stop it.* You're *frantic,"* Jane shouted at him.

"What do you mean 'frantic'? Why? Why stop what? What am I doing?" he shouted back. He looked around as if to call for support. He looked up at her. "I'm your husband." He proclaimed it; he hit himself on the chest. He felt like she had slapped him. What was wrong with her? Why did she have to say that? Why couldn't she ever pick up with him his excitements? It had always been that way. He stood up.

"Oh Alex, just shut up and get out of here. Just go away." She could have wept. "I'm tired. I'm tired like an old woman. Leave me alone. Just go." He started to. But he turned.

"Wait a minute. Wait a *minute!* What do you mean 'go'? This is *my* apartment. *I* live here. If I'm not your husband, then who are you? What is this? What WHAT?" he bellowed. "So if it's over, then it's over. And if it is to end, then let it end here. Enough."

"Forget it," she said rising. "Marty and I will sleep in the park." She called her son to her.

"Aaaagh," Alex Blatt said, packing a bag for overnight and leaving. Three days later he returned for more. But it was nearly three weeks before he could get her out and himself back into his cage of an apartment.

Jane took an apartment about two blocks from Alex's. He had fought with her about that but she prevailed: "It's for Marty. This way he'll hardly know that his father's gone."

He fought with her about her unexpectedly dropping in on him and at any hour: "What should I tell your son when he wants you? And when he knows where you are? Besides, there are things we've got to talk about, to settle." He lost there too. He fought with her about car expenses, doctors' visits, clothing bills. He fought with her about everything. He recalled that, married, they had hardly fought at all, only normally.

And Selene had dropped out of the center of his life to linger, nervously, on the edges of it. Having encountered Jane twice at Alex's, the girl was frightened: it was tough to be brave in the nude.

Finally, their being here instead of in California cost him more money. The paper-thin margin he lived on got crumpled by the nickle-and-dime demands of their casual requirements: a lunch for Marty two or three times a week, a toy, a sudden prescription that he was called upon to pick up at the drugstore. What could he say? No? His son with a temperature of 103 and he should say no? Or ask for $4.85 as Jane took the antibiotic at the door and closed it in his face? Or deduct it from her monthly check? Here and there he ended up living on nothing, nearly nothing at all. In a month he lost the ten pounds he had been trying to lose for five years.

"No," Reibner told him. "I can't give you a raise. Look, you get the same base as anyone else and the same commissions. Who ever heard of a salesman getting a raise? Sell more so you make more. So Alex," Reibner leaned over and bobbed his head vigorously, "is that not so?" Blatt grunted. What he wanted was money, not truth. "Besides," Reibner went on, "until your grief the money you made here was good enough. And it still is." He swiveled to Blatt. It seemed to Alex that Reibner never left his chair. "Alex, let me tell you. If you're going to lead two or three lives, what you need isn't a raise, it's two or three jobs. Free is not such a cheap thing."

In late October, in the small park near the office, where so often in their past they had met to eat lunch or simply to matter to each other, Alex and Jane Blatt, under the golden chips of elm leaves, decided to give it another go. What had done it, he could not say, for he had forgotten nothing of what he had remembered tasting from his grail in his deep dreams of abandon, though there had been nothing real or tactile to compare to that dream in his waking hours. Maybe that was it. Or maybe he hadn't been prepared. But by the late afternoon of their *rapprochement* he was already tightening. Still, he beat that down and locked it up and they celebrated and worked upon each other the night through.

It took until near Thanksgiving to get rid of their two apartments and to settle into another (smaller than the one they had given up three months earlier), for now there were debts—his, hers, theirs. But Thanksgiving Day, and three more, they spent in or near the hospital, in which Martin Blatt lay in an oxygen tent: pneumonia brought on, the doctor said, by the conglomerated weakening of his lungs by his numerous allergies.

Did Martin Blatt have allergies! Bread, milk, tomatoes, twelve kinds of vegetables, pork, half the spices known to western man, and new stuff that the doctors were discovering weekly.

"What is it?" his father had once asked annoyed and abraded during a long Sunday of Martin's wheezing, coughing, gagging, and choking. "He can't wait to find something he doesn't agree with?"

"For God's sake, Alex," Jane said, "He's not doing it on purpose. It's not *fun* for him."

"Sometimes I wonder," he said, and fled to the freezing streets for an hour off.

Then Jane read in *The Reader's Digest* about theories that allergies were psychosomatic, frequently the result of childhood trauma. For her it was like a religious revelation: unalterable truth seen bare. So now she knew why her poor Martin had suffered so badly in California, what with no father. She explained it all to Alex. Time and again.

But on Thanksgiving they were in a hospital worrying together.

Monday the boy was safe, Tuesday well, Wednesday home. Alex Blatt was deeply poor, out of his bed, tired. And on Thursday it snowed for the earliest time in his city's history. Not a lot but enough to compound his life, which by then was misery, or so he thought.

Three days after he and Jane had returned to each other back in October all the feelings for why he had left her returned. He had fought with them, the shapes and desires and tastes of a condition he could not clearly see and doubted he could ever have. But if *that*—whatever it was, wherever—wasn't for him, then neither was this. Dreams, visions, aches: they, like his sorrow for his discomfort now, were not matters of blame or responsibility. They simply *were.* Alex Blatt raged about, banging into the tightening wall of his life. Sometimes, like his son, he awoke at night to chew in terror at the thin dark air.

When April came they left each other again.

"It's very simple," she said to him as she roughly packed his clothes, throwing things into a suitcase. "You're crazy. You're a twelve-year-old who is also crazy." What could he say? Yes or no, maybe she was right. But that didn't matter. What he had to be was who he was.

"I've got to be who I am," he said. He was sitting on the edge of the bed. "I never said I was right. I never blamed you for anything." She stopped.

"Listen you . . . you jerk!" She turned to face him directly, her long dark hair free across her back, her hands on her sharp hips. "You've got all your life to make a decision. Marry *or not.* Have children *or not.* Do this, *do that.* You can do whatever you want. But once you decide, like for me or for Martin, so you take our choices away. Listen! You make a son, you don't have a choice anymore." She turned back and dropped a ball of his underwear into the suitcase.

"What does all that matter?" he said jumping up. He had to explain. "It's what I *feel.* If a man has a lump, he has it cut. Me, I've got . . . I've got . . . I've got . . . ."

"What ?" she laughed, mocked.

Strangely, what he had at that moment was desire for his wife.

"I've got this for you," he said, grabbing his crotch and giggling. Jane was stunned. She dropped her arms straight and stiff by her side. Was he, after all, truly mad?

"Get out!" she screamed throwing his T-shirts at him. "Get out!"

Where he lived in that summer was too hot for sorrow or anger or hope. It was where people went in the end—alone or dying or embittered. Only for Blatt the reasons were easier: he was poor. Too poor for any comfort or even for the energy he would need to avoid the tortures of his August bed. He would walk the streets till two or three in the morning before going to his fourth floor room. All night the streets were full of worn people like himself. He didn't even dream about women anymore. The heat, the poverty, where he lived, and the soreness in his heart were complexities enough. There wasn't room for feeling anymore of anything just then. It was plenty just to get up and get through a day selling what Reibner had stumbled upon.

He despised all his discomforts, but even at worst there was a lucid happiness, too—tiny, a whisper, but that sustained him: he was where he had brought himself. But Blatt was not a reader, not a reflective man, and so there was nothing to feed the small contentment, no soil for the small slip to root and grow in, no chance of it bearing anything: it was all. And what might have been the monkish liberation out of which a Newton or a Milton came, was, instead, nothing more than the cold accomplishment itself. On Labor Day, with no one in his building going anywhere, that day or later, he couldn't hear the whisper.

He lay on his bed and wept.

Evenings later he went to Jane's apartment and knocked. When she opened the door he didn't understand at first; her soft perfume, the rich fabric of her dress, the careful liner to her deep black eyes.

"Please," she said quietly. "Go away." Past her right, shimmering, concentric circles earring he saw a neat man sitting on the green sofa. He was smoking and looking easily at the door, at Alex, looking out at him as if he were a delivery boy. "Please," Jane said again, but evenly. "Go away." He left.

From the beginning he had thought that she would get married again; he even considered her sleeping with a man here or there until she did. But until now, he knew now, he had not lost the habit of possessing, had not yet learned to give her over. With an actual man in his apartment—*her* apartment—he was a cuckold. Walking quickly through the streets back to his cubicle he thought about what he felt and what he should do. Near to his tenement he began roaring. He hammered up the stairs, bouncing sometimes from wall to wall, rising on his puffing, snorting laughter. No one listened, even if they heard. Where he lived no one laughed in humor.

And two days later, two days in which he had not worked nor eaten nor slept, he ran back through the streets to Jane, resolved. He didn't understand it; he didn't entirely care to. It was like knowing he knew something without knowing what, or being able to name it, describe it. It was like knowing what God must be like. He thought to call it love, only the name was too small for what was moving him, and through him.

He got to her apartment at nine o'clock. Martin would be in nursery school. He rang the bell. Jane came to the door, dressed, ready for housework.

"What?" she said. She was surprised.

"Listen," he said to her. She looked hard at his excitement. "Listen," he said again, walking in, backing her in. "I think I've figured some things out." He took her two hands. "Will you listen to me? Will you just not say *anything,* just let me finish?" She nodded. "Just let me explain the whole thing to you, from beginning to end, even if it makes sense or not. Afterwards you can ask questions. Just listen." He shook her two hands up and down like children do in playground dancing. He smiled at her. She smiled at him.

"Ok, ok," she said. "I'll listen."

And then it was all gone. Totally. Nothing. Alex Blatt was terrified. He was sweating *inside* his skull. He stood in the middle of the room, white and draining. He dropped her hands. If he had finally come to his utter truth, he had taken a terrible way.

"Alex?" Jane said.

"Ooooooh," he groaned and ran into the bathroom and vomited. When he returned he walked by her and out the door without a glance.

Even so, in two days, he returned.

"What I don't understand," Reibner said, "is her . . . . You I understand." He made a corkscrew motion with a finger pointed at his head. "But her? Why she should go back to you escapes me. Not completely, actually. I can think of reasons, like for Martin, for instance. And other reasons. But I always thought she was smarter. So? When?"

"Next week. That's what I'm telling you. We're sending the boy to her mother's. I'm taking off from work. Ten days in Puerto Rico. The two of us. Can I get an advance? Five hundred dollars?"

"A second honeymoon?" Reibner said.

"Yeah," Blatt said smiling.

"Actually," Reibner corrected, "it's more like a third or fourth. But good luck. Yes," he said. "Here." He pushed away a pile of invoices for four-headed balloons, imitation ivory-handled shoehorns, necklaces made from cantalope seeds, and wrote out the check. He handed it to Blatt. "Good luck. Good luck."

"I think it will work this time," Blatt said getting up. But he was wrong.

On the sixth day they flew home, each certain of one thing. Alex: "I can't help being who I am." And without questioning or caring anymore who he was, Jane: "I can't live my life expecting anything from you."

Although he had given up his fourth floor room, it had not been rented yet, and he came back to it easily. Frying an egg on his hot plate he thought about the dinners in the Caribbean, the exotic fish, the fanciful vegetables, the nectarish drinks. He thought of the love they had made each night after the light days on the beaches. What, then, was there to be gay for now, or ever again? Still, he could not find in all the bleakness of his existence any permanent sorrow or even discontent. There was sorrow and discontent in plenty, but like the phase sign on an oscilliscope, there was as much above the line as below. Blatt lived, for what it was worth, in the tension between.

His room was as hot in February as it had been in August, only drier now and not as humid.

Sixteen months later, from working two jobs and weekends, he was out of debt and able to move to an apartment that lent itself, no matter how slightly, to life. And even after the enormous repair bill on the car (transmission *and* valves) and the terrible illness of the boy (infected adenoids with complications into the ears), he could hang on by his fingertips.

Another year after that he could even drop his second job and, if he was careful, get by. Which meant he could look for a partner. He found one (Selene had married long before). And then another. And another. After a while it was easy and regular.

About once a year, or sometimes even twice, like the anniversary of comets, he and Jane fell into each other's field, so that it came to be structural, a subsumptive agony, though neither imagined it that way. When in some accidental crossing they drew together, what followed was always removed from time and experience, like observers in a dream watching other characters acting out a fantasy. Their force was sincerity. Alex never doubted, in the middle of his yearly domestic week or sometimes month, that whatever he had granted to the necessity of impulse in the past was payment to a debt of the blood now discharged. It was good to be back finally and for good. Each time he always believed that. And Jane, with all her weary knowledge growing heavier each year, agreed, and even when she no longer agreed or expected, allowed.

So that was the way it was for them, free at last.

In Excelsis Deo

EDDIE RINGLEMAN WAS strong—tough—outside, but inside his heart was like honey, although he did not know that in the beginning. In the beginning it was only the strength. He was smaller than most men and appeared to be less muscular, less solid, even fragile sometimes. An illusion. In high school and later in college, where he had played defensive end on the football teams, it was his pleasure to watch in the early plays of the game a big wing-back or a squat guard who had pulled out to lead a sweep around his end come at him with contemptous expectation in his eyes as he bore down, and then to see the surprise and anger as he, Eddie, hit him harder than the player could have known he would, or to knife quickly by the blocker to tackle the ball carrier directly. After some of that, the personal game played in his sector equalized—strength against strength—until usually in the last quarter, when the bigger men slowed a little from the pounding afternoon, but Ringleman did not. Then he would maul them.

His body was usefully strong and he could last. His coaches learned that, and as each game progressed, secure on their left, they shifted their defensive thrust into a concentrated right. It made an important difference. Ringleman's three varsity years at college were good ones for the team, and in his senior year he made second team little All-American.

In college he had majored in English because in high school he had liked to read, for no other reason. So when he graduated in some June he had no where to go, no future to go into, nothing necessary to do. Above all, he wasn't worried about it. He floated around, the summer on the Cape at odd jobs, October and November in Miami Beach as a waiter. In December he was drafted into the army; on January 5 he reported for duty. Pleasantly, warmly, he got to take all of his training in the southwest—Fort Hood, Texas—but if it had been in the cold north, like Fort Meade, Maryland, he could have stood it ok. He was Ringleman, as tough as they came.

He was sent to Korea soon after the truce and spent close to two years there, a clerk in an administrative battalion headquarters, typing, filing, reading, prowling, remembering. When he got out of the army he had the GI Bill, so he went back to school and got a Masters and even a Ph.D. He didn't like that so much as he did college, when he could just read the books, but the money was good—free, at least—and there was nothing pressingly better for him to do, so he did what he did. There was no other reason.

During that period of his life he met Connie Fine, a pretty applied arts major, and fell consumingly in love with her. In less than a year they were married and in another year, even before he graduated, she bore him a son of immense beauty, and like his father, destined to be strong and a thinker too.

About that time—he could never remember for certain whether it was before or after the birth of Joseph (named for a deceased grandfather)—Ringleman began to have Jewish twinges. They came to him, at first, at night in his dreams, but later they came in the day time too. All they amounted to, really, were ethnic remembrances—quick scenes from a wedding, a view of a grandmother in synagogue on Yom Kippur, the symbolic platter at Passover. What made them at all remarkable to Eddie was *why*. Why, all of a sudden in his life, should these forgotten memories come to him? True, he had been raised as a Jew, but far from the intense ghetto-ness he had read so much about; and although he had been *bar mitzvahed,* it had meant nothing to him, then or now. He had never understood a single word of what he had ritually chanted on his chosen day. And after that, after two days of binding himself in the phylacteries and *dovening,* he had given it up. He had grown up in a Jewish tradition all right, but there had been nothing yiddish or kosher about it.

Nor had he felt quilty at wanting to deny or angry at the inhibitions imposed by his Jewishness as had many of his friends when they went into the world and knew better the meaning of things. He had had his run-ins, had smarted at the anti-semetic quip, the wisecrack, the stereotyping attitudes and hatreds, but who hadn't? No. Ringleman's Jewishness, such as it was, sat upon him easily, neither much nor nothing. All the more reason for wondering about his sudden Jewish dreams.

He told Connie about them and together they decided it was because now as a husband and soon (was it already?) as a father, he was naturally remembering, trying to remember, his own youth. Or as a psychology friend put it neatly: as his child (son) replaced him, became the new son, so he replaced his father, became *his* father. So that was that.

Finally he graduated, and while others, exhausted and lacerated by the ordeal of graduate school, stumbled out to a career of sinecure or cynical ease or recuperation, he, Ringleman, strong, never broke stride. He got a decent paying job teaching composition and literature at a clean, friendly, and not entirely unheard of small college and excited it. But not at first.

At first he prepared his department courses thoroughly according to the department abstract and his own courses according to the ways that they had been taught to him. He did private research and wrote and published over three years four respectable articles and one note in *Notes and Queries.* He served on his share of committees, the useful and the futile. He and Connie were occasional chaperones at sorority and fraternity parties. They made a lot of acquaintances and a few good friends. Eddie stayed in shape playing handball, swimming, and running around the gym. They had another child, another son, as beautiful and healthy as the first, but fuller of laughter. Aaron he was called. The clown.

Eddie's Jewish twinges came and went; that is, they occurred in clusters. Sometimes for months, nothing, and then a week or two of memories. He was surprised at how much of his life, at least as viewed through whatever psychic filter was doing the selecting, had been touched by, involved in, his religion's culture—Eddie always considered his Jewishness a cultural and not a religious event.

And then he started to get Korean twinges, too, as well as other kinds. Only they were ugly.

One Saturday night he and Connie were watching a TV program about two lawyers, a father and son, who had to defend a man who had clearly killed another. The story was about a Jewish survivor from Dachau who calmly shot and killed a famous expatriate German doctor at a testimonial dinner at which the doctor was being honored for his accomplishments in science. As the trial of the Jew developed, it was revealed that the doctor was by merest chance the nominal head for one day only of the section in Dachau where the Jew's wife and crippled son were gassed, and on that day. The dead doctor's wife's argument against her husband's guilt was that he had done much—as much as could be done—to lessen the suffering in Dachau; it turned on the point of what could he have done, one man in one day? The Jew's argument was simple, fierce, and colossally tragic: the doctor could have done *something;* he could have given his wife and son another day of life.

But what was important about the program to Eddie Ringleman was this: When the Jew described the central event of his existence, he told them—the audience in the court. the Ringlemans in their happy lives—that in the gray, morning yard of Dachau that day, of the four in his family—he, his wife, a whole son and a crippled one—only the crippled one was singled out for the chambers. As the soldiers herded the lame one out, only ten years, his mother had rushed through the soldiers to him and would not leave him. The soldiers struck her and dragged at her, but she would not let go of the boy. She would not let the terrified child die alone. Finally they let her go with him into the black mouth. The father and the whole son lived with that.

In the dark silence that filled the courtroom and the Ringleman's house, a shrieking wail went up. Connie turned to her husband to see him weeping, his face distorted and wrinkled in every way, gasping and choking on the clotted sorrow in his throat. "Eddie, Eddie," she had said, frightened, but then quickly she cradled and comforted him.

Through his shirt she felt all his fine muscles snapping and jerking in jagged edges of grief. "Eddie, Eddie," she crooned to him as she sometimes crooned to Joseph, their eldest. "It's all right now," she said. "It's all right now, baby. It's all right." She swayed. She put her arms more tightly around him over his shoulders and squeezed him tightly so that he wouldn't break apart with his great unrhythmed heaving. "It's all right," she said. "Please stop crying." But it wasn't all right. And Eddie Ringleman never stopped crying again.

From then on he twinged like a man with St. Vitus dance in his soul. He could partake of little, nothing, less than nothing in his world anymore without weeping or without fighting the weeping down into a sore-throated silence, though never away. It cost him enormously. For anything—a trivial movie, a TV commerical, a walk down a human street—he paid. He would get halfway through books that he dared not finish. Sometimes the desperately revelatory essay of a wounded freshman would break him open. Discriminating taste left him, fled before his terrific vision, so that the heroism of Cordelia and Kent in *Lear* or the courage of Lassie saving a woodland friend became as one and worked him to a moral groaning.

Anymore the only comprehensive truth to him was Mercy, of which he saw little in life, though the need immense; and what little of Mercy or Courage or Love that he did see through the hovering shadows overwhelmed him: young people holding hands in the bright public, some father playing catch with his son, rheumy old men, a woman singing at a task, a pheasant guarding her flock across a road, any honesty at all. High and noble or sentimentally low did not matter, only the particular gesture which sprang whichever way out of the unassailable Ideals themselves. So he wept in joy for the crumbs; and he wept in rage against the encroachers everywhere, the bastards of the earth.

It wasn't that he hadn't been aware of all of this before; for one so widely read in the history and observations of human agony, how would he have been able to miss it? It was that never before had he been so vividly, so personally susceptible, so present himself in it all. Nothing was too trite or mawkish or inconsiderable now for his compassion. Everything for Eddie Ringleman lived, and what ever lived, he saw in woe, lived against its doom.

He lost some weight and got baggy under the eyes. And there were other changes too. Some of his acquaintances began to get edgy near him, for he had begun to glow, deeply, like they say in the old books consumptives did before they turned on the outside like transluscent ivory with red patches on the cheeks. Eddie's eyes shone partly from the constant emotional fire in him, partly because his eyes were seldom wholely dry. The entire range of his speaking voice had raised, tautened, in pitch two whole tones, from a comfortable baritone C to a tenorish E, giving his words a ringing, sometimes a piercing sharpness. And there were many more words now, cataracts of them. While never reticent before, Eddie was turning into a non-stop talker, and a dramatizing one. Whole scenes would ravel out of him, soliloquies and asides, after dinner jokes and banter, a drenching rain of puns. Massive intellectual and verbal conceits would billow up into daring Baroque swirls of imagining. Laughter was everywhere, but it fell upon his listeners not pleasurably but like a lash. One always heard the muffled sob out of which it grew. And, sometimes, in a hallway passing, through a partition, over a transom, one heard the sob itself. All in all, some said Eddie was moving toward a nervous breakdown, and then speculated why.

But others were attracted, students particularly, unconsciously engaged and warmed by his heat and thrilled by his open and constant admonition that the only reason for learning anything was to do something Good with it. And by Good he meant clear and simple things: don't hurt, be nice. At last it was all that he taught in his classes, whatever the course might be called.

Gradually, one by three by eight, he became central and oracular for those who heard him and listened, like a *tsadig* of old. They sought him out in their desperate hours to be saved, and some wept upon him.

Eddie Ringleman went on weeping for them all. He wept louder and longer, increasing in every dimension of weeping, expanding every degree and nuance, discovering unheard subtleties. Eventually Connie his wife wept with him. Sometimes, lying together in the other's arms, they wept deep into the bitter night. Sometimes Joseph, the brilliant son, would cry a little, a soft whimper. Only Aaron, the earthbound, was silent.

In time their weeping grew so great, so resonant and insistent, that the sound of it reached to God, who heard and summoned them to Him.

Connie was frightened and fell to her knees. She dropped her head down and clasped her hands over it and trembled. But Eddie Ringleman, who was badly frightened himself, stood up and looked around. All about were huge gray smudges like clouds floating softly wrapping him. Or were they small, tiny wisps of smoke and it was he who had become like a mountain? Was he in them or they in him? He could not tell.

What God wanted to know from Eddie Ringleman was why there was no bound to his sorrow. Eddie told him: because there was no bound to the suffering he wept *about,* none now or ever to come that he could see or imagine.

God granted that it wasn't a pleasant thing to behold, but that, after all, was the way it was.

"Some way," Eddie said.

"Now *listen,*" God said. "Cut that out. Where wast thou when I created the . . . ."

"Sha!" Eddie shouted waving both his hands in front of

him wiping at God. "Sha," he said. "You loused it up. You loused it up good."

The smudges, in or out of Eddie, darkened and God blew Eddie and Connie Ringleman like a milkweed tuft back gently to their home. What else could he do?

Eddie pried Connie up from the rug in the living room. She was white and rigid, catatonic. He hugged her and kissed her back to life.

"Oh Eddie," she said as she recovered. "I was so scared."

"Me too," he told her kissing her eyes, her ears, her brow. "Me too."

"What happened?" she asked. "What did He want?" He told her. Overhead Joseph thumped in a corner of his mother's studio. Aaron giggled in a distant room. "What now?" she asked, tears already coming into her eyes.

"Nothing's changed," he answered, sobbing.

And Their Fathers Who Begat Them

THE SLOW, DULL clatter of the old alarm clock began, but was cut off in seconds. It was six-thirty of a mid-September morning, already light. Yorst Inman Broctor was awake, was, once more, alive. He thought of that and got out of his bed, his feet landing precisely upon an old but still firm pair of leather slippers. He put them on and walked into the small, gleaming, adjoining bathroom and looked carefully at his face in the mirror over the sink. The eyes, already out of sleep, were clear and dry. The flesh under the stubble was weathered and taut but pinkish. And the teeth, the teeth (he clacked them together solidly a few times) were all there and his. At seventy-eight years Yorst Inman Broctor could have been much younger. He would ("by Christ") live to be much older.

He shaved and showered. In the shower he ran his hands across his flat belly. He slapped himself there. He looked at the granulated, saggy skin of his old arms and smiled as, tensing his biceps, the bulges rose to give those arms again the shape and feel of strength. He dressed, then went into the kitchen and prepared his breakfast. As he slid his fried egg onto his plate he heard the first sounds of awakening overhead. The sway of the bed, the creaking of the floor. That would be Margaret getting up. He followed her padding footsteps across the ceiling into the children's room. I hear pretty good, he thought. By the time Margaret came downstairs, Yorst had finished eating and washing his few dishes. He had even set the table for the family.

"Good morning, father," Margaret said sleepily.

"Good morning, Margaret. Sleep well?"

"Uh huh." Margaret poured herself a cup of coffee Yorst had made and began to prepare herself for the impact of the day. "Going out?" she asked her father. She always asked, even though he always went out immediately after breakfast, if the weather was possible. A long walk after breakfast was good for the bowels he had once told her. She had forgotten when.

"Yes," he said as he walked into his room. He came out soon with his coat on and upon his head a greyed, stained hat from the Thirties. "Nippy already," he explained. And then he walked out the back door, holding the knob turned so that the door did not click loudly when it closed. He would disturb nothing and nobody.

By leaving the house every morning at about seven-thirty, Yorst managed not to meet his son-in-law, Ernst, until suppertime, five days out of seven. On the weekends Ernst was up early too. Never in the seventeen years of Margaret's marriage or in the seven years of his life with them had Yorst found cause for unfriendliness between himself and his son-in-law. Nor did he actually dislike him. But, Yorst had reasoned when he first moved in with them after Hanna's death, he was a stranger in this house, not a part of it, an imposition, no matter how small a one. Well, the less he was around the less of an imposition he would be. What you didn't see you didn't care about.

Ernst Robinson cared plenty. "What the hell is he always spooking around about?" he had asked his wife.

"Shsh," she said. "What do you care as long as he doesn't bother you. You should be happy."

"He bothers me like a ghost would bother me. What's he got against me that he never spends any more time than is absolutely necessary in my presence? He eats supper, then, boom!—gone! He won't even watch TV in the living room. Oh, no. He's got to watch his own TV in his own room—the same station even. What's he got against me?"

"Nothing," Margaret answered. "Nothing at all." She was wrong.

In the Second World War, at Anzio, Ernst Robinson was wounded in the chest by a grenade fragment. His left lung had collapsed and was still collapsed. When, in 1948, he and Margaret announced they were getting married, Yorst had checked around and found that the life expectancy of people with a collapsed lung was—statistically—considerably shorter than for two-lunged men. The thought that Ernst might die soon or sooner than most and especially while young, revolted Yorst. It was disgusting to him. It was almost obscene. He had, for seventeen years, been quietly nervous in the presence of this half-dead man.

Outside the house, in the backyard, he noticed that the supply of sunflower seeds he had placed in the bird feeder was almost gone. It was really too early in the year to need to feed the birds, but Yorst enjoyed indulging them. Birds had a tough row to hoe, all right. In the deep winter he would check the feeder twice a day and had even bought a special heater to keep the water in the birdbath from freezing. And there was always a piece of suet hanging in a mesh bag from the corner willow. He remembered reading once in a newspaper that bird mortality was extremely high, that for a sparrow-size bird to reach three years was almost rare. And yet, in all his life, Yorst had never seen a dead bird—not counting stuffed ones—not even a pigeon or a robin. He wondered where they went to die. Maybe they were like the elephants and had a special place to go. But for all their dying, that he should never have seen a single corpse, never have come suddenly upon their graceless death in some gutter or alley, amazed and gratified him.

Yorst Inman Broctor had been a bricklayer for his entire life. Back in the old country, into the years he could only slightly remember, he had been apprenticed to a master. When his family immigrated suddenly to America, he began where he had left off, but at a better—if low—and democratic wage, with a hod on his shoulder. Through his years he had put brick everywhere. Unending rows and days of brick and mortar. He had married, by traditional arrangement but pleasantly enough, Hanna, who bore him

Margaret. Besides her, Hanna, and a cousin or two, he had not bothered much about friends. At Hanna's death, Yorst had acquiesced to his daughter's plea for him to retire—bricklaying, even part-time, at seventy-one appalled her—and come and live with her. He did and, with the exception of working and another thing, went on doing what he had always done with his life: nothing exact, nowhere committed with any passion to any idea or interest or concern. Uncomplex, compliant to almost all that man is born into, Yorst Inman Broctor lived with his daughter and her husband and their children as he always had, in the utter simplicity of his strong tendons and bones, and he thought, naturally enough, if he thought about it at all, that a good digestion was about as far as human felicity could reach. Only in the seven years there were the children.

Yorst came out to the front of the house, turned left, and moved into his gait. He was a tall man and still erect and a good walker. When he first came to live with his daughter and her husband, he had bought a map of the city and had, quadrant by quadrant, examined it on his feet. Sometimes he had walked from near dawn to night. But now, even though he would sometimes visit areas of good memory, his day was more prescribed. Now he would walk, in any direction, a distance always equal to the time it would take him to walk back to the high school to see his grandchildren mixing in front of the mock-Gothic building, to see Kenneth and Greg, who, at sixteen and fourteen, stood already blond-headed and high above their peers, manhood stretching them in the chest early.

He could have seen them at home, could have eaten breakfast with them and their father (thank God collapsed lungs weren't hereditary), but he liked his first sight of them of the day to be this way. Later, in the heavy snows and cold winter, when walking was impossible and the children went directly inside anyway, he would settle for the suppressed breakfast table. But this way was better, here where he could see and smile fully at their size and their strength and their popularity.

Standing in the entrance of a nearby building or under the heavy sycamores across from the school, unobserved, Yorst would watch them as they swung off the public bus into the yelping greetings and the puppyish wrestling. Kenneth, already a promising athlete, a swift, high-reaching end in football, was, in this his season, especially sought out, his strength and height, his hint of a lurking power to come a talisman for the weaker rest. Greg, a sophomore, lived now in his brother's reflected light, but his time was coming too, and soon. Yorst watched them and did not question at all the great difference in the immense size of his feeling about them and about all the rest of all the other things of his life. But what did it matter? On this good morning of September twenty-first, Yorst Inman Broctor was well and was alive in all of his generations. Was there more to know than that?

After the bell summoned the children in, Yorst would stop at a nearby luncheonette—minutes earlier packed with high-schoolers—and drink a cup of coffee. He had an hour before his next appointment and it was only a twenty-minute walk to it. In the luncheonette and at that time, about nine-ten, there was inevitably a knot of students who were "cutting." Some, it seemed to Yorst, were always "cutting." Two, at least, seemed always there. He had learned their names. The girl—Beverly Laskow, the boy—Alan Kramer. The boy was a clown and a shrimp—loud, already pimply beyond repair, and yellowish-green. But the girl's beauty made even the old man remember. The sheen and luster of the blackness of her hair stabbed out the eyes; the hauteur of her body, her stance, could demand a grace from others—and did. From all but Alan Kramer. Once when he slapped Beverly on her behind, Yorst had half risen to take the filthy, disfiguring lout by the neck and pluck him out, but he had restrained himself and sank back to his coffee. Still, he wondered that such as she could permit him, apparently alone, his freedoms, and wondered even more that she should seem so pleased to be the object of them.

"Hey Bev bay-bee," Alan Kramer screeched above the others as he swung into the coffee shop that morning. He stopped about ten feet before her, and with his arms outstretched and raised up, wiggled his hips in a gross, waddling parody of some twisting dance. "How about you and me studying some square roots today? Huh, bay-bee?" A few others near them laughed. Almost gagging, Yorst observed the girl obliquely from his end-of-the-counter stool. Uninvolved, she yet smiled happily at the boy, whose face already sweaty, the crusts of broken pustules hanging from him, flickered over all the variations of leer. And her teeth, white to glory, so young, so strong. Yorst left his coffee and left.

Outside, striking off northwest across the city to where he was going next, in the new, slight breeze which had come up, he felt better, cooled and soothed like a man waking from an ugly dream, but slowly. He just couldn't understand it. Is she blind? Is she stupid? But he knew that she was neither. What there was there for the two of them to share in was beyond him to know. Block by block he walked the irk out of himself. And then he arrived.

Yorst sat down on one of the benches of the little park and took out from his coat pocket the morning newspaper. It was nine-thirty. In about fifteen minutes they would be coming out. The breeze blew a little stronger and for a moment Yorst worried that it would be too much for them. Still, the sun was very good that morning, and between the gusts, the day would be a warm one. At precisely nine-forty, the oldest one came out of the converted hotel across the street from the park in which Yorst sat and went to his customary bench. It was always that way. Soon others followed and by ten o'clock they were all there, about twenty of them; they on one side of the street, Yorst on the other.

Ordinarily he would sit on his bench for about an hour and a half reading his paper a little and watching them die. In the three years since he had started his attendance he had followed the pathological progression of eight of them to their graves and had begun anew to follow their replacements. Even across the little street, his sharp, strong, glassless eyes had recorded each increasing degree of someone's palsied failure of muscle and bone. He had watched bladders collapse, the breath shorten, and memory crumble away. It was not exactly or simply pleasure that he took, his being on his side of the street, they on theirs, but rather something like strength. When, around eleven-thirty or twelve, the nurses would come, often with wheelchairs, to gather up their charges, Yorst would always feel through his whole body a great collapsing, a total, sickening melt of substances. He would stand up then and flex to straining the long, full muscles of his thighs and walk off feeling now the hard, smooth, easy swivel of every joint in its place. And now he would be exhilarated in his strength and walk more quickly and breathe more deeply into the day. And now, at noon, life would flare up and fill him. It was all that Yorst Inman Broctor had. It was, he thought, enough.

Today, however, at about eleven o'clock, a quick and harder gust of wind lifted Yorst's hat from his head and blew it across the street. He sprang after it. The hat bounced away and blew up against the legs of one of the two men who had been sitting on the bench opposed to Yorst's.

"Excuse me," Yorst said as he strode up to them. "My hat," he said. "The wind. It blew it and . . . I . . . ."

"Of course," one of the men—the well-dressed one—said and leaned over to pick the hat up, but Yorst bent more quickly and retrieved it himself. For an instant their heads were close together, the mouth of one close to the ear of the other as if some secret were being quickly passed. Then Yorst stood up and the man leaned back.

"Thank you," Yorst said. "Thank you."

"But for what?" the man said, "I have done nothing. Still, you are welcome. Tell me, please, what is your name?" About the man there was a subtle elegance. Beyond his physical decrepitude, the liver spots that designed the skin of his hands, the impossible pallor of his face, the purple lips, something—a tone of voice? a gesture of the eyes?—played like whimsy, like wiseness. Whatever, it held Yorst, for he did not walk away as all of him wanted to do, but stayed and answered.

"Broctor," he said. "Yorst Inman Broctor." The man lifted his hand. At first Yorst was puzzled, and then he realized that the man was offering him his hand to shake. Yorst, caught, took it. It was what he imagined a skeleton to be like, the lightness of bones with the marrow long dried out of them. Holding death by the hand, revulsion rose up in him and he felt his mouth drying. The man did not leave go but turned instead to the other man of the bench.

"Mr. Broctor," he said with high civility, "my name is Franz Appel. Permit me to introduce you to my good friend and companion, Moses Schreiber. Moses," he went on in superb decorum, "please be introduced to Mr. Yorst Inman Broctor. He has come to watch us die." Yorst blanched. Appel released Yorst's hand, but before Yorst could take it back, Franz Appel's good friend and companion Moses Schreiber had it. If the touch of death could be light and cool, it could also be sweaty, hot, and violent. For the first time in his life Yorst thought he might faint.

"No better place. No better place," Moses Schreiber screamed at him. "See him over there?" He motioned with a jerk of his head. "The one in the dark glasses? Him I don't give a month. Three weeks even. His kidneys. All gone." By now enough of his spittle had bubbled out of and around his mouth to run down his chin in a trickle and onto his grimy shirt collar. Suddenly he gave up Yorst's hand and poked him sharply in his body. "But *you* know. You *know,* don't you?" He began to laugh until he began to cough and then he coughed up a lunger of something and hawked it expertly out past the bench onto the grass. Yorst quivered.

"I must go," he said, and started to.

"Please," Franz Appel said. "Don't be offended by our frankness. Don't be frightened. We are seldom with others and so forget to . . . be restrained. Will you not stop and sit with us a moment. After finally meeting, after all these months, would it not be a pity to have you leave so soon?"

"Some other time maybe," Yorst said. "But now I really have to go." He turned and walked away as quickly as he ever had.

All that afternoon he walked and near suppertime called his daughter to tell her that he wouldn't be there for supper.

And he walked on until ten o'clock, when he walked home. He slept that night, but for the first time since the year following his Hanna's death, he slept badly.

Although Yorst continued to go to his morning post across from the high school to observe his grandchildren, he stopped his visits to the park across from the nursing home. Besides his confused embarrassment at being exposed in his morbid superiority, he would not again willingly risk coming into such close contact with them. To see and know was one something, no matter how old, anew, what Yorst responded to was morning's leisured arrogance that there was time could be strong; on their side of the street he had become, for the brief moments of their encounter, like them. It was all too real to bear.

After his coffee in the lucheonette now, he would wander the city as he had before the boys were in high school or when he had first come to live with Margaret and as he did even now during many of his open, uncluttered afternoons. Without exactly knowing it, he found that mornings were different from afternoons, that what people did, how they moved in doing it, was different and better before lunch. Besides the quicker pace expected after a night's sleep, besides the natural heightening that comes with starting something, no matter how old, anew, what Yorst responded to was morning's leisured arrogance that there was time enough. In the morning, people, easy in time like children, were better and happier to be around.

The coolish but clear weather of September and October held, and Yorst, freed of his obligating deathwatch, pursued throughout the markets, libraries, factories, stores, and peopled places of the day what pleased him most. Now he was feeding off of the very twitch and pulse of the urging quick, not as in the little park. And here, in the midst, he paid no price. It was for Yorst his most ebullient autumn.

Still, there were times when he could not help but wonder about the dying men, even, with remembered queasiness, about Franz Appel and Moses Schreiber. They had been, after all, all of them, the closest thing he had to companions in the past three years.

One afternoon, near four o'clock, when none of them would be there, for "old times" sake, he went back. It was safe, he knew, for whatever else they did in their day, they did it late in the afternoon. He walked back, but as he approached the park, Franz Appel and Moses Schreiber came, slowly, out of the building and tottered toward their bench, each upon the other's arm. Yorst turned quickly. He didn't know if they had seen him, but if he got away quickly enough it wouldn't matter. To hell with them, anyway, Yorst thought, in his chagrin at being caught again.

Close to him, walking toward him, was Alan Kramer, his hand upon the neck up under the luxuriant hair of Beverly Laskow.

"Hi, Pops," Alan Kramer shouted, loudly even for him, and waved vigorously. "How the old bones doing?" The girl smiled and waved, too. Yorst stopped. Doubly confused, doubly caught, affronted now beyond enduring by this impudent vermin, his dirty hand upon her, Yorst prepared to make, in his anger, his stand.

"Now see here young . . . ," he began as the couple reached him, but they didn't stop; they didn't even see him. They walked on together past him and across the street to the bench. Yorst watched the girl bend and kiss Moses Schreiber. At that moment Franz Appel clearly and unmistakably signaled for him to join them. Dutifully, but with dread, Yorst did.

"Ah, Mr. Broctor. What a pleasant surprise," Franz Appel greeted him, the other three looking on. "Permit me to introduce you. This is Beverly Laskow, the granddaughter of my good friend and companion, Moses, whom you have already met. And this is Alan Kramer, my . . . "

"We've met, we've met already, Pops," the boy interrupted.

". . . grandson," Franz Appel concluded.

Yorst started visibly. Would the shocks of this day never cease? Franz Appel reached up and lightly took Yorst by the elbow and brought him down to sit upon the bench.

"Yes," Beverly Laskow added. "Many times. But never formally. How do you do," she said, and extended her hand. Yorst took it. It was a woman's hand. He looked at her and all her manner seemed to say to him that when he would betray her, as in a moment he would have to, that it was all right. She forgave him. She understood.

"How is that?" Moses asked looking at him, at Franz Appel, at them all. "How could you have met many times?" Yorst told them that it was in the luncheonette near the high school in the morning. Maybe Moses would let it go at that. But he didn't.

"What were you doing there?" he pushed on. "What were *they* doing there?"

"Well," Yorst began, not knowing how to go on, how to put the words around his reasons, and desperately not wanting to, not here.

"Where have you been for so long, Mr. Broctor? We have missed you," Franz Appel interrupted to change the subject. But Alan Kramer interrupted him to bring it back.

"We were 'cutting,' is what we were doing," he brazened. "We were trying to stay out of that cruddy school and away from them stupid teachers before some of their dumbness rubbed off on us." Choleric anyway, the boy glowed now. "Like I *need* to know the eighteen thousand causes of the French Revolution. Y'know? Like I really, really *need* that crap!"

"Alan," his grandfather attempted to gentle him. "We can't always see immediately *why* learning something is important or good, but learning *itself* is good as its own . . . ."

"Aahhh, come on, Pops," the boy said, shaking off the old man's decency. "I was just answering Mosey's question. There's nothing that dump's got that I want or need, so I cut out whenever I can get away with it. Him," he said, gesturing with a quick, across-the-chest flick of his thumb, "he comes to spy on his grandsons. You know," he said to the girl, "Kenny Robinson, the big jock?"

"It's not *spying,*" Yorst blurted, shouted. "It's my . . . it's . . . I . . . ." He was almost standing. He was on his way up. He couldn't say with words what it was, but that didn't make any less real what he felt. And why should he have to say it? Could any of them see what it was anyway? And who was this miserable punk to call Kenneth a name, Kenneth who could break . . . . And again he had been discovered by . . . by these *people* before he had discovered himself. Wound on wound and not knowing why and the dirty lout sassing him. Yorst had beaten two men in his life; in the flashing seconds to come he was about to beat his first boy. But Franz Appel put a finger upon Yorst's thick wrist, who turned a moment and in that moment saw that someone could see, that Franz Appel knew why Yorst looked for his grandchildren in the morning and what it was like to want to look for them. It surprised him at first that another could know, but Yorst sat back down. Pierced by Appel's touch, he was caught and crushed in the vacuum left by his escaping frustration and anger; emptied and confused, he floundered about against this tide. For the first time in his life that he could remember, his breath was short and labored; he had to think to breathe, to concentrate on doing it. An hour earlier, this shortness of breath, would have struck him, omen-like, with a thin terror. But now the excitement bred in his blasting yet grateful and saving contact with Franz Appel came flooding in to fill him out again and to push him on into a strange and mystifying region, boundless and without proportion, where he had seldom been before and never for long—outside of his body, beyond his flesh. Sometimes, so long ago, before there was time with Hanna, after the last brick had been placed into a good house, there had been something like this. Was there a name for it? Yorst had closed his eyes. His breath was coming back and his color subsiding, but this sudden new thing in his head, this seed, he would have to learn to live with; he would have to make something out of it. He felt anticipatory, expectant, verging. Murkily he felt that with Franz Appel's help, something good was going to happen. Something important was going to be understood. But it was all so strange. With so little in himself he felt oddly light and vulnerable. Still, it was not unpleasant.

"Hey, you better take it easy, Dad," Alan Kramer said. He hadn't given an inch, his tone and manner as full of contempt as ever. Yorst opened his eyes and looked at him. He didn't matter so much anymore. He wasn't Yorst's. He wasn't Yorst's sorrow. He was someone else's. Let him go at that.

After the merest conversation, the girl again kissed her grandfather. The boy said to Franz Appel, "Mom said she'll be down to see you Sunday, Pops. Maybe I'll see you next week." The two of them left, going back in the direction from which they had come, Alan Kramer, hardly taller than the girl, dark and ape-like, walking close beside her, his arm around her, provocative and low upon her hip. The three old men on the bench watched them out of sight.

"Is it not something of a wonder, Mr. Broctor, that I should be the grandfather of that boy?" Franz Appel said. Yorst had thought that himself as soon as he heard they were related. But what could he say?

"Or that I should be the grandfather of that queen?" Moses Schreiber put in. Yorst had thought that too, but, as with so much else with these people, he was again unprepared, unready to hear these men—any men—address their lives with such candor. It occurred to Yorst—dimly, half-formed—that maybe when you were close enough to the grave you were willing to look at things, whatever way they were, the way they were. And it occurred to him then, too, that just then he had had his first open and calm thought about death.

"I suppose so," Yorst said to the statements of both, at once sorry that he had said anything that, even in agreement, was so uncomplimentary in its implications. "I mean," he went on, "I mean you would think it would be reversed." But that wasn't right either. He started to flush. "I mean . . . I mean . . . ."

"It is all right, Mr. Broctor," Franz Appel said, smiling. "We know exactly what you mean. We have often thought so ourselves. Yes, Moses?"

"A dozen times a day at least," Moses assured him. He blew his nose into an ancient handkerchief. "It's my postnasal drip," he informed Yorst. "Yaaah. I leak everywhere," he announced in disgust.

"How does it happen?" Yorst asked quietly. Not counting street directions or the time of the day, it was the first question Yorst Inman Broctor had asked another man in a score of years.

"Well," Moses began, "you start with the adenoids." He pointed a finger to where he thought his adenoids were.

"No, no," Yorst stopped him. "I mean how did you get the grandchildren . . . that . . . you got?"

"Oh that," Moses said. "It's from her father. His side. What a gorgeous man! What a family he comes from! Every one of them a beauty! Every one of them a prince! *A Prince!* My wife used to say to me, we go to a family affair, I should put my head in a paper bag." Moses giggled highly. "Selma, my daughter, isn't so good-looking. Not a pig, but no Beverly, believe me. But she knew how to get her man, huh? Where he lives, right? Where he *lives!*" He yowled, elbowing Yorst sharply in the ribs. "You know? You *know?*" Moses Schreiber dissolved into a laughing, snorting, wheezing appreciation of his Selma's wits. He grasped Yorst by the wrist, part of his stained, greasy tie caught in his yellow hand. "She had what it takes," he sputtered. "Like *all* women got." His voice had reached its highest pitch, his glee uncontainable. "But she knew what to do with it, huh? *Huh?*" He poked again. "You know? You *know?*"

But Yorst Inman Broctor did not know. At best, appalled, he suspected. His own memory of Hanna, neither idealized nor passionate, was all that women had meant to him or meant to him now. He knew there were other "kinds" of women—he had read in the papers, he had seen on the TV, he had heard—but he had never considered them as real. Hanna was real. Hanna had married and had borne a child. Did Selmas bear children too? Did Selmas bear Beverlys? Yorst edged back from the abyss of a terrible knowledge.

"With Allia it was different," Franz Appel began. "She was—is—a great beauty herself. Here." He took out a photograph, a recent one, of his daughter. He was right. Allia was a beautiful woman, in her picture a decade younger than she was. "She married a handsome man and now a successful one. But after the child, Alan, the home was never really good." He paused, as though giving Yorst a chance to brace, for he went on, "She didn't know what was good for a man." He paused again. "She didn't understand the bed." Yorst didn't want to hear any more, but Franz Appel continued. "You see," he said, "for all that I could and did teach her, there were obviously some things I couldn't. Unfortunately, neither could her mother." He was looking now across the street where Yorst used to sit. "Why he looks the way he does? Who can say? But he is what he is and what he will be because of his father. Like last year, for an instance, when he took the boy to a cockeyed-Jenny. A whore," he interpreted for Yorst.

"Too bad," Yorst said, softly, gently commiserate.

"Oh no," Franz Appel said abruptly, turning on the bench to look at him. "Oh *no!* Not at all. Not at *all.*"

"What's the matter with you," Moses Schreiber shouted at Yorst, his impatience veined with anger. "Don't you understand? Don't you understand *anything?*"

It had grown close to darkness. Only the unusual warmth of the late autumn day had allowed them to sit as long as they had, and the warmth had gone with the light. The streetlights coming on reminded them of their chill. Franz Appel got up.

"It is late and it is cold," he said. "We must be getting in." He put a hand upon Yorst's shoulder, as before, light to nothingness. "It has been a great, great pleasure seeing you again and talking with you. Promise us that you'll come again shortly." Moses Schreiber now was up too, his arm locked in Appel's.

"Right," he said. "Come soon."

"I will," Yorst said. "I will." And then they all moved away.

Walking home Yorst twisted. He knew for certain something had happened to him, but he could not say what. He knew for certain, though, that there were new things in his head, things that he couldn't make do what he wanted. Instead of cataloging the different kinds of bricks in the buildings he passed while walking or recounting the simple impersonal incidents he had encountered in his day, there flickered through him instead bits of memories—dim tastes and smells from the old country that he did not remember tasting and smelling; a brick-carrying contest he had won—fifteen hods in an hour; Hanna mostly—Hanna cooking for him, Hanna rubbing his back, Hanna in silence doing for him and Margaret. But he could not remember his passion. He could not remember her's. Great hollow globes of memory kept bursting around him. He stopped walking and leaned his head against a building and tried to fight back to his wedding night. With all his strength, what he had now and all that he had ever had, he hurled himself at every barrier and restraint until each cracked before him and he broke through to find only the strength itself and nothing, nothing else.

"Are you all right, buddy?" the policeman said. Yorst looked up.

"Yes," he said. "All right. A little dizziness is all."

"You're bleeding a little," the policeman said, pointing to Yorst's forehead. "You sure you're okay? Do you want me to call a patrol car?" By the way he was breathing in deeply through his nose Yorst knew the policeman was trying to find out if he had been drinking.

"No," Yorst said again. "I'm all right now. Anyway, I just live two blocks from here. I'll make it the rest of the way."

"Okay," the policeman said, watching as Yorst walked off.

The last, sudden warmth of the year brought with it the last rain, which had begun to fall easily. By the time Yorst entered Margaret's kitchen he was wet enough.

Supper that night was, as were most of the meals in that house, reserved—not entirely cold but oddly nonsocial: Margaret and Ernst saving their intimacies, such as they were, for their private evening following the dishes; the boys, deep now in the heedlessness of adolescence, had nothing to say that they could imagine their parents would be interested in—or should be interested in; and Yorst, never much of a talker, was a stone. It was a house distant, never brought together. Tonight it was so quiet that Ernst, annoyed, remarked:

"What is it? What are we, in mourning or something? Nobody's said a thing at this table since we sat down." He waited for them to take him up on it. Margaret helped a little with some trivia of the day, but that sputtered out. They were all silent again, the only sound the scraping of forks through the apple pie.

Ernst went at it again. "How's the football team, Kenny? Are they going to be 'up' for the West Side game?"

"Yeah," Kenny said. And that was all.

"Is that all you can say," Ernst pushed him. "Come on, tell us something about practice. What about Davis? Is his arm better? Are there any new plays, anything special we should look for at the game?"

"Aw, dad, you know. It's always the same thing at practice—run, stop, hit, run, stop, hit. That's all."

Ernst said, "You don't sound too happy about it. I mean you seem to have lost your enthusiasm. Is something the matter?"

"No," Kenny said.

Greg snickered. "He's in love."

"*You shut up,*" Kenny screamed at him. "*You shut up, you little bastard.*" He spun in his chair and hit his brother hard on the arm, knocking the boy to the floor, jarring the table so the coffee slopped out of the cups.

"*Kenneth!*" Margaret shouted at him. "Don't you *ever* use such language. Do you hear *me? Never!* And don't you hit your brother."

"He should keep his big mouth shut before he gets it shut for him." In the bosom of his family, beneath his mother's anger, his brother at his feet, a girl in his guts, the boy looked down in red-faced misery.

"I don't care about anything. Keep your hands to *yourself!*" The boy could take no more of any of it. He got up and thumped quickly from the room.

In the morning it was raining still. And Yorst was getting the first cold he had had in a dozen years. From Moses Schreiber, I'll bet, he thought. Breakfast was a little more animated than supper had been, as though a common pain had brought it closer, but when Kenneth, last, sat down to eat, things faltered a bit under the elaborate and heavy delicacy of the rest for his embarrassment. After they all left, Yorst made himself a scalding glass of strong tea with lemon and poured in an inch of whiskey. He sweetened it with a tablespoon of honey.

"Best cold remedy in the whole world," he said to Margaret as he sat down at the cleared table across from her. She had already begun to prepare some of the foods for the day.

"Imagine you getting a cold," she said to him. "How do you feel?"

"Oh, not so bad," he said. Colds in the head he could take. It was the rest that was hurting him, all the rest that so suddenly, so knifelike, he had gone through yesterday that had ravaged his peace through the night. And now the boy. Yorst took a gulp of the hot tea to burn himself back into focus. This wandering, this complexity was unfamiliar. That he might be beginning to slip in the head was half a worry to him too.

"Margaret," he said so that it made her look up.

"What is it, father?"

"Kenneth is sixteen, you know," he said.

"Yes," she said. "Sure I know." She smiled, waiting.

"Well," he said, "has anyone told him about girls? I mean does he know about . . . babies . . . and . . . all?" Margaret smiled lovingly and stopped peeling the potatoes.

"I haven't," she said. "And I don't know if Ernst has. But you know, times have changed. Kids today get to know about such things by themselves—almost, well, automatically, I guess. Kenny'll be all right." She said it with the confidence of a mother who, having borne such fine sons, need not worry overmuch about them. She picked up her paring knife.

"Still," Yorst insisted, "it wouldn't hurt if you and Ernst were sure that he knew." He stopped, drank half his tea, still hot to hurting, and then did something he hadn't done in the seventeen years of their marriage. He butted in directly.

"Margaret," he said to her, "I want you to do me a favor. I want you to find out if Ernst has told him. And if he hasn't, I want you to get him to." Margaret peeled on for a few moments, the skin lengthening until it broke.

"Okay, father," she said, but it sounded to Yorst more like pacification than agreement, more like the humoring of the old. He was not satisfied.

Yorst's cold got worse until, hardly believing it, he found himself, after three days, in bed, visited by a doctor at Margaret's demand, and taking expensive pills. He had been ordered to bed for a week. On the fifth day, Greg, visiting with his grandfather in his room after school (a duty imposed by his mother), had had drawn out of him the name of Kenneth's love: a girl called Beverly Laskow. And it was going badly. She wouldn't accept any of his requests for a date or hardly even any of his attentions. She wouldn't even be nice. As Greg put it: "The big jerk is making a jerk out of himself. She's just teasing him. Boy, is she ever! Boy, he doesn't even know if he's coming or going." His brotherly loyalty and affection were welling up. "It's terrible. Him running after her, trying to look like he doesn't really care too much about the whole thing and everybody knowing, especially her, that he does. And what's so bad," he was almost strident now, "is that she just won't turn him off. Oh, no! She's playing him like a big dumb fish, laughing at him all the time. She won't turn him loose and she won't keep him. The *bitch!*" he shouted, carried into the word by his ardor. He looked up quickly at his grandfather, apprehensive and tensed at his liberty. But Yorst calmed him at once.

"You're right, Greg. A *bitch* is just the word."

He asked about Alan Kramer. Greg wrinkled his nose.

"That smelly rat? Yeah, he's all over her. I can't see how she stands it. And boy, you ought to hear the stuff he says about Ken. You ought to hear the fun he makes of *him!*" But Yorst had heard enough.

That had been the fifth day. On the sixth he was up getting his legs back, relapsing a little but not much, and fending off Margaret's frantic protests. "You're seventy-eight years old," she had shouted at him once.

"Don't I know it," he had answered her with what, for Yorst, amounted to ironic wit. He had come a long way; he had a way to go. Friday, the seventh day, he started.

On that morning he waited until the worst of the night's coldness had subsided and then left the house. He walked, only a little shaky, to Franz Appel and Moses Schreiber. When he got to the converted hotel he walked right in and up to the former check-in counter and asked the just slightly grim secretary-nurse-telephone operator behind it if she would call Franz Appel and Moses Schreiber. She reached over to the switchboard and threw a switch. And then she looked at him, obviously appraising him. Then she said, "Mr. Appel died last week. Pneumonia." Yorst was still standing there when Moses came up and took him by the arm and led him away to a corner of the winter-lighted foyer. They sat, but not for a whole minute did either speak.

"Just like that," Moses said. "One day a cold, the next day pneumonia, the next day dead." He was still Moses Schreiber.

"I am very sorry to hear this," Yorst said. "He was a fine man." Yorst paused and went on. "And I wanted to talk to him—and to you. There were things I thought you could tell me."

"Yes, yes," Moses said in quiet agreement. "Franz knew. I know. You have so much to learn. There is so much you don't understand, have never understood. Here." He reached into his inside breast pocket before Yorst could say anything and withdrew a soiled envelope. "For you. From him. He wrote it when his fever was high, but it's his." Yorst opened it.

"Dear Yorst Broctor," it began, the handwriting uneven: "Your health is very good and so it is quite possible that you will live for many more years, but even if you do not it is important to know this: all we can give is what we have. Don't torture yourself about the rest. Franz Appel." Yorst read it again, the enigma that had recently spread disruptively through his life, his soul, deepening. He had come today to clarify, to settle; he had gotten instead death and mystery.

"What have I got to give them? What have I ever given them?" he blurted out, torn between exposing and hiding. Moses Schreiber had taken the letter and read it. "My grandson Kenneth is in love with your granddaughter, Beverly. He suffers. She is cruel to him. What can I do about it?" Had his life, all of it, come down to this? "Moses," he said, grasping him gently by the wrist, "how can it be? How can she prefer an Alan Kramer to a . . . a *beauty* like Kenneth? Is it because of religion?"

"A little, maybe," Moses Schreiber said. "But that's not what the more important thing is. It's what's between the legs that counts. That dirty pig Kramer and Bevy got the same thing going inside them—a big, hot need. They are the same people. But don't worry! He ain't ever going to touch her, not that pig. She's too smart, like Selma, her mother. Ya, Bevy knows what she got and she ain't wasting it on no dirty pig like Kramer, but, *oi,* does she like being *looked* at the way he looks at her! Does she like what's in his head! Him? For him it's something good to jerk-off about at night. They understand each other, them two. For a couple of years it's a good arrangement, you know? Look, someday his skin will clear up a little and some woman will marry him for *her* hot need and she'll be his and he'll get what he wants, so things will work out. Your boy? I guess he's got no sex, at least not yet. Maybe never. Who knows? Most people never get no sex going in them. Like Franz. Like you. That's the way it is." Moses sounded weary, tired out by truth. Yorst let it in, not angry, not repulsed, no longer able to afford his revulsion.

"Then there's nothing I can do for the boy, is there?" Yorst said more than asked. "Nothing now? Nothing ever?"

" 'All we can give is what we have,' " Moses read aloud

from the letter and then handed it back to Yorst. "What else is there to say?" There was nothing else.

"Good-bye, Moses," Yorst said, getting up. They shook hands.

"Good-bye, Yorst," Moses said.

Outside, back on the street on the way home, Yorst bent under his thoughts, an aged man intent. There was nothing he had ever given to his grandchildren or to anyone else. He had only taken. He had given them no guidance, no knowledge of life, no toughness to the world. He had fed them and clothed them. It was all he had. Alan Kramer's father had taken him to a whore, while Yorst, even now, agonized if his grandson knew where babies came from. How do you not torture yourself about the rest? he lashed at himself. How do you not suffer? Was it by doing something, he wondered, even if it was anything at all? The random winds of November and other vagaries blew him about.

One day later Yorst attempted to tell Kenneth about girls, about sex. It was a disaster. Shocked into defensive range by the embarrassment talking about sex with an adult, a *grandfather,* forced him into, Kenneth hit and hurt back. "What do you think I am?" he demanded, "some kind of stupid little kid? Where do you think I've been? Where have *you* been? All my life you've got nothing to say to me and now you're full of it. Just . . . just . . . just leave me alone," he stammered, guilt and sorrow at his harshness to the old man already softening him. He left his grandfather quickly, plunged a little deeper into the painful confusion his life in his sixteenth winter had become, one more knot in him, Yorst, in his own guilt and sorrow, knew.

A bitter week went by. The already recently heightened constraint at the supper table lengthened, rayed out, and hardened, some inexplicable vortex of life spinning them away from each other. Ernst, frustrated and upset by the changing, showed it variously but mainly by shouting a lot. Kenneth, embattled, shrank now from all family contact. Yorst, fearful to offend, frequently retreated into a staring vacancy. Greg, by nature a chatterer, succumbed beneath the weight of their silence and his father's touchiness. Margaret worried slowly about them all. By that Saturday night it came to seem that the central and binding intimacy of easy, open love—always limited in the family—was gone away, had maybe never strongly been. Had it? Yorst wondered. Had it gone away? Had it ever been? *Was what was happening here me all over again?* Food, clothes, a house? Where was what mattered? Yorst got in between the sheets and tossed about. Margaret and Ernst had gone out, bad as the weather was, to a late movie. The boys, before the muffled, droning TV in the living room, would, Yorst knew, soon be in bed themselves. He closed his eyes and finally sank through all of what was bothering him to sleep.

The first sharp crack that brought Yorst out of sleep sounded to him like a rifle report from a cowboy Western. But the second explosion sounded close to his ear and brought with it the smoke of fire. The house was burning down. Yorst knew it at once. He jumped out of bed, skidding a little on his old slippers, and felt the hotness of the floor on his bare feet. In the basement, he thought. Probably the furnace. It was the last clear thought he had except for one, for his still adequate nerve, corpuscle, cell, trained by decades of fleshly self-concern, calculated flashingly to live. They grasped Yorst and threw him through the door of his bedroom into the thick, killing smoke of the kitchen, gropingly but surely toward the kitchen door through which awaited the fifteen or even twenty years more of life he could expect. But the arithmetic of it was all wrong. Loyal to no life but only to life, his flesh recalculated. The years of them upstairs outbalanced those left for him. Life, as Yorst Inman Broctor had always wanted it to, won. He thought about it, not without terror, and, madly buoyant, his hand upon the kitchen doorknob, turned, took his last total breath, and ran up the stairs to the room Kenneth and Greg slept in, to give them what he had.

In the room the boys had passed out, falling into a heap upon each other before the tightly closed window and storm window. Yorst, blinded, his chest tight to bursting, called up the proud strength he had saved through his years, flexed his arms again into power and smashed at the windows with his great fists. He ripped and tore and kicked and butted the frames with his hands and feet and head, his blood now upon him everywhere, until there was no more breath in him at all and he fell to his knees, the lungs reflexively drawing into themselves the black, superheated smoke. The last pain Yorst ever felt was his throat cauterizing. But he would not die. He dragged Greg to the window and rolled him out of it. A siren screamed. People were below. Flame roared up through the bedroom floor. Yorst burned. But he would not die. He found Kenneth. He took him in his arms and shielded him and he stood up as in miracle and walked to the window and threw the boy out and then, having done something, died.

Tickets

MORRIS JACOBI SAT at his kitchen table with his forearms resting on the damp plastic tablecloth. His wife Helen had just wiped it with a sponge for the third time in the half hour of his warmed-over supper. Had Morris noticed, he would have expected the scene to which his wife's insistent cleaning was always prelude. But he was weary and did not notice. The time was seven-thirty.

Morris held an empty dessert cup in one hand and with the spoon in his other hand scored channels in the remaining traces of chocolate pudding. From time to time he would put the empty spoon, upside down, into his mouth and leave it there for maybe a minute. In such an interval Helen turned away from the sink to him.

"You want another?" He forgot about the spoon in his mouth and started to answer her. He stopped trying to speak and removed it.

"What?"

"You want another pudding? You've been scraping the cup now for so long I don't even have to wash it. You still hungry?" The thought that he could still be hungry, or might be hungry, caused her to frown. She left the sink and came to the table.

"Some coffee, maybe," he said.

"Coffee keeps you up. Even the Sanka keeps you up," she reminded him. "With you I think maybe it's mental. So many things are mental today. You know what I mean?"

"Tea, then," he said.

After Helen had boiled the water and poured him the cup of tea and cut a wedge of lemon, she sat down opposite him and began to turn slowly the pages of a *Woman's Day* that lay in front of her. Morris, with his tea as with his chocolate pudding, seemed to ruminate. He sipped slowly and only at long intervals. The tea became cool. Morris was silent. After fifteen minutes, the tea almost gone, Helen looked up from her magazine and told her husband that Mr. Feldman from the synagogue had stopped by that morning and wanted to know whether the Jacobi family wanted the fifty or the one hundred dollar seat tickets. Morris looked at his wife without pain, and with certainty said, "None of them. Not the ones for fifty or a hundred." Then, "What seats? What tickets?"

Helen told him they were seat tickets for the high holidays.

"Yeah," Morris said, "well, we don't need seats for a hundred dollars or even fifty. We can sit on the benches downstairs like always and for nothing. God's God," he added.

"Out here," Helen explained, "they don't have a downstairs. You can't even get inside without having tickets."

"So we don't go," Morris answered. "What? It's the first time we ever missed?"

"It's different out here, Morris," Helen said, finally allowing her voice to rise. She closed the *Woman's Day.* "Out here I got to see these women almost every day. You go to the city and who knows you? But me, every day, every single day except I should be sick or something I got to see them. So how can I explain not having tickets for the holidays?"

"Explain to them you are up to your ears in debt. Explain to them you just bought one half of a shoe-store and one whole house in Green Acres, where the tax assessment is fifty bucks a thousand." Morris got up. "Tell them you can't afford it. Tell them the truth." He had finished. He walked into the living room, but even before he could turn on the TV Helen was at his ear demanding, now stridently, "What? Are you crazy?"

It was a question to which Morris had addressed himself with frequency in the past six months.

Riding in the dirty train that brought him slowly out of the city to his home he would ask himself if, in fact, he were not crazy. Especially on Thursday and Friday nights, when he would not get home until after ten or eleven o'clock (the store stayed open for a special shopping night and for stock taking), would he question the sanity of his motives and gains. His observations were direct and his conclusions, like an unbalanced ledger, fierce.

For twenty years come April he had sold shoes for Slotkin and Novick—Sampler Shoes, Inc. Slotkin was now dead for over a year and Novick, too old himself (though hale) to handle the business alone, convinced, easily and sensibly, the Widow Slotkin to sell her half of the business to Morris. It was for all three parties a solution, or, to Morris at that time, so it had appeared. Now he wondered.

Before he became a partner he had earned less money, so spent less, lived less spaciously but in greater communion with his wife and daughter and son, and had come to move well and fondly in a neighborhood whose identity in the city had not been lost. All these conditions of his middle-age life had been changed. In place of his substantial savings stood debts which he often felt would be liquidated only with part of (God forbid!) his life insurance. For the frenetic, suffocating joys of his children growing up stood now the boundlessness of the late trains and his weariness. And—stone upon stone—for twenty years of faces and colors and shapes stood the cold, treeless silence of Green Acres and the dogs which charged at him out of, it seemed, all the driveways on the long block at whose end he lived. Morris alone in Green Acres owned no car.

Jolting through the night Morris would look at himself in the train window and try to catch his reflected eyes. He could not escape his own arithmetic. He had traded in one whole existence for another, disagreeable one. Tricked by the convenience of Slotkin's death and Novick's need,

Morris had reached out and taken. In an easy, pleasant, lawyer-ish afternoon he had attained the long goal of many men. It was not until some little time after that he realized such a goal had never been his. He felt, as in a bad tasting business deal, that he had been taken advantage of by life. For what? For this had he gone down on his knees to the world for twenty years? Was this what twenty years of sweaty feet added up to? "Shmuck," he hissed at his companion cringing in the window.

"Never again will I ever leave this house, Morris Jacobi, I shouldn't be able to go to *shule* on Yom Kippur. And the children? Think of the children. All their new friends inside and them standing out front, alone." Helen groaned and sank down on the sofa.

"What are you talking about," Morris countered. "That's all them kids go to the synagogue for anyway, to stand outside and *kibbitz.* You think any of them know or care what's going on inside. Ha! Don't make me laugh. A couple of days off from school, that's all it means. The Yom Kippur Social Club. Ha! Don't make me laugh." But Helen was at him.

"You should talk. You're such a good Jewish man? Look who's making who laugh. Besides, they should be able to go if they want to." Again she sank back in the sofa. Two small fists inside of him beat quickly and sharply at Morris's heart. "Gas," he thought, but he was wrong. He turned on the TV and a dark truce fell upon the house until morning.

Morning, breakfast particularly, had become the best part of Morris's day. It was the one family meal throughout the week, not counting Sundays. Both he and the children had to take buses, he to the train station and they to the regional school four miles away. After breakfast Morris, Harry, fifteen, and Barbara, thirteen, would walk the long block together to the bus stop, the children animatedly challenging the day, Morris listening, occasionally questioning, and always being asked to assent to something. Joy of his joys. Five minutes. At the bus stop they cut him cold to join their respective knots of new, quickly-made friends. His bus came first, and without a wave, he mounted to be torn even further away. "Aaaah," his breath would escape from him.

That morning at breakfast Helen continued her offensive. As soon as she had placed the grapefruit, unscalloped, in front of them she began. "When are the holidays, children?"

Harry answered, "Late, this year. Rosh Hashonah starts sundown the eighteenth. Yom Kippur the twenty-seventh."

"No school. No school for three days this year," Barbara added.

"This year you'll go to school . . . all three days, too," Helen threw at them and turned quickly away to the stove for the coffee.

"What?" the children screamed together.

"You heard me," Helen screamed back at and over them. "Ask your father." Morris gagged on his toast.

"Why are you torturing the children," he asked of her, quietly. Shame flickered in her eyes, but what was begun was begun. Morris said, "Always the children have never gone to school on the high holidays. This year is no different." Harry and Barbara hoorayed.

"Sha!" Helen silenced them. "O but this year *is* different. Before always, *always,* they had a synagogue to go to. This year, no. So, no synagogue, so no sense not going to school. The three days shouldn't be a total loss. That's that."

"What do you mean we don't have a synagogue?" Harry asked his father. "What about Beth Israel? We just joined it."

"Get your coats," Morris said. "Hurry. We'll miss our buses."

Surprisingly and, to Morris, gratifyingly, for four and a half minutes of their walk to the buses the children said nothing. Only when the three were almost upon the bus stop did Harry ask,

"What's going on Dad? Are we going to *shule* for the holidays or not?" What could Morris say?

"Harry, I don't know." His bus had arrived. Morris sprang eagerly toward it, but before he could bring himself to enter he turned and called out after the boy moving toward his school friends, "Harry, Harry. I don't think so." And then he was in the bus convincing himself that biting off the tongue already poised between his teeth would solve nothing.

Business was unusually—unreasonably—good that morning. Even so, though it absorbed much of Morris, it did not absorb all of him. Nor did the hurried business conference in which he and Novick, but especially he, decided to reorder double on the imitation Capezios which had sold so incredibly fast (one hundred pair in a week) absorb all of him. It took a solid hour of shouting on the telephone to bludgeon out of Krinsky the jobber a promise that was worth something, a promise that he would deliver the shoes by tomorrow, and a lunch-hour rush that lasted two lunch hours to totally absorb Morris. At two-thirty he settled down to a sandwich and coffee in the box-crowded, leathery-smelling backroom. Out in front it was absolutely quiet, for once a good sound, for once, even, satisfying. Morris bit into the sandwich with appetite.

Halfway through Morris's lunch Novick came back to him, worried. "Morris," he worried out loud, "two-hundred-fifty Capezios is a lot of Capezios. You think maybe we should maybe order half?"

Morris smiled, finished the last eighth of his sandwich, and said, "Abe, we got a good price on them because of the size of the order, right? Right! And who was it twenty years ago said to the young salesman, 'You got to have the stock. It's stock makes sales'? So, what do you think? I ordered two-hundred-fifty pairs of *black* Capezios? Abe, Abe, we got every kind of Capezio made and backups." Morris was feeling good, positively. He waxed on. "And Abe, look at the price. For what we bought them even if we sell only half we almost break even." Morris settled back pleased, but the look on Abe Novick's face did not change.

"Morris," he began, "it ain't none of all you said, which is true, but something else altogether. These crazy demands, like for the Capezios. They don't last long. All my life in this business I've seen the same thing. All of a sudden like, they want something. One, maybe two weeks, and you couldn't give it away. And especially with the Capezios. We don't sell them now, before it gets cold and rainy, we ain't *going* to sell them this year." Novick frowned deeper. "That's a lot of money locked up in stock," he added after a moment. His visage was black.

Morris was perturbed. Not that it was uncharacteristic of Novick to worry and to disturb others with his worries; Morris was used to that. But he was not used to Novick worrying so deeply, so insistently, especially when he, Morris, could not see the cause of it. After all, even though what Novick said was true, it was still all hypothetical. What, under the sun, *couldn't* happen? Finally, why hadn't Novick thought of all this when he consented to the order in the first place. Why was he coming now to lay this thing at his feet?

"So?" Morris asked, a touch sharply. "If the fad lasts one week or two weeks what's the difference? At the rate we're selling we'll get rid of enough. Some stock you always got to end up with."

"No, no," said Novick shaking his head in gentle, preparatory commiseration. "You don't understand."

"Frankly, I don't," Morris broke in. He got up, ready—wanting—to return to the store, to the selling of the damned Capezios. "Frankly, Abe, I just don't know what you're talking about." He turned and started out.

"The holidays," the old man called after him. Morris spun around.

"What? WHAT?" Morris shouted at him, visions of conspiracy racing through him. Novick, frightened at the sudden turn, drew his left shoulder up an inch and inclined his head down an inch in gesture of defense.

"The holidays," he whined. "We got to close for the holidays. Three days this year."

"*Oi gotteneu,*" Morris groaned, turning white. He sank back into the leathery smell of the storeroom onto a shipping carton and groaned again.

Novick was to him in a moment, solicitous, hovering, fretful. Morris, in turn, felt impelled to calm the agitated older man. And both were returned, outwardly at least, to stableness, to the decorum of businessmen, as two customers entered the store.

"I'll get them," Morris said, rising from the carton. Waiting on people was what he was best at. It calmed him to do something he could. To Novick he said, "Call Krinsky and halve the order." But Novick's eyes pleaded. "O.K.," Morris relented, "cut it two-thirds." Novick smiled for the first time that afternoon and went for the phone.

As Morris entered the front he felt a little restored. Part of his pre-lunch ease he had forced to return. "So, look," he reflected to himself, "the world is still turning. Who said it should all be smooth?" But in three seconds even this glaze of calm was shattered. The two superbly dressed men waiting for him were no customers. They were Feldman and Katz from Beth Israel. They had come to sell him tickets.

After introducing themselves Mr. Feldman said, "A nice business you got here Mr. Jacobi." Mr. Katz nodded. Both of them cast about appreciatively.

Morris said, "A nice business I'll *have* when, I should live long enough, it's paid for. And then only half. My partner Novick is over there." He pointed to the cash-out counter behind which Novick was talking into the phone. Feldman and Katz didn't bother to look. They took his word? They didn't care. "What do you want?" Morris asked.

"Could we talk to you? A minute? In the back maybe?" Katz spoke and gestured to the storeroom with his eyes. Morris turned and led them there. They entered and all sat down on the cartons. Feldman began.

"Your wife called me this morning and asked me to talk to you about the tickets."

"Did she tell you why?" Morris asked. "Did she tell you I said we wouldn't buy any tickets? Did she tell you that?" Feldman flushed slightly. Morris knew that Helen didn't tell him anything. She didn't have to. Feldmans always knew such things. Feldmans also knew how to twist your arm. But not this time. Morris braced himself.

"No," Feldman said, "your wife didn't say anything. She just asked I talk to you about the tickets. You say you don't want any. You don't have to tell me anything, but I ask, as a Jew, as belonging to the same congregation, why?"

"I can't afford it, and besides, I just paid two hundred dollars not so long ago just to join Beth Israel. Why should I pay extra for the holidays?"

Feldman smiled, It was the answer, the reaction, he wanted and expected. He attacked swiftly and with a merciless reasonableness. "Mr. Jacobi, Beth Israel couldn't exist on membership dues alone. The additional assessment for seats at the high holidays is really part of the congregation's financial responsibility." Morris waited for more, but there was no more. Who needed more?

"Why, why is the financial responsibility so high in Green Acres?" Morris asked. "Why does God cost so much?" Feldman, Katz, and even Morris himself were surprised and embarrassed at the question. What, after all, had God to do with all this? Katz tittered.

"Why does *everything* cost so much in Green Acres?" Katz and Feldman laughed appropriately, but Morris thought it was a good question. And then Novick entered, distraught, miserable, his sparse white hair flattened down on his soaking pink head.

"Go," he muttered, fluttering toward the telephone with his hand. "Go, Krinsky." Morris dashed out of the storeroom.

During the first ten minutes he argued on the phone with Krinsky about reducing the order, two customers came into the store. Novick did not reappear and Morris could not chance letting Krinsky go. His whole argument turned on convincing Krinsky that it was not too late to cancel, that it was not out of Krinsky's capable hands nor, even, out of the large province of his heart. The customers, annoyed, left. Feldman and Katz came forward, themselves caught by their desires to pull Morris into the holiday congregation and by their own, other temporal demands. A third customer entered the store, but Krinsky's capitulation was nowhere in sight. Where was Novick? "Abe," Morris shouted toward the storeroom, but there was no Novick nor an answer. Krinsky became obstinate, Morris frenzied (was Novick dead?). "Nazi," he shouted into the telephone. "Do you want our blood?" Krinsky hung up. Morris groaned. He had gone too far. The third cusomer left. Novick reappeared.

"I was on the toilet," he explained, apologetically. Morris spun on Feldman and Katz.

"You want to look at a nice pair of shoes, maybe?" He was shaking. His eyes were antic. Feldman and Katz looked at each other quickly and then away. They started toward the door.

"What's the matter?" Morris demanded. "I got the only shoe store from Green Acres, from Beth Israel even. Why don't you buy your shoes from me?" He looked at their shoes and saw his answer. Leather like that even Morris' jobbers didn't see. The door eased itself pneumatically shut after them. Morris ran for the back room. He came out with his hat on, his coat partly. He ran for the door.

"Where are you going?" Novick screeched after him, clawing the air.

"Out," Morris shouted, and, even louder, "for a walk." But the phone rang to arrest him. Maybe it was Krinsky? It was Helen.

"Morris, Morris, speak to Barbara, speak to our baby. What did you tell Harry this morning? Tell the baby it isn't so. Tell her she can go to *shule*." Her voice rang with the great histrionic Jewish sense of tragedy.

"It is so," Morris blasted back at her. "She can't go." He hung up and walked out into the busy flush of people and was swirled away.

Morris walked a good distance but not aimlessly. He walked back to the neighborhood in which he had lived for the twenty years before the arrival of his swift sloop of fortune, of partnership and Green Acres. In this place he had become a husband and a father. Among these people of these streets he was neither more nor less than what he was. He was Morris Jacobi, seller of shoes, married to Helen, getting matronly fat, father of Barbara and Harry who had a good head for numbers, should maybe someday be an accountant. That was Morris Jacobi, but who was this stranger walking up the five steps of the synagogue entrance?

"Who are you," the *shamus* asked. Morris groaned. He could not say. "What do you want?" he asked, now suspiciously. Fremick, the old *shamus,* was dead, had died just four months ago—Morris had heard. Fremick would have known him. But this new *shamus?* this alien? Morris caught himself. Who was new here, who was the alien?

"Again I ask you, Mister," the *shamus* broke in on him. "What do you want here?" He was insistent.

"I want to see the rabbi," Morris blurted out. He had not come to the synagogue to say that, or to say anything, but having said it, now it seemed right.

"The rabbi's not here. Come back for evening services." The *shamus* folded his arms. Then Morris asked the *shamus* if he could bring his family to the synagogue for the high holidays. The *shamus's* lips tightened across his teeth, his nostrils sprang hissing into the air, and the cleft between his eyes became a crevice.

"Only," he struck out at him, "if you're a Jew."

Morris fled.

Riding homeward that evening Morris, soul-sore and troubled, had his solution. He and his family would worship at Rodeph Sholom just as in all the years past. Indeed, the solution became more than a solution, it became a pleasure, a warm indulgence. Not even the occasional thought of two-hundred-fifty pairs of Capezios marching through the night toward his store could much disturb him. He settled back into his seat and, at partial peace, watched out of the window the autumn-touched September day conclude.

Morris entered his home to be attacked by his wife's strident accusations and by his children's cold, demanding eyes. They, the children, had been brought up to respect always their father but, alas for this moment anyway, Morris thought, to believe always their mother. Nevertheless, he thought, he had a good hand. For a minute or two more he would play it close to the vest. Why not? For what he had paid let him enjoy himself a little. Finally he held up his hands, over his head, like Moses.

"Enough," he said, and they were silent. "We'll go to *shule.*"

"Yaaah," they shouted, laughing. The children hopped.

"To Rodeph Sholom," he added.

"O no," they screamed. Barbara began to cry, Helen to pull her hair. Morris, stunned, considered himself. "Some card player," he thought. Putz, shmuck, schlemeil, dope, nut, jerk. To that cadence he moved into his gleaming kitchen to serve himself supper. But who could eat?

In the darkened living room Morris sat before the unfocused TV. He saw nothing. Somewhere behind and above him his alienated family moved. A slammed door, a call, a sewing machine—all insistently, reproachfully excluding him. Inside of him the little fists beat him black and blue. "Mercy," he pleaded, but nothing happened. At nine-thirty the doorbell rang. It was Uncle Charlie, Helen's uncle, Uncle Charlie who had been very good to the Jacobis, had, even, been the co-signer of the great loan which had bought for Morris all he now had. Uncle Charlie was a rich and successful man and a leader of the congregation.

"Hel-*lo* Morris. What are you doing, contemplating your navel here in the darkness? Ho Ho." Some kidder, Uncle Charlie.

"Hello Charlie," Morris said, "Come on in." But Charlie was in. "Let me help you with your coat." But the coat was already off. "I'll call Helen." But Helen, who had heard the doorbell, was already there. Morris tried to wonder why Charlie had come to his house at nine-thirty that night, but he knew.

"Uncle Charlie," Helen said with affection, and went to embrace him.

"*Mädchen,*" he answered. They hugged. "How about a nice hot tea?"

"Of course," she said. She took him by the hand and led him into the kitchen. Morris followed, snapping off the TV as he passed it.

They sat around in the small talk of families and friends while Helen made the tea. The tea made and half drunk, Charlie began.

"What's this Helen says you're not going to synagogue for the holidays?"

"We are going," Morris answered.

"O?" Charlie smiled, glancing at Helen questioningly.

"To Rodeph Sholom," Morris added.

"O!" Charlie frowned. "Why to Rodeph Sholom and not Beth Israel? You belong to Beth Israel." The phone rang before Morris could answer. It was Krinsky.

"Jacobi," he said, "I can cancel half but not two-thirds, certainly not two-thirds at the price I'm giving you . . . or anywhere near the price I'm giving you. A half but not two-thirds." There was a silence before Morris answered.

"Fine," he said. "A half will be fine." Another silence. "Krinsky. What I said this afternoon. I'm sorry."

"Forget it," Krinsky said. And then he said, "Right then I could have cancelled half." And then, low, "I should have. It wasn't right. Who can sell Capezios Rosh Hashonah, Yom Kippur?" He added his goodnight, Morris his, and they hung up. Morris came back to the table.

"So," Charlie said, "I repeat. You belong to Beth Israel. How come you're not going there for the holidays?"

"Beth Israel wants to sell me tickets. At Rodeph Sholom it's free." Suddenly dizzied with fear at what was about to race out of him into words, he struggled to embrace the hard rock of experience of this life his years had won him, to cling to the mountain's striated face and walk its slim but certain path. But he tripped and, though at once sickeningly spun about by the vagaries of his belief, said, "Like it should be." Out of the dimmest gene and corpuscle sprang five millennia of suffering to assail him. Morris was scared, but the little fists of pain were gone.

"What do you mean 'Free?' " Charlie snapped at him, his blood rising, his ears red. "In this world nothing's 'free.' Was your store 'free?' Was your house 'free?' When you joined the synagogue why didn't you talk about 'free' then? Here!"

Charlie reached into his breast pocket and withdrew a check. He flipped it onto the table. "A hundred dollars. Two tickets."

"No," Morris said. Helen caught her breath.

"No? NO?" Charlie couldn't believe it. Neither, quite, could Morris, who could? "So if 'no' explain, please, why not."

"It's a matter of . . . principle," Morris said, the word almost sticking in him.

"*Principle,*" exploded Charlie in thunder. "What's a man your age, married, two kids yet got to do with principle?" Morris, himself, wondered. "And let me tell you, Mister *principle,* something else. It ain't *principle* what built Beth Israel *or* Rodeph Sholom. It's this." He hit his fist down upon the check. "And lots more of it." But there, Morris knew, Charlie was wrong.

Charlie rose, picked up the check, and walked over to Helen. "Here," he said, "you keep this until your *meshugana* husband wises up. I got to go." He and Helen walked out of the room. Morris, after a moment, followed.

At the door, ready to leave, Charlie paused and, calmly and softly, said to Morris, "You should think some about your wife and kids before you do this thing." He paused. "And about me, too. What would it look like for me, my own family don't show up? Good night," he said and left. But in two seconds there was pounding on the door. Morris opened it. Charlie stood before him, livid. "For shame," he shouted. "For shame you should do this to me and your family." He clenched a fist and raised it above his head, shaking. "When you needed help for the business did I come? Now what is it so big a thing we ask of you? On your knees, you should go down on your knees praying from us forgiveness. For shame you should do such a thing."

"For shame I do it," Morris shouted back and slammed the door in his face. He jumped back from the door, and from his wife demanded candles.

"What?" asked Helen.

"Candles," he demanded, louder, angry. "*Shabbas* candles."

"What?" she asked again, frozen. But Morris was gone, into the kitchen, into her precise, determined cupboards rooting about in frenzy. She followed him. He emerged from the scattered cupboards holding in his hands two *Jahrzeit* candles, memorials for the dead.

"These were all I could find," he shouted, as if to make it clear to her. He smashed the two drinking glasses of wax against the enameled drain board of the sink, chunks and splinters of glass pattering and tinkling everywhere, specks and smears of blood springing out upon his hands. It was not to death that he would offer.

"O God," Helen screamed. The children, dumb, appeared in the doorway. Morris jammed the mounds of candles down on the table, searched for and found a match and struck it. He lit the candles.

"*Oi, oi, oi, oi,*" Helen moaned. The children came to her. Morris extended his arms, his palms flat out in front of him high over the burning candles, and then brought his hands back to his face, his bloodied fingers covering his eyes. He repeated the gesture.

"Morris, Morris. What are you doing?" Helen called to him.

"Praying," he said, and did. "*Boruch Ato Adonoy Eloheynu Melech Ho-olom Borey Pree Hagofen.*"

"Morris," Helen screamed, chilled. "That's the blessing for wine."

"It's the only prayer I know," he said. And lifting his wounded fingers again and again to his eyes, prayed on into the night.

Elizabeth Lanier

THERE WAS MORE to her perfect Beauty than what she looked like: there was her allure, that net of her own richer hunger which she threw out over us in our mad, urgent bewilderment. In the dazzle of our own raging blood she stalked us as the legend cobra stalks her prey, holding her victims in a spell of their own longings, by the undulations of a hooded grace, in the swirl of shivering ringlets, the paradoxic promise of illimitable joy to be had—where else—but in the mouth of death.

But who could resist? Who would think to want to?

Elizabeth Lanier took us, one by one, into her amazing arms, between her corruscating legs, and gave us birth. And gave us then to William, her brother, to be beaten.

It happened this way.

Tevis Anderson tried to speak clearly through the wire clenched teeth of his swollen, broken jaw. But what he was trying to say was too large, too compelling, too elating for him to manage it. I had been away for a week—an after-the-school-year present to Washington and Williamsburg with my parents and had not heard until now of Tevis' misfortune, or, far more importantly to him, his great good fortune.

"I got laid," he finally made his garble understood.

I made him say it again slower, and then again more slowly yet. I wanted to be sure. He wanted me to be sure. I was delighted for him, awed, but awash, too, in envy, half a hope away from wanting it not to be true, from wanting not to be left alone, for of the four of us—Tevis Anderson, John Pritchard, Bart Ford, myself—this made him the first. And so the pressure into manhood had begun for certain now. Nor could there be doubt, for in the solemn and honorable and unspoke compacts of young male good friends, one did not lie about one's virginity—not the possessing of it, not the losing. And not with whom.

"Who?"

He looked at me through his one unblackened eye, not *with* but *through* that eye as though he, the real Tevis Anderson, the deflowered Tevis Anderson, were inside himself in a cavern golden with achievement and that was what was raying out. Perhaps it was his tight-mouthed, tight-eyes generally puffed appearance that made him seem that way to me; but perhaps, too, there *was* an inner light of glory rising from a fire newly struck. At any rate, I felt its heat and pulsed to its high frequency.

"Elizabeth Lanier," he said.

I plummeted. Not because it was she but because I didn't believe him. He had tricked me into a false and vicarious exultation. He had lied. I felt cold and dull.

"Like hell," I said. It was inconceivable that Elizabeth Lanier would even have dated Tevis Anderson, let alone have had sex with him. She was, first of all, seventeen, a year ahead of us in school, a serious but not impossible prohibition. More serious was Charles Hinton, her rumored boyfriend.

Charles Hinton was a senior at nearby Lyle Prepatory School for Boys. We called them "lepers," though not Charles Hinton, who was all that elegance meant to us. He was older, easy in his bearing, assured and lofty even, casual about smoking a cigarette in public. He drove his own car when he visited on his vacations and in the summer. But what truly sanctified him was Elizabeth Lanier. No one who could drive down our small town avenues with Elizabeth Lanier beside him in a crimson MG could be called a "leper." That Elizabeth Lanier would foresake the worldly

Charles Hinton for the emergent Tevis Anderson was preposterous.

But the most formidable prohibition of all was herself. She was simply too proximate to the utlimate anima for us even to dare to desire her, even secretly, as though the *thought* of such an encounter would itself be a dooming sacrilege, a calling down of a blighting curse upon our sexual aspirations, a *hubris* too unnerving for mortals to contemplate. Like Artemis must from Diana have bent, so we avoided Elizabeth Lanier even in our most soaring and audacious masturbatorial dreams.

"No. It's true," he said. And as quickly as I had disbelieved him, I believed him again. The light in him was too genuine, the claim itself too vaunting for it to be otherwise. And of course I was consumed by the mystery of it: that in one short week Tevis Anderson should leap out of his virginal anxiety to become the sexual conqueror of Elizabeth Lanier was a story I would want to hear, true or not.

"But . . . but *how?*" was what I think I said, though Tevis needed no urging questions.

What follows is what he said, nearly enough anyway, as I reconstructed it out of the hot, broken mouthed buzz of his tumult.

"I was walking home from the bus stop. You know, up the long hill, Raymond Street?"

I nodded.

"Past her house?"

I nodded again.

"It was Sunday. It was about three o'clock. I was walking by her house when she came out on the front steps. She called me."

"She knew your name?" A spasm of jealous hatred sprang through me. Why him? Why should she know *his* name? I soothed myself that they were nearly neighbors, were neighbors.

"Yeah. She called me over. 'Tevis Anderson, come in here please,' she said. I followed her into the house right through it to a big TV room in the back. 'Do you dance?' she said.

There was a tape on, slow stuff. So we start dancing. Then she starts kissing me. Soon we're on the sofa, kissing away like crazy. Then she puts my hand on her tit. Then she grabs my crotch. And then our clothes are off. And then I'm on top of her. And then, well, I did it."

But he had told me nothing of what I wanted to know, nor could he. *Why*. I wanted to know; but so did he. And more, I wanted to know what I would feel like, but the details of my own imaginings could not be spoken to by his. That, I suppose, is what the poets are for. Still, I asked, "How was it?"

"Terrific," he said. What else is there to say? "Actually it was over pretty fast. I was pretty excited, you know? Actually she had to show me a lot. And then her brother walked in as soon as it was over."

"Jesus!" I stood up, frightened even at this distance, appalled and embarrassed. "Her *brother?*" The pieces of the idyll came splintering down around me. "My God!"

"Yeah. He kicked the shit out of me. I was trying to pull my pants on and he was punching me out. Oh man, what a scene. He must have knocked me out or something because after awhile it all stopped and then I can get my shirt on and I stumble home. I can hardly see. My parents were at the club. I look in a mirror. Holy Shit! I wasn't scared till then. I called a cab and go to the hospital. They fix me up. My parents come get me. Anyway, so here I am."

"What did you tell them? *Did* you tell them?"

"A fight. I told them some hoods jumped me down on Hillary Street."

"Do they believe you? What would you be doing on Hillary Street?"

"Maybe they do, maybe not. But they leave it alone." He got up from the edge of the bed he was sitting on and walked about. "I'll eat again in five weeks. I'm young. I'm strong. I mend fast, the doctor said."

Tevis Anderson did not seem to mind his jaw and face, the terror and ignominy of the event. If that was the price he had to pay, then he was yet glad to have had the chance to be a buyer.

Through the rest of that afternoon and in the days following, we, the four of us, talked about nothing else. But gradually the unfathomable and inexplicable gave way to simpler and, indeed, more reasonable and obvious solutions: that Elizabeth Lanier, for all else, was just a "broad with hot pants," as John Pritchard bravely put it. Yes, we had to agree, that is what it seemed. "When they want it, they *want* it," John Pritchard went on knowledgeably, a sexual theorist as absolute in his pronouncements and as secure in them as a chaste monk. Who else, after all, can know the flesh better than those able to view it distantly?

The misadventure with the brother? Well, that was just one of those comic things, something—or something like it—that we had all seen a thousand times on TV.

By the time Tevis Anderson was eating solid food again and looking at the world through two clear eyes, the grand adventure had slipped back into the larger and more compelling sexual context within which we still lived. For if Tevis Anderson was no longer a virgin, he was yet far from what his fantasies had tutored him to hope for: the first time is not important afterwards but as a beginning. And for the rest of us, well, the terrible hunt went on at its stumbling pace through the miasmatic fume of our necessity.

Only Charles Hinton seemed significantly altered by all this (not that he knew that), for now when he would drive down out of whatever high blue hills he lived in to our village to spend a day or so or a weekend with his beloved, now we would freely imagine him and Elizabeth Lanier in embraces splendid to behold as we would, for each other, behold them. Into what woods and dells his lust-red MG would take them! And she would surely go with him anywhere, into anything. We knew that now. John Pritchard was right. If not with us, with him. Charles Hinton, yes!

In early August William Lanier beat up Bartholomew Ford, though not so badly as Tevis Anderson. (Bart had his clothes on and could, to some degree, escape.)

I had finished for the day at Northside Market, where I was stacking grocery shelves for the summer. I walked out of the store in a work-ending buoy-ing cloud of release, alert to the evening and night that came as a remission to the daily boredom of columns and pyramids of soap boxes and toilet paper. I saw Bart across the street. I shouted to him. He stopped and waited for me, but as though he might in a moment move off. As soon as I crossed the street and saw him, puffed, reddened and deeply cut on his left upper lip, I assumed what turned out to be the truth, as though there could be only one explanation for violence in our lives any longer.

We looked at each other quietly. Bart was a less ebullient type than Tevis Anderson; he had a greater density, you might say, and was more complicated by life. If he had gotten off better physically than had Tevis, he had gotten off worse in his soul.

"The son of a bitch," he said and turned away. I had assumed correctly. I walked with him for half an hour and then I called my home and told my mother that I would be eating supper with Bart. We walked for an hour more. To no where. There wasn't much to say. She had driven by him in her father's car in early evening yesterday. He was mowing the lawn and hadn't noticed more than the car passing, a great beige El Dorado, until it returned.

"Get in," she had called to him from the car over the roaring lawn mower. He shut the machine off to hear her, though he had read her lips and all the rest. "Get in," she had said again.

"The lawn," he had said, pleaded. She said nothing, only looked at him across from her seat through the opposite window at which he stood. She wore brief white shorts. He looked down at her legs. All of her was legs. She pressed a lever and the window moved up out of the door with his hands over it. He let go and opened the door and got in. And they drove off.

"Going to work this morning, I walked around the corner and there he was. I was too surprised for anything. He hit me about three times before I even could realize it. I pushed him off and ran. That's it." We walked on.

"Do you want to eat?" I asked. "I'm hungry. I want to eat. MacDonalds?"

"No. I'm not hungry. I'll go with you."

And we were silent again.

"Look," I said. "It's over. Forget it."

"Forget it?" he shouted. "How can I forget it. She *told* him. Don't you see that?"

I hadn't even thought about it, but I saw that he was right. "So?"

"So that's goddam sick is what."

"So all right, it's sick. But that doesn't mean it isn't over. What are you letting it eat at you for?" We entered the MacDonalds.

"It isn't fair," Bart Ford said while I waited for my food. He wanted justice, a court, a trial, an appeal, but there was no way to have it, and where would the indictment begin and end? He could never know why she had done this. And as certain as he was that she had told her brother, he was yet not as certain as he would want to be. Only if he confronted her could he gain that, perhaps, and that he could not do, or would not. What would he have said?

"Let's call Tevis and John," I said as I finished eating. He would rather not, but had no choice: whatever he was in, we appeared to be in, and together.

That night under the moth-flickered streetlights that ringed the small community park we used as our summer base, we talked it over and over. There was no understanding it. John Pritchard had offered that she was just a "mean bitch." He had read about women who got their kicks beating on guys with a whip. That's what she was like, he said. Tevis Anderson corrected him. It was the men, he said, who got *their* kicks by having the woman hit them. But John Pritchard found that too unlikely to accept, though he dropped his explanation anyway. He said no more. The mystery was silencing him, the fog palpable and stifling.

"What about Charles Hinton? Why doesn't she tell on him?" I asked.

"Maybe he isn't getting any," Tevis Anderson answered. But that seemed too unlikely as well.

So the evening ended where it began. If we concluded anything at all it was maybe that she hadn't told, at least on purpose, after all. Tevis's discovery had been bad luck. And maybe her brother or some one else had seen Bart driving in the car with her. Maybe her brother was suspicious now and had gotten it out of her against her true will. We worked at the possibilities of accident and coincidence, of chance. It was easier to bear than conspiracy.

At eleven o'clock we rose to go our ways, the night air cooler now though none of us noticed or cared. What a thing is a man!

"Two down, two to go," Tevis Anderson laughed. "You live by the sword, you die by the sword," he poked Bart Ford and whooped under the spotlight.

"Shut up," Bart Ford said, not yet used to his bruises.

"Up yours," Tevis Anderson said. "Just watch your step you guys," he said to me and John Pritchard as he danced away from us backwards into the dark.

"Don't worry," John Pritchard shouted after him, "I will."

But he did not.

At the very end of late, dogged August John Pritchard phoned me even as I finished my supper.

"Listen," he said. "I'm in big trouble. I've got to see you."

"Come over," I said.

"I can't. I can't leave the house."

"What do you mean you can't? Did you break a leg?"

"I just *can't*, ok?" He was suddenly strident with his fear, brittle. "What am I asking from you, huh? *Come over.* Get Tevis and Bart, too."

"All right, all right. But can't you tell me anything?"

"He's outside. He drives past the house, back and forth."

"He?" I waited.

"William Lanier," he said after a long pause.

"You didn't," I said after my own long pause.

"Goddamn it, are you going to come over or not," he shouted, screamed.

"Ok," I said and hung up.

What I thought of first was my trouble more than John Pritchard's. Everyone had found his way now but me. It would be everyone's good summer but mine. I thought more certainly now than ever that I would go down to the city to a whore house and get it over with. If I could have found a whore house. But that act was a tainted one, unmanly, we had all decided in our earthy discussions long ago, not the same thing as *earning* it, though how my friends could consider that they had earned Elizabeth Lanier escaped me. Except with their blood, of course. Anyway, I was alone now for sure. And when that solitude would end I could in no way tell, foresee, or even confidently imagine. I rode my bike over to John Pritchard's and only then thought of him. Sure enough, William Lanier drove by.

Tevis Anderson had gotten there before me. Bart Ford arrived soon after. John Pritchard was chained up in suffocating anticipation. It was understandable that he should be, for neither Tevis nor Bart could have known their fate as they dove into their brief ecstasy, but John Pritchard, from when she sat down beside him in the library to now, knew. Two days ago a free boy, tonight a fugitive, if a man.

"I couldn't resist," he moaned to us shaking his head, holding it sometimes in his hands. "I couldn't resist." He was working in the municipal library for the summer. She had deftly drawn him into a musty storeroom and had taken him there and had left him there in a blasting moment to contemplate the avenging Fury who even now was circling his house.

"He's crazy," Bart Ford said of William Lanier. "The whole family's crazy. They ought to lock the two of them up."

"I'll say," Tevis Anderson agreed.

But then I thought, and said so, that no matter what, if they all had the chance to have Elizabeth Lanier again, that they would.

"*No way,*" Bart Ford insisted for them all. They shouted their support. But they were wrong. They would have her again if it was possible and always would, because what we are is not different from what we become. What changes is our procedures, not what we want. And Elizabeth Lanier was still flesh too quintessential for us ever to reject it. Right then I *knew* that, even if I did not know at the same time what to do with such knowledge. So my summer had not been altogether useless after all.

As for John Pritchard, he would have to sweat it out. We all agreed that he couldn't tell his own father about William Lanier without telling him about his sister. It did not occur to us that his, or any of our fathers, would be sympathetic. We did not think that they would be angry either. Only that they did not belong in the fundamental affair. And of course he could not tell William Lanier's father. All he could do was what he was going to do: in the morning he was leaving for a two week visit to his grandmother's on the Maryland coast. He had called her that afternoon and she was pleased to have him. He had called the library and made his excuses: he felt ill, exhausted he told them, and he wanted a rest before school. Besides, he only left them five days before he would normally have left. He had called the airlines and made a reservation. In the morning his mother would drive him the thirty miles to the airport. The visit to his grandmother would take him almost to the start of school. Perhaps by his return William Lanier, who was heading for college, would be gone. Perhaps he would forget, or at least care less.

William Lanier never did catch up with John Pritchard although I think that John may have suffered the most of us all. Even in Maryland he sought out every shadow, turned quickly at the ringing of his grandmother's doorbell. He even lost, he related months after, a fine opportunity for sex with a cute waitress by the warm September sea, struck down by trepidations spored in the humid library basement in his hometown. Dread is the worst of punishments. Some lessons are simply learned, and learned forever.

We did not see Charles Hinton fallen, but only heard. He visited her over the Labor Day weekend and on the last day of it, William Lanier forced Hinton's glorious MG to the side of the road crumpling a fender and then began to beat on him. Elizabeth was there to stop most of it, she and a police car that happened by.

So it was not just us.

Football practice had finished early. September had turned hotter than August had been, and after the fourth player fainted the coach gave it up. When I came out of the locker room, showered, changed, feeling leafy and loose the way you do after a shower after a game, Elizabeth Lanier was standing nearby. The school and the athletic field were close enough for her naturally to have been there, even at four-thirty. She had nothing to do with me. I walked by. She called. I turned to her and she walked up.

"Hello," she said.

"Hello."

"Don't call me Betty," she said. "I hate it when people call me Betty. People do that, you know, call Elizabeths Betty. Don't you think Betty is an awful name?"

We were walking together down the long block of the school to the bus stop. We were walking together, a boy and a girl, like we belonged together in the way that the young belong together. Already I noticed quickly that two of my teammates had noticed us. I saw that they wished they were me. Where were we going? I did not care. To be here was overwhelmingly enough. I heard the echoes of the summer dark and sharply like caligraphic signs of danger, but such brightness fell from her and raveled me up in it that I knew that I would go with her into whatever she would lead. What had drawn my friends was drawing me. But there would be terms, I vowed, for if secrecy did not save my friends, nor propriety Charles Hinton, then there would have to be another way. I promised myself that because I could not leave her if what I prayed was to happen was to happen. But I could not go on into disaster, if disaster it would be, unprepared. So we promise ourselves what we need, whatever we need. But *what* I was to do I had no mind for.

"Yes," I said, "Betty is awful. It's a shame that people take a nice name like Elizabeth and make it into Betty. Why do they do that?"

"I don't know," she said. "Just a custom, I guess. How's the team?"

"Good. Real good. We could have a great season if no one gets hurt."

"What about you?"

"What do you mean?"

"Are you going to play?"

"Yes, I think so. I don't think I'll start but I'll probably play a lot." We had gotten to the bus stop.

"Will you go out with me tomorrow night? Eight o'clock? We could go to a movie." I did not breathe.

"Yes," she said and turned away and walked back in the direction we had walked from, probably to her own car. Soon the bus came and I stumbled into it. From then until eight o'clock the following night I thought of nothing else, or rather, I thought of only one thing.

After the movie I bought her a hamburger and coke at the A&W Drive-In on the frayed edge of town, the north edge, near to the heavier wooded part of the county, the deep rutted back roads.

"Take me somewhere to park," she said after she finished eating. And so I did, and so at last arrived at my venture. After the usual high school groping, she made herself more available. And so did I.

"Why me?" I asked her later even as she still sat there partly dressed. She was smoking a cigarette and the glow of it would light up the smoky cloud about her head and that would reflect for a moment her features, her nose, her brow, a glittering eye, depending as the cloud shifted. Even in that softened darkness she was a ravening pleasure that I could not sum up nor comprehend. Whatever else I had expected, I had not expected that I would have fallen into love, dropped into it like a stone into a canyon deeper than the eye or ear can measure. The wind rushed by me.

"I like you," she said. "That's why."

"But you don't even know me."

"Well, I do now, don't I? And I like you now, don't I?" She reached across and kissed me. And still I fell.

"Why my friends?" I had to ask. She smoked on and I thought she would not answer, but she did.

"Because I *enjoy* this—sex—you know? Do you think I'm going to wait until I'm married for something as good as this?" She smashed out her cigarette and dressed completely. Still we sat there. She did not seem to want to go. I thought I might have made her angry. But she wasn't. She had stated her position: get what you want.

"I guess I meant something else, something more," I went against myself. "Why did you tell your brother."

I think she must have known that the question would come someday, that even if no one actually asked her, she would have had to ask herself, probably had already. Anyway, she was prepared, not surprised.

"It drives him crazy," she said. "He can't stand it, me having sex. He loves me. He doesn't want to see me hurt. I'll ruin myself, he says. And do you know something?" She turned in the seat and took my arm and shook it to make sure I was listening, to insist, as if what she was saying might escape my attention. "I think he's jealous. I think he'd like to have me himself. Sometimes he looks at me. I can tell." She settled back. She lit another cigarette. Dwell on that, she implied, her answer held out like a weapon.

But I could understand. Who could look at her without desire? And now I too wanted her safe from all the others, wanted to run before her smoothing the road, throwing cloaks over puddles, building citadels. Why should even a brother be proof against paragons? It was a wide and deep pool I had plunged into at the bottom of my canyon, but I was not drowning in it.

"I'm sorry about the boys getting hurt. I guess I wanted someone to beat *him* up. To make him stop protecting me or whatever. I guess I still do."

"Does that mean me?" I said.

"Maybe," she said. "Are you scared?"

"Maybe," I said and started the car and drove her home.

By the middle of October we were going steady. She wore my ring on a chain around her neck. Whatever mild shock that had rippled through the school at a senior going with a junior passed quickly. I was not unpresentable and, more effectively, whatever Elizabeth Lanier presumed to do made it valid. Additionally, I was having my own successes on the football field, now starting at left offensive end, where I had already caught four touchdown passes. Together we made a nice pair. We did all those things that most young lovers do except perhaps we had sex more frequently. Sometimes we even feinted at the future: where she might go to college, where might I, marriage even, for our love would last.

But above all I felt a great security, felt that the *details* of my present high, perhaps dangerous and exotic, existence were far less important—for good or ill—than was my doing what I was doing. I felt *right* to be in love with, to be the lover of, Elizabeth Lanier.

It interested me that she had no "reputation," for though I never spoke to her about it, surely she had had sex with others besides my friends and Charles Hinton. Nor can I tell how many others fell to her brother's fists. Perhaps their silence was the silence of the defeated. My own friends did not take my laison with her pleasantly. As my affection for her became more apparent, at least more apparently established as we walked about the school halls and the autumn-y streets hand in hand, Tevis Anderson and Bart Ford and John Pritchard grew colder toward me. It was difficult, of course, for us all to be together; there was too much intimate history that we had shared for that. Polite and decorous as we might be at school or social functions, under it all was a bridling current. Nor were they without jealousy.

But to them I had betrayed them: I had deserted to an enemy. Only once did we four old friends speak about it, their resentment cresting finally in Bart's calling her a slut. I told them then that I loved her and that I wouldn't have any one calling her a slut or anything else. So perhaps they were right. I had gone over to the other side, to William Lanier's side, though in a better position. Or so I thought.

Our last game was Thanksgiving Day against our traditional rival Voorheesville, a contest which, along with the week of civic fanfare, the morning pagent preceding the game, and the elaborate halftime display, allowed our region its most atavistic moment of the year. We won the game and I played well. But after the game Elizabeth was not waiting for me as we had planned. I went home to a houseful of cheering relatives, all of whom had come to the game to support me and to the Thanksgiving feast. After enough greetings I excused myself and called her.

"It's my brother," she said. "He's come home from college." She sounded haggard, uncharacteristic, weepy.

"Have you been crying, Elizabeth?"

"I told him," she said.

"Have you been crying?" I asked again wanting like a madness for her to say yes, yes. "Elizabeth?" But she had hung up.

Thanksgiving dinner passed the way they always do, in an uproar of eating, in a glut which is the true sign of thanks, in indigestion. What I ate tasted like straw. My inattention when noticed was dismissed by the rigor of my game or more likely was swept under the shouting uncles and the scurrying aunts, the bric-a-brac of families in festival. After the second round of desserts I got up to my room and lay down.

What I thought made me think that I was asleep and dreaming: the seamless quality of my life now, the amorphous bubbling of it. Nothing of firm morning was left, nothing of the swift certitude of the afternoon game where I danced and leaped the precise yards. And no plans. The family boiling in the rooms below me was like what my life had become: a chaos of ingredients, a stupefaction of tastes. I struggled for Order that would come when I awoke. But I was awake.

At noon the next day William Lanier called me at home and said he wanted to see me. He described a more secluded area of our small city park. Room enough to fight in, I thought, and private enough for it. He must have known that I would know what he intended. And he must, too, have realized that knowing that I could more easily avoid him. Was he certain that I would come to fight him? Why did he think that I was different from my friends and could be confronted directly rather than surprised or ambushed? Was it because I was larger and stronger than they? Or was it because Elizabeth had told him more about me than she had about the rest? But what? Was she seeking her salvation? Was she, perhaps, seeking his? Or even mine?

I could not tell then and still cannot. What I learned was not the answer to questions—there are no answers as such. What I learned was about the stances available to us, and what mine was. We fought and I beat him with less effort than I thought, or hoped, it would be. It was not a terrible fight. I exhausted him, depleted him, blocking him with my shoulders and arms. When I hit him I hit him in the body so that when he fell at last he was not bloody but helpless. We never spoke. He looked up at me without any emotion that I could see. I never saw him again. And when I walked away I was whole.

For perhaps it is only the knots we tie, get tied in, that are real, and that it is only in our tension to engage or to be free that we gain from the knots whatever realities we have or believe in. So one strikes out or strikes back, gives or takes, wonders or fears. Only this I know, that there *is* victory and defeat, primal urgencies that the soul comprehends beyond events, knowledges more complex than are the thin accounts by which we measure such things. There is victory and defeat, the *synapse* of it, and the taste of purest triumph is maybe an elixir and maybe a subtle poison. For to have once won enormously and well is searing, a hot kindling of light, an illumination ever after as though you have no choice any more to ever lose or be dark again. So did I once make love to the most beautiful woman in the world.

And that has made all the difference.

"... *and still the heart doth sing.*"

THE FIRST POEM that Gaffney read began,

> This is for my little dog Johnny
> Who I love and always give a hug
> Even if he goes wee-wee
> All over the living room rug.

The poem went on in like manner for five more quantrains. Paper-clipped to it was a three-by-four polaroid snapshot of what could have been a dog—Johnny—sitting down up to his neck in a field of weeds.

My God, Gaffney thought. He looked around his office. He looked at the thick black moulding framed pictures of the literati of five decades, the great and the nearly great, mosaiced on the wall. All of them had contributed to the pages of *New Literature*. Gaffney looked back at Mrs. Wilcox's poem. It must be a joke. It must be the standard gag put on a new poetry editor. Gaffney thought of some of his great predecessors—Cowley, Williams, Schwartz, Kunitz—getting the "new editor's treatment." At *New Literature* traditions of every kind were everywhere. Gaffney rose from his desk and stalked from his poetry editor's office to take his part.

"All right," he shouted, but smiling. He stood in the middle of the large working room where secretaries and initial readers and friends sat around coffee and foot-high piles of manuscripts. They all looked up. "All right, all right. Who's the clown?" Then he read the poem, flourishing melodramatically with voice and gesture. But when he finished no one was laughing. Or caring at all. One girl started back to typing, another slit open envelopes with a real dagger. Gaffney went to Phyllis Havermeyer, who ran the work room and had been at *New Literature* for twenty of its fifty years.

"I don't get it," Gaffney said. "I thought it was a gag, an office gag. It *is* a gag, isn't it?" He held out the poem to her, but she didn't take it. She didn't even look at it.

"No," she said. "It's not a gag."

"But . . . ." But that was all he could say. He turned and went into his office.

Three hours later Gaffney leaned back. Before him were five piles of poems rising and falling like a perfect bell curve: a tiny pile of poems he would accept; a large pile of poems that were almost (but not) good enough; the largest pile of poems, which were bad in all the ways that calculated writing workshop poetry could be bad; a fourth pile as large as the second but as far from life as the second was near; and a final pile as small as the first. In this pile was Mrs. Wilcox's poem, two poems from Steve Kranoff, two poems from Grace Petersen, and six poems from Zahir Lanthi. These last came from India, from Rhajustan in India.

The three middle piles of poems would be rejected *pro forma* by a polite printed slip. The two small piles would get personal letters.

Part of a letter to pile one, the accepted poems:

> *Dear George* (Gaffney knew most of the people in this pile),
>
> *As I've said before, to you and elsewhere, the "nature-will-save-us-if-we-give-her-a-chance" theme is about as irrelevant in this apocalyptic decade as it probably has been for the past fifty years. Instead, it seems to me it is us who have to save nature. I KNOW. I KNOW all the implications in that last statement. Screw it. I am publishing your two poems in* New Lit *because*

they are lovely, even if wrong-headed. Because they are memorials to language and to an important craft called poetry. Because it is language used well that will probably save us (if anything can . . . or will) faster than your god damn trees. But of course you must continue to look well at the trees. How are Mary and the kids? I may be out your way in the Spring . . . .

The letter trailed off into personal things and professional gossip.

The letter to Mrs. Wilcox:

Dear Mrs. Wilcox,

I do not usually write personal letters of rejection but I think in your case I must make a special exception. Dear Mrs. Wilcox, there is no way in which I can begin to make clear to you why your "poem" about your dog Johnny isn't a poem, isn't poetry. What poetry is concerned with and how it, poetry, goes about organizing that concern through language are ideas that just can't be made to relate to your effort. Mrs. Wilcox, whoever would write poetry must first (and continuously) read it. Read poetry, Mrs. Wilcox! Read!

Most Sincerely Yours,
John Gaffney, Poetry Editor

He wrote letters to the other three as well.

Why did he write those letters at all?

Gaffney knew about the Mrs. Wilcoxes and the Steve Kranoffs of the world, the Grace Petersens and even the Zahir Lanthis. He had been in poetry long enough to have heard of and from its every dimension. He just hadn't expected to confront all of them at *New Literature*. Anywhere else, maybe, but not here.

John Gaffney was a poet whose reputation was the kind you get from writing a relatively few poems so good that everyone who reads poetry seriously knows them. The size of his imagination and his rigorous beauty of language made his poetic sensibility one of the quiet touchstones of contemporary literature. For fifteen years he had published infrequently and only in the journals and magazines like *Poetry, Partisan Review, Kenyon Review, The Quarterly Review of Literature,* and, of course, *New Literature.* He had had no volume for a long time, though he had been often urged to one. When, however, he did put his first book together, it won the Lamont Poetry Prize, the National Book Award, and was nominated for a Pulitzer, which it would have won had it not been in competition with the posthumous collection of Robinson Jeffers that year.

It had taken him fifteen years, from age twenty to thirty-five, to make and collect sixty poems, every one of which was worth it—the lonely effort, the courage of discipline, the distillation of intelligence.

He wrote to Mrs. Wilcox and the others without scorn or rancour. If he felt anger anywhere it was toward the pretentiousness and arrogance of the other, failed, piles, towards those who *had* read poetry and deserted it. If he had a mind to defend language from their likes he would do it by not publishing them, by reviewing badly those who did some way stumble into a volume. And by other means.

But he wrote to Mrs. Wilcox and the others because they were innocent yet, and he would preserve them if he could.

> Listen all you people smoking cigarettes out there!
> What do you think it is like having to breath in the air?
> Do you think it is fun sitting in a crowded bus with a cigar going off?
> No! It is not fun! It makes you sneeze and wheeze and cough!

Steve Kranoff had written this as part of ten inches of angry couplets.

> *Dear Mr. Kranoff,*
>
> *Why do you write about air pollution in couplets? And why fifty-eight lines that usually repeat your idea rather than develop it? And why are all the lines of any which length? Come, Mr. Kranoff, do you think of any of these things when you write your poems? Mr. Kranoff, do you*

think you need a poem to express what you want to express? Consider! Consider!

Grace Petersen:

I found it was no use waiting for Death,
Expecting him to call,
Tap on the door with his bones
Saying "Ready all?"

So I decided to seek him out
With the aid of a sharp slim knife,
But found I was too squeamish thus
To loose my hold on life.

I got a gun and loaded it
And put it to my head;
I pulled the trigger once but found
I still was far from dead.

The gun misfired; the knife was out;
The poison that I bought
Smelled utterly vile, so here I am,
My neck quite neatly caught

Within this noose, I plan to jump,
Breaking my neck and strangling.
All that stops me now is the thought
Of the indignity of dangling.

Dear Miss Petersen,
Death is a fearful thing, and suicide, which grows out of despair, is even more fearful. But your poem treats Death and suicide lightly, *though it doesn't mean to. Or does it? You see, there's no way of knowing what your poem is about. Try this. Ask yourself if you can say what you poem is about, what a reader is supposed to think and feel after reading it. And try this: read the poetry of Emily Dickinson. Have you heard of Emily Dickinson, Miss Petersen?*

Zahir Lanthi:

If God is love
God lives in my love for you
deeper even than you know
I feel His awesome presence in our moments shared,
so sweet with peace, so warm with all
the secrets only we two know.
God is in the wordless closeness of our
being together, and in the way your fingers
curl around my own, and in the slow
deepening of your smile.
God is in my big need of you, and in the aching
hurt of hours we do not share.
Still, you're with me always, as He is beyond
all barriers of time and space.
If God is love, I know Him well, for I know
you, beloved!

Dear Mr. Lanthi,
You are trying to say an abstract thing abstractly, which equals double vague. And God as a metaphor for anything *anymore has pretty well had it by about this time in our millenium. I take it from your name and your address that you are Indian. Why not write about its culture, and its idiom and ideas and insights? And use India's little magazines, newspapers, and journals of opinion.*

It pained Gaffney to think of Zahir Lanthi continuing to send envelopes 12,000 miles one way and 12,000 miles back.

Phyllis Havermeyer came into the office bearing two feet of thin poetry books as Gaffney finished his note to Zahir Lanthi. He put it and the poems back into their return addressed envelope and licked it closed.

"Do you still want to see all the poems that come in in a day?" Phyllis Havermeyer asked him.

"No. God no. This has been enough to give me an idea. It's not, alas, as different from other places as I'd hoped."

"Worse. Everyone wants to be printed in *New Literature.* People have been known to parlay an appearance in *New Literature* into a career." She put down the stack of books. "I've made suggestions about possible reviewers. I put their names on these slips in the book. But that's the old way, so don't feel funny about changing it all around. I'm a quick study. I learn my editors fast." But Gaffney was still thinking of the submissions.

"I guess I really knew that, that people wanted to get into *New Literature.* I suppose I hoped they would understand what they were reading in it and be frightened off. By the quality I mean. How's that for naiveté?"

"Listen," Phyllis Havermeyer said. "If half the people who send stuff in read *New Literature* and a quarter of them bought the magazine, we'd be running ads for Chevys and Fords against *Life* and *Look.* And taking vacations in Bermuda." She looked at his desk, at the five piles of manuscripts.

"Yeah, I guess I knew that too. Take these four," he told her.

"What's this last pile?" She picked up the piles for rejection. She saw that four envelopes were already sealed.

"Don't ask," he laughed. "And let's use the old system. Just show me what the readers like and anything that is personally addressed to me."

"And messages from the Gods?"

"Ah yes. All messages from the Gods."

Phyllis Havermeyer walked toward his door with the manuscripts in her arms and bundled against her.

"Hey," she turned. "Don't forget the Waggoner reception tonight. Stay loose."

"Why not? I'll know everybody there."

"That was before. Now you're *New Literature.* Everything will change."

Everything did change.

John Gaffney got his job as poetry editor of *New Literature* (one of the very few truly paying editorships in *belle lettres*) pretty much the way a king was chosen in the Feudal Age: the barons of the realm got together and voted him in. Although there was an actual Board of Directors for *New Literature,* even a Board Chairman, the decision that really counted was the one arrived at by about fifteen writers and critics, America's elite, who had been assembled for the purpose by Franklin Carter, editor-in-chief of *New Literature* and son of the owner and publisher, Martha Grant Carter.

After it was clear that Kunitz was not going to resume the poetry editorship when he returned from Italy, Franklin Carter assembled the lords, and in an easy but deliberative afternoon they decided upon John Gaffney.

It was an important decision because *New Literature* was the preeminent journal of literary accomplishment and opinion in the English speaking world, at once a seismic force and a recorder of it, a light and a mirror. What happened in *New Literature* mattered more than what happened anywhere else. And it was an important decision because although John Gaffney was chosen by his barons and, in effect, continued to rule by their leave, as with any king, once he was a king, duly annointed and consecrated, getting him off the throne was always harder than putting him on it, should the necessity arise.

But the barons were all pleased with their choice of John Gaffney. He had in his career avoided the skirmishes and literary wars that had scarred so many of the others. He had developed no allegiances to "schools" or "aesthetic positions," had created no "arrangements" with little magazines or with other poets, and had, in his poetry particularly, remained aloof, lonely. It was *sui generis,* defendable within its own perimeters. And so was he.

As with any king, he was soon harried by his vassals' (and *their* vassals') homage and entreaty. Everyone, it seemed, had a cause to plead and a protegé to advance. What surprised Gaffney most was not the fact but the intensity of it all, the *desperation* with which people were willing (compelled?) to cast their lives upon the ephemera of little magazine fame. How insubstantial were the imaginations of such! How clearly was that vacuity of spirit reflected in their hollow poetry! Poetry indeed!

For John Gaffney, who had all his literary life carved his sensibility in the stone of language like Callimichus carved marble, the spectacle of that egoistic moil over which he had some rule was frequently depressing. But not defeating. For if his weapon in the past was the single spear of his own strong voice, now he had the armèd might of *New Literature.* If he had to drink a little of disappointment in scrabbling poets every day, at least he also got to drink to the pleasurable dregs of power used in a righteous cause. In six months he made some enemies, but he made *New Literature* ring as it had not even in its own splendid past, insisting upon excellences from established poets, searching out and printing fresh, early, and brightening voices.

If Gaffney had wanted to he could have lived upon the fat of the literary land. There were endless invitations to food, drink, parties, infinite cultural events, weekends, summers, cruises, sails, flights. There were women who wanted to sleep with him to get their poems printed and those who would just so they could claim that they had. He became a celebrity, in small circles to be sure, but important ones.

What he said became significant. In any issue of any literary publication he might find himself quoted, as often incorrectly as not. Often he would find himself credited, or blamed, for something he did not say and never would have thought. He was asked to be on every panel and jury in the country. Lecturing offers fell like snowflakes. Fourteen colleges wanted to give him honorary degrees.

Phyllis Havermeyer had been right. Everything had changed. Nothing could happen anymore without its potential for consequences looming up behind it. Even those ancient personal friends whom he held in the heart's core were affected, held by him for their own protection at slighter distances, for the light shed by a king is often hot but seldom warming. And his own poetry, which he had always made slowly and in small quantity, he now made less and less of. It wasn't just the time that he didn't have.

What didn't change was Mrs. Wilcox, Steve Kranoff, Grace Petersen, and Zahir Lanthi, from whom he continued to hear often. There must have been others, of course, but he never knew of them directly. After that first day they, those others, never got past the desk of the clever and pretty first reader, a year out of Skidmore College. But with those four, that he should have answered them personally at all wedged an opening in the *New Literature* phalanx of editorial assistants. Mrs. Wilcox *et al.* wrote directly and too personally to Gaffney to be put off. He had invited it. Or perhaps it was just the pretty first reader's running joke. Whatever, in any week or month, on the top of his mail would be Grace Petersen, say, or Steve Kranoff.

> *Listen Mr. Gaffney,*
> *Maybe you don't know it but the air of this whole world is dying and what that means is that all the things, which is everything, which depend upon that air, is dying too. So that is why I write ten inches of poetry about it. For emphasis. And did you ever hear of Alexander Pope? Well you check an anthology of English Poetry and I'm sure you'll see that he writes nothing but couplets. And as for the varied length of my lines, this is the twentieth century and things have changed. Hoping that you'll keep all of the above in mind, I submit the enclosed.*
> *P.S. Walt Whitman didn't worry about the length of his lines.*

> The rivers are all rotten, solid with filth. They stink.
> You, America, are guilty, throwing everything, even the kitchen sink
>
> Into the once proud nation's burbling rocks and rills.
> Now with you it is all cutting up the woods and knocking down the hills.

and on and on.

Dear Mr. Gaffney,

Thank you so much for your words of encouragement. I went right out and got from the library a collection of Emily Dickinson's poetry. You certainly are right. She certainly is wonderful. I am about half way through her book. She has certainly inspired me to new efforts, some of which is below.

I'll never be lonely
for friends that I knew
I'll never be lonely
I only need you.

I'll never be missing
Another boy's kissing
I love reminiscing
But only with you.

I'll never be lonely
Your hand holding mine
Is warmer than sunshine
And sweeter than wine.

I've never been lonely
Since you came to me
I'll always be loving you constantly
For loving you only
Is so heavenly.

And on.

Dear Mr. "Johnny" Gaffney (Get it?)

Of course it must be hard seeing my poem about my dog Johnny as a poem because what you saw is only part *of a larger work called "The Johnny Poems." When it is completed and you can see all the parts in relationship to each other, then I think it will all be more understandable. Actually, I have already begun negotiations with a publisher, Exposition Press (Have you heard of them?)*

that has responded quite favorably to what they have seen of my work and I would appreciate any advice from you that you might care to give about this matter. It is exciting and scary getting out your first book of poems as I'm sure you must know. To give you some idea of my range I've included a poem herein with the hope that you might consider using it in your fine magazine.

God gave me my brain
I have the upper hand
With intelligence I reign
The strongest I command.

Yet my brain is a curse!
I envy dumb creatures.
Is there anything worse
Than perceiving my future?

And on.

Dear Sir,
I have looked for India and believe that I have found it. Thank you for your suggestion.

See the egg of the mouse.
See the kitten suck of the hen.
The sun and the moon are in the sky together
Lighting each other up.

It went on that way for eighteen pages. It cost Zahir Lanthi $5.74 each way.

In late July Franklin Carter came back from Martha's Vineyard, where he summered, to attend to various of his interests. After a day he came to the office and took Gaffney to a good lunch. They talked about *New Literature,* about literary friends they held in common, about the trick of sailing in between Martha's Vineyard and Nantucket. They made small plans for the two weeks in August when Gaffney would be visiting. Any of the *New Literature* staff could come to the Carter estate on the island during the summer. It was a policy, an attitude, as old as the magazine itself. Secretaries included.

Lunch over, outside the restaurant, Franklin Carter going one way, Gaffney back to the office, Carter handed him an envelope.

"There are some frightfully good things here, I think," he said. "I hope you can use something." He held on to the envelope as he spoke as though unwilling to release something so precious. Then he let go. "See you in a couple of weeks." And he was gone.

Franklin Carter was an editor-in-chief who left his staff alone. It had been clear to chief editors before him that what truly determined *New Literature* had to be the taste of the individual editors in poetry, fiction, and opinion. You could never get the individual editor you wanted unless he were guaranteed his critical autonomy. All his decisions were the final ones. It had always been that way. Besides, the credo of *New Literature,* fifty years strong, was that it was obligated only to quality, not to a fashion, mode, or ideology. All an editor-in-chief *could* do was, much as a producer of a film, keep it all together and running. And to do that Franklin Carter had Phyllis Havermeyer who, in turn, had all the bright and productive help she wanted. Altogether, then, there were never problems about editorial decisions at *New Literature.* Maybe that was why it had lasted so long and so well. For that reason and because of the Carter money. And Franklin Carter, who was literate and effective, was also interested in much else. He did not need *New Literature* to *Be,* nor did it need him, although both functioned better because of their easy contact. It was a proper journalist's job for an intelligent, wealthy gentleman, no less, no more.

In his office Gaffney looked at the poems in the envelope that Carter had just given him. Even before he read them he puzzled at the personal treatment. Why hadn't Carter just dropped the poems in the "In" basket of Miss Lindstrom's desk? And as he read the poems, though authentic, they were clearly undistinguished. Third pile poetry if ever he saw it.

The sails are full tonight with the wind
And I am full with you tonight, my skipper.

> Steer a careful course to where your compass points.
> And don't let the north star fool you.

etcetera. The poems were written by someone called Virginia Mannion.

Gaffney called Phyllis Havermeyer into his office, told her it all, and asked her what she thought.

"A love affair," she said, certainly.

"A what?"

"An affair. You know, with a woman? Oh come on," she said to the face on him. "You're not really that easily shocked, are you?"

"No," Gaffney said. "I guess not. Just at first. Why the hell doesn't he just use money? Why mess around with the magazine?"

"That's the first question all you editors ask."

"This isn't a new thing?"

"Hardly. Once or twice a year. It's been going on for a long time."

"Sort of a tradition."

"Right."

"Nothing like an old institution for traditions."

"Anyway, the women he gets involved with are usually writer-types, real or imagined. That's why they go after him, among other reasons. But *you* must know about that by now yourself."

"OK," Gaffney said.

"And he doesn't give them money because while it lasts they get from him all that money can buy anyway. What they want is the ultimate experience—what money can't buy. They want their name—somehow, somewhere, even once—to appear in *New Literature*."

"So why doesn't he just accept something of theirs. He's got areas of the magazine that he controls directly. Or does if he wants to. What does he come to me for?"

"Well, sometimes he does accept something like a book review or a letter. But you see, it depends upon what *she* has written. What *she* wants. It depends upon what she thinks of herself. And even if he just *ordered* a poem or a story printed, which he has never done, it wouldn't be the same. These girls know the score. They know what *New Literature* is. They know how it works. It doesn't count unless they get accepted by the editors who accept all the rest."

"Even if the big boss is putting in a very good word for them?"

"Right."

"God damn." Gaffney pushed back from the desk.

Phyllis Havermeyer held up her hand. "*New Literature* has gotten more than a few good things this way, you know. They're not all Virginia Mannions. I could drop you a couple of names that would ring loud bells."

"Son of a bitch," Gaffney said. He wondered if he would always be learning after all the rest what was the perfectly obvious. Maybe that was why it took him so long to write things. "Son of a bitch," he repeated. "Well, what do I do now?"

"No problem. Just tell him the poetry is substandard and you won't print it."

Two weeks later, even as they were driving away from the ferry depot at Oak Bluffs, Gaffney told Franklin Carter just that. Carter laughed and drove on as if it had never happened. And in the following two weeks, good weeks, Gaffney got to meet and see frequently Virginia Mannion herself, who was beautiful enough for him to understand why Carter would want to do things for her. And she was intelligent and gracious, witty, urbane, sincere, and memorable. But no poet after all.

Back on the mainland he was busy with the last problems of the September issue, which were not great problems. In two more days he would finish and then resume the rest of his vacation, this time two weeks in the Chesapeake region of his growing up. And to writing. In the late Friday mail there was a letter for him from Mrs. Wilcox.

> *Dear "Johnny," (sorry, but I can't resist it)*
>
> *Thank you for your advice. Yes, I know that Exposition Press is what is called a "vanity press" (Imagine!*

Me with vanity!) and that I'll have to pay for the printing, but as Mr. Grolier explained to me, if even half the books sell, I'll make my money back. Maybe a profit even. We are sending notices to at least a thousand libraries. And what with the bookstore sales I may just make it. Also, many great writers in the past have had to pay to have their books published, so there is really no great crime that way. After all, I'm sure there are probably many more fine writers than there is room for them in the publishers. Also, Mr. Grolier showed me some of the fine things said by important and tasteful people about many of the books his company has published. Scientists, opera stars, college professors with Ph.D.'s write lovely comments on the back of the dust jackets. And he showed me many of the reviews. Real reviews in newspapers, the Watertown (N.Y.) Gazette, the Messina (also N.Y.) Times, the Tipton (Texas) Patriot, and lots more. So thank you again for your advice but I must go where my heart dictates and hope for the best.

The Johnny poems—or Poem—is coming along just fine. The title of the book will be "The Johnny Cantos and other Poems" (Mr. Grolier's suggestion). I've included a few of the new Johnny poems in case you might want to use them in forthcoming issues of New Literature.

Johnny, Johnny, get out of the brussels sprouts.
That dog, he runs through the garden like an army routs.
If I don't shout at him . . .

But here Gaffney dropped the sheaf and held his head. Should he laugh or weep?

There are places in the tidewaters of the Chesapeake that none can know of but natives: places too difficult to be accidentally found by the occasional summer wanderer, too dangerous to be forgotten once discovered. There small creeks run from the estuaries to end against a mud dam of fiddler crabs. You have to slide a flat bottom garvey over the dam and then onward to get to the reed hidden bays and the rush surrounded coves beyond. You get there when you are young, when *all* purposes are discovery. John Gaffney drifted into his first marsh pond when he was twelve. That first time he came too quickly and frightened upward the rafts and rafts of waterfowl. They arose like an explosion. It was like all the earth swooping into the sky. He never forgot that. He thought that if he ever forgot that—the way that his heart had leaped in a spasm of fright and lovely awe—that he would be dead. That was why it was a dangerous place. This was where he spent his two weeks.

He came back to *New Literature* tuned and strengthened. He had been on the job nearly a year now and had not seen how much the job had drawn from him in small pieces. For all his accomplishment with the magazine and his pleasure in it, his renewal in the marshes reminded him that he would have to save more of himself for who he was: a poet, but more—a man who was given to think about life in precise and wondering terms; a lonely man committed to artifacts and what he hoped they could mean. Out of the material of the marsh, his response to it, *he* would make the revealing patterns and forms: the high human endeavor.

Gaffney came back to *New Literature* and to Mrs. Wilcox ("Two weeks! In two weeks 'The Johnny Cantos and Other Poems' will see the light of day. I am so excited . . ."), Grace Petersen ("I cannot smell the blue of September/I cannot eat the hum of a peach"), Steve Kranoff ("What is so terrible as War/That kills our young men galore?"), and from Zahir Lanthi, a letter.

> *Dear Sir,*
> *I am alive with my pursuit. Your words have meant everything to me. Tomorrow I go on a religious retreat into the foothills of mountains one hundred miles northeast of Rhajustan. Perhaps I will stay and go higher into the mountains. Perhaps I will write new poems, without pen and paper. With, perhaps, the contemplation of the life in the seed of the pepper plant.*

Peace to you my good friend and good advisor. May all my poems be dedicated to you.

Gaffney felt terrible. What had he done to these people? What had he done to Zahir Lanthi?

There was also a sealed envelope of poems from Virginia Mannion. Gaffney found out from Miss Lindstrom that she had not seen them first. He found out from Phyllis Havermeyer that she had not seen them either. So it must have been from Franklin Carter.

But it was not.

The envelope of poems had come from Virginia Mannion herself. She had put them on Gaffney's desk one recent evening when she had stopped into the offices with Carter. She told him all of this herself in Carter's office to which Gaffney had gone with her envelope still in his hand. Carter's private secretary had announced him, and when he walked into the comfortable dark office, she was there. She saw her envelope. And she saw him.

"You're either thrilled with the poems or angry at me, but Carter doesn't know anything about it, so spare him." Then she explained to both men. And then she talked about the wonderful two weeks they all had on the island. And of her time since. And about how good the last issue of *New Literature* was. It was all so civilized. It was all so pleasant. And of course no one could speak of the circumstances at hand. After a bit Gaffney returned to his own office.

In an hour Franklin Carter came to him. It was a good, clean talk.

"The fact of the matter is, John, that I've never felt about anyone the way I feel about Virginia." He had been walking around the office; he stopped. "I'm thinking of marrying her. I mean I'm *going* to marry her."

"That's fine, Franklin. That's actually wonderful. Virginia is splendid. She's beautiful and all the rest." He stood up and put out his hand, which Carter shook. Then they both sat down. "Does that have anything to do with her poetry? With *New Literature?*"

"I'm afraid that it does," Franklin Carter said. "There's nothing I wouldn't give her, John. Nothing." He looked right at him.

"What about them?" Gaffney asked, waving his hand at the wall of photographs.

"Them?" Carter looked where Gaffney waved, finding, after a moment, the implication. "Oh," he laughed a little. "They're all dead. Almost." He stood up. "Read her poems, John. Give them a chance. I read them and I think they're grand. But of course I read them through a lover's eyes." He was at the door. "But that's important. *Please,* John. Consider them carefully, will you."

Gaffney considered the poems carefully and then wrote a detailed rejection of them. There was no address and no return envelope with the poems. But why bother. Three days after their talk Gaffney sent everything into Carter's office. For two days he waited for a response, but there was nothing. Even after two weeks there was nothing, and so he let it go.

And by now the fall literary season was fully upon him. The colleges were full again, the manuscripts of the fruitful summer cascaded in, Miss Lindstrom was getting married to a junior editor at *Harpers* and would have to be replaced, celebration of mind and spirit was everywhere. The mechanism was gearing up, spinning ever more quickly around its shaft, which was where men like John Gaffney were. In the back of his mind mallards rose into the air like artillery.

The Johnny Cantos and Other Poems arrived. Inscribed inside the cover: "To John 'Johnny' Gaffney, for his attention, advice, and respect, I present this fruit of my labor with sincere affection." It was signed: Alma Clifford Wilcox. Gaffney handled the book. It was typical: cheap paper, gross typography, and a squib on the back cover written by (or for) Zoltan Cherney, who was identified as an important European concert violinist. Mrs. Wilcox, it turned out, was fifty-three. She had two sons living on the west coast. Her hobby was gardening, indoor gardening: house plants.

Dear Mrs. Wilcox,
Thank you for the book.

He was going to write more. He was going to write as he always had, what he thought. But what the hell. Nothing he had said before had mattered, and it was too late now. If anything mattered it was a year ago when he had answered her and the others. *He* had made them poets by being their audience, for every poet must have an audience to exist; that is an ontological truth. Even if it is an audience of one. So that was all he wrote: "Thank you for the book." And bore his responsibility.

Days and weeks and manuscripts and *The New York Review Of Books* went on. Miss Lindstrom was married (he had gone to the reception) and she had been replaced by Margaret Southern, who was as skillful as Miss Lindstrom had been though less beautiful. She was from Barnard and possibly lacked her predecessor's humor. At least Gaffney heard no more of Grace Petersen and Steve Kranoff. Perhaps Grace Petersen had transcended in an unutterable sentiment. Perhaps Steve Kranoff had burst into his true fulminating fire and been consumed. Perhaps, as Alma Clifford Wilcox had become a poet, so Zahir Lanthi ahd become a holy man. What was there after all that the Will could not affect? Or perhaps it was only the serious defense of Margaret Southern at the first desk, who was standing for no nonsense at all.

Gaffney came back from the Random House party for their new young writers with maybe a drink too many in him for doing the kind of work that was waiting for him. There would be the afternoon mail, official and personal, but more important and more difficult were the galleys of the January issue. He liked to work on his galleys himself. He would let the staff check him. But this evening, 4:30 already, he would only glance over them.

What he saw on the fifth galley was four poems by Virginia Mannion. They were four of those he had rejected and which he had sent back through Carter, reasons and all.

There it is, he thought. His extra drink reeled around in his head a little but not much now. God damn it to hell. He thumbed through the rest of the galleys, but the small inevitable rising he always felt in handling new print on long paper was gone. He didn't feel so very creative now, only like somebody who worked. He felt very down, like losing in an important game. But he was a professional after all, and it was the season, not a game, that counted; the percentage, not a score. And there would be tomorrow. He looked out of his small window at the night.

He riffled quickly through his mail looking for a friend's name, someone who would be writing to him about the rising cost of milk, a new car, a broken finger, a promotion, a memory. But all there was that caught his quick attention was a letter from Alma Clifford Wilcox. He opened it. Inside there was only a poem.

> My dog Johnny is dead.
> He was hit by a car smashing his head.
> His little bowl is empty.
> His little bed empty.
> I am empty.

He sat for a long time with her poem in his hand.

He put it down, picked up the galleys, and on the fifth sheet pulled a long blue X through Virginia Mannion's poems. "Delete" he signaled largely in the margin. Then he spun a piece of paper into his typewriter and wrote.

> *The Johnny Cantos and Other Poems,* Alma Clifford Wilcox, Exposition Press, 64 pages. $4.95.

"Insert this under Announcements," he ordered below it.

About the Author

BARRY TARGAN is the assistant director of the University Without Walls at Skidmore College, Saratoga Springs, New York. He studied British and American literature at Rutgers University (B.A.), University of Chicago (M.A.), and Brandeis University (Ph.D.). He has published numerous poems, essays, and short stories in magazines and journals. Several of his stories have appeared in collections such as *Best American Short Stories.* His book of poems *Let The Wild Rumpus Start* was published in 1971 by Best Cellar Press, and he plans to publish a second book of poetry this year.

The Iowa Arts Council provides the one thousand dollar prize for the Iowa School of Letters Award for Short Fiction.